BANK

ACTIVE CH

249 1 2 3 4 5 6 7 8 9 10 12776
▲ ▲ ▲ ▲ ▲ ▲ ▲ ▲ ▲ ▲

The ULTIMATE SCANNER

DEMOD MSK SCAN VSAT-ON

Electronics publications by
Bill Cheek

World Scanner Report
Scanner Modification Handbook, Vol 1
Scanner Modification Handbook, Vol 2
The Ultimate Scanner

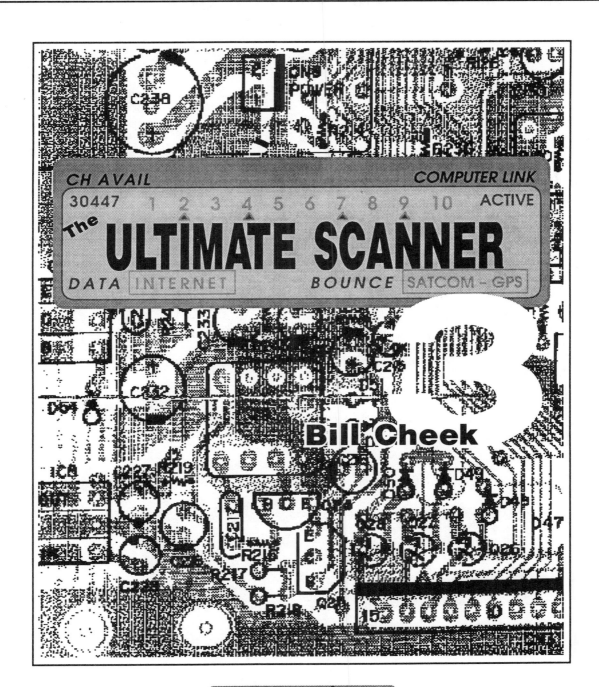

CH AVAIL   COMPUTER LINK

30447   1   2   3   4   5   6   7   8   9   10   ACTIVE

The ULTIMATE SCANNER

DATA   INTERNET   BOUNCE   SATCOM – GPS

Bill Cheek

Index Publishing Group
San Diego, California

The ULTIMATE SCANNER
(CHEEK³)

by

Bill Cheek

Copyright © 1995 by
Index Publishing Group, Inc.

Published by
INDEX PUBLISHING GROUP, INC.
3368 Governor Drive, Suite 273
San Diego, CA 92122

Library of Congress Catalog Card Number 95-075846

Cheek, Bill.
The ultimate scanner / Bill Cheek.
P. cm.
Includes bibliographical references and index.
ISBN: 1-56866-058-8

1. Radio--Monitoring receivers--Amateurs' manuals.   I. Title.

TK9956.C54 1995   621.384'54
                              QBI95-20063

Produced in San Diego by SOS Printing

4 5 6 7 8 9

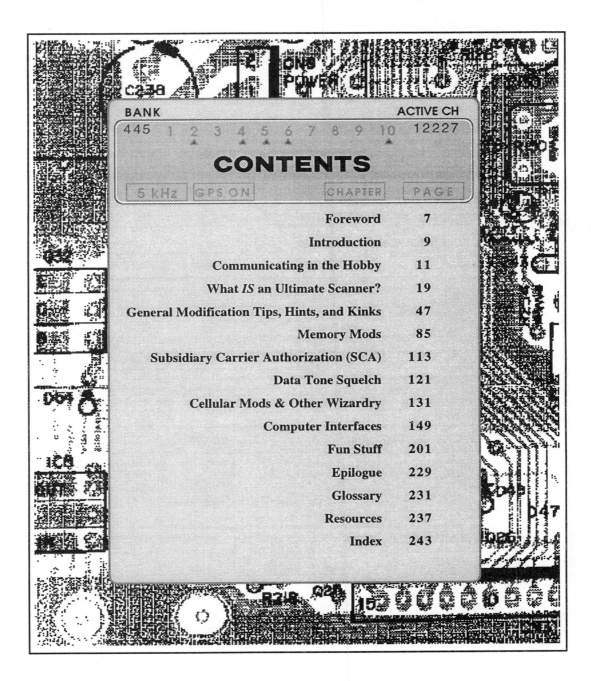

BANK   ACTIVE CH

445   1 2 3 4 5 6 7 8 9 10   12227

CONTENTS

5 kHz   GPS ON   CHAPTER   PAGE

Foreword	7
Introduction	9
Communicating in the Hobby	11
What *IS* an Ultimate Scanner?	19
General Modification Tips, Hints, and Kinks	47
Memory Mods	85
Subsidiary Carrier Authorization (SCA)	113
Data Tone Squelch	121
Cellular Mods & Other Wizardry	131
Computer Interfaces	149
Fun Stuff	201
Epilogue	229
Glossary	231
Resources	237
Index	243

This project is dedicated to my:

patient, beautiful, wonderful wife, Cindy
brilliant, lovely daughter, Allison
strapping, fine son, Ryan
ornery Pit Bulls, Sheba & Gonad

of whom all missed me these many months while I was writing,

and...

to daring Hackers everywhere, without whom this work would have
been impossible.

I owe debts of gratitude to:

"Professor Peabody" and "Sherman" for their endless contributions
"Mr. Digital," Mark Persson, who kept me on the righteous path
Bill Gillie and Dan Hughes for steady encouragement
Chuck Pergrim for launching me into CD-ROMs
Marv Shelton for what is yet to come
Tom Kneitel for opening the door
Skip Arey for whooping it up
Tom McKee, the Big Hacker
Ken Wells for the pin-line ideas
Fred Hatfield for persistently urging me on
Brian Greer for accelerating me into computers
The incredibly loyal Readers of the *World Scanner Report*
The FidoNet ScanRadio Echo gang for their endless demands and ideas
Linton Vandiver, my terrific publisher, who nagged only at the bitter end

FOREWORD

As a youth I read Heinlein. I'm glad to be around today, if only to see this amazing conversion of science fiction to reality. One night in Vietnam, after a few drinks, pilots in my squadron guessed when they'd die; the average life expectancy was only about 35. My estimate was also pessimistic, and once again I'm happy to be wrong. Even in the 1960's I saw clues that something exciting was happening, and I didn't want to miss it.

It's 30 years later, and I'm still here, and it's getting more exciting by the moment.

Unless you live in a cave, you're a witness to the accelerating pace of technology. Some experts believe the sum of human knowledge has doubled every seven months for the last five years.

Other experts disagree. *Their* research argues that the rate is every seven weeks. And then there's that group on a distant mountaintop that believes that mankind has already learned everything we need to know. But they're in the minority.

As for me, I want it all. Even if our knowledge doubled every seven *minutes* I'd say the same thing. The tools for increasing and managing our knowledge become more efficient every day, but what we discover is that the amount of possible knowledge is infinite, and as we grow more capable of collecting and processing information, the more we realize how very little we *do* know.

But the situation is improving, and communication is a major part of that improvement.

Both Elephants and Jackasses are trying to take credit for something called the "Information Superhighway," a road traveled by an infinitesimal percentage of humankind.

Today, the nature of cyberspace access means that only about 50 million of the world's people can get there. So one limitation is that the population of cyberspace is so small. Worse, access takes special skills, and works so slowly!

You see, the Internet, Prodigy, Delphi, AOL, Compuserve, and a near-infinity of BBSs all connect their memberships with strands of copper wire and fiberoptic cable.

That was advanced technology in 1975, when such systems were being conceived and developed. It worked well, and it works today.

But our information has at least tripled since then, right? And the next leap forward will handle an order of magnitude more information at an order of magnitude greater speed... but wirelessly. Here's what's happening, and why the savvy scannist is prepared for it.

First, the telephone system is slow. Twisted copper and fundamental physics limit its speed, and it cannot even go fast enough to support conventional television. Second, being connected to the world through a modem might be exciting, but because that connection is a wire you're not mobile! Worse, the interface to cyberspace is hand-typed words! How exciting can it be when you must sit down to enjoy it, and must use a keyboard?

But in either seven days or seven years (or sometime in between) a combination of wireless and speech recognition will change all that. The "rest of the world" will get hooked up not with expensive and vulnerable copper cables strung from poles, but with wireless links to hubs that uplink to satellites and then downlink into the network. "Wireless?" It's cellular, Personal Communication Systems, VSAT (very small aperture terminal), Personal Communication Networks, HandyPhone, Cellular Technology Two (CT2), and wireless modems by the truckload.

In this country, the FCC has allocated personal communication frequencies in high UHF, in low - microwave, and in mid-microwave. And the industry is moving rapidly to provide the low cost, high reliability, easy to implement components required by cost-effective hardware designed for those bands. Specifications that cost $50 two years ago are $5 today, and those parts are not only cheaper, they're better.

What can you expect? I would say "a wrist-watch pager," but the new Seiko unit just hit the local market. How about a 5.4 GHz shirt-pocket personal micro-communicator (MC). Like the Newton, but with voice recognition instead of handwriting recognition – and with a wireless link to the Superhighway.

I'll bet that (long) before the year 2000 you'll be able to buy an integrated unit that's simultaneously a personal telephone, data manager, tape recorder, answering machine, pager, security system, shopping system, newsgatherer, location system, address book, fax machine, garage door opener, stock market reporting system, weather data display, sports information display, pet-, kid-, and wife-finder, clock, computer, port to cyberspace, and coffee-maker. Okay, forget the coffee... Besides, the coffee accessory makes it larger than a pocket calculator, and the marketers say that's the limit we consumers will accept. And just who are the designers of such wonders?

In 1960, if someone said he was an "electronic engineer" you knew exactly who you were talking to. For the past two decades (as information increased by a factor of at least eight!), the world has watched the electronics industry divide into two separate parts: computing and communication. Radio engineers and the computer people each suspected the other of smoking and eating red meat, and they rarely talked face-to-face. Well, that's over.

The next generation of personal electronics will combine these once diverse functions, leading to yet another revolution in growth of information and our ability to collect and manage it. And in a Darwinian way, the universities are already spitting out engineers who can talk both topics! The world is moving rapidly toward goals that few understand today... but some of us will develop that understanding, and will take advantage of it.

Now, what about you? Because you already know how to spell "RF," can use a computer (you can, right??), have one or more radios, are technically nosy, and are very smart (check the glossary under Hacker), you're a super candidate for the new generation in communication and personal computing. There's already a small computer in your scanner, so the next step is to hook it up to a bigger one.

Bill Cheek's Ultimate Scanner differs from scanners of the past by many factors, of which the most important is the cable to a computer. When I first picked up this manuscript I expected to see a prescription for a new sort of scanner that could be built from scraps in my junkbox. But when I reached for a VCO and a bag of GaAsFETs, Bill slapped my hand away and told me that to have an ultimate scanner requires only a commitment to a goal on which the world electronic industry is already spending billions (trillions?).

That goal is a combination of radio plus computer. Okay, Bill's got me aboard. He's right... there's just too much information to handle with the old techniques. I'm tired of 3x5 cards, scraps of paper everywhere, and calluses on my programming finger.

Bill says that this book is only the first in a new series. Boy, am I glad! I was afraid that "ultimate" meant this was my *last* chance to enjoy the style and wit of that crazy fountain of knowledge. In fact, it's my *first* look at the next generation of our wonderful hobby: the marriage of the scanner and the computer.

And who else but Bill could send us there? He paid for your ticket! This book contains complete plans, procedures, sources, and parts lists for his computer interface, and he *gives* us the software! And if you decide to write the software yourself, Bill will even give you the Software Developer's Kit... *also* free!

As Bill says, "it's time to rev up your computer." Have you got one? No? So what's *your* excuse? If you don't have a computer, maybe you can trade in this book for a buggy whip.

And if you do have one, this book is the path to the future of our hobby.

You're gonna love it!

Henry Eisenson
LtCol USMC (ret)

Co-founder: *Sciteq Electronics*
Author: *Scanners & Secret Frequencies*
Audio Modification Manual
Rotary Wing Aerodynamics
The Television Gray Market
TravelScan

INTRODUCTION

Hot stuff coming down, Hackers!

A river of blood, tears, and wine cut new channels in the land since my original *Scanner Modification Handbooks* were unleashed. Laws changed; technology changed; ways of life changed; and I changed. You changed, too.

A metamorphosis ripped through as a blur in some areas, while others lagged and dragged, like growing grass and drying paint. Some were as pleasant as a root canal; others were as painful as winning the lottery. Many were subtle, unnoticeable. My life underwent some of the most notable of changes.

My two *Scanner Modification Handbooks* were banged out on an Apple IIe computer with AppleWorks software. I dabbled in electronic communications on a few BBS's with a new 2,400-bps modem that cost the better part of $200. State-of-the-art modems were 9,600-bps and priced upwards of $600.

Drafts of my *Scanner Modification Handbooks* were printed on daisy wheel and dot-matrix printers. In stark contrast, *The Ultimate Scanner* drafts were printed on a laser printer while others were transmitted to the publisher via the Internet, or on my BBS.

The Apple IIe gathers dust now, as a fleet of state-of-the-art PC's work full time around my shop and home on a local area network (LAN). Several computers are strategically located in my work station alone, while Cindy and the kids each have one or more. A notebook computer floats around the family circle to whomever needs it most at the time. Sometimes there is a scramble. We often need two or more computers at a time.

At least one and sometimes two computers are dedicated to my scanners and electronic workbench. One computer runs the Hertzian Intercept BBS, and functions as the LAN post office and server to the Internet – and to other worldwide electronic forums. Our computers are equipped with fax and connections to the Internet, BBS's, and information services with high speed 28,800-bps modems. Some of our family computers are "stuck" with cheap 14,400-bps snail modems. The kids won't touch a 2,400-bps modem now.

Getting the picture? Something happened! The common denominator is change. The times, they are a'changing, and we hackers have no choice but to go along because the nature of what we do is to react to the communication industry. And, overall, it's changing a lot, and rapidly.

Strangely, scanners haven't changed much, and the PRO-2004 remains a state-of-the-art receiver. It may be the best scanner of all time. Differences between the 1995 PRO-2035 and the 1986 PRO-2004 are less "radio technology" than appearance and software. This is opposite to the progress in the computer hippodrome, where there is no comparison between 1986 and 1995 PCs! How can the scanner and computer scenes be so dissimilar?

Scanners are not the only hardware on the Hobby Radio scene to suffer from stymied progress. Frankly, there has been little real advancement in any aspect of Hobby Radio for nearly ten years.

The 1978 Cobra 2000 GTL and Cobra 148 GTL remain the top runners on the Citizens Band scene. Ham radios come and go, but the top performers of five and ten years ago remain competitive today. Shortwave radios haven't made any quantum leaps in the last ten years. Radio saw progress, but not *Hobby* Radio...

Ten years ago, cellular telephones were black magic hardware, so costly that only the more affluent could afford them and the service. Nowadays, cellular phones are almost free. Before long, cellular phones might be worn on your wrist, like today's smallest pagers. You once could recognize a doctor by his pager, but today they're everywhere!

Cordless telephones have leaped into spread spectrum in the 900MHz band. And 800MHz trunked radios are ever-evolving to higher states of the art that help both industry and public safety agencies run efficiently and privately. VCR, television, and home entertainment systems are racing to keep pace with the technology, and new features appear every day as developers push to produce salable innovation.

As I see it, the thread common to those areas where radio is evolving at the highest rate is... *computers!* And that stands to reason, because the science of combining computing and communication is *the* leading edge of technological advancement. So why aren't hobby radios advancing at a comparable pace?

I don't know. Perhaps it is because hobbyist consumers are slowpokes on the computer scene. Perhaps the casual hobbyist is still content to manually punch in 400 channels worth of programming into a PRO-2006.

I do know that by and large, radio hobbyists are not very interested in computers, and most are no more interested than they have to be. Computing and radioing are pursuits in two different directions... or, they used to be. Today, they are converging.

Business and industry, however, know a little secret driven by economics: computers control communication systems more effectively, and at a lower cost, than humans can. Few hobbyists relate to that.

Sure, there are exceptions, and I am one. I wasn't always computer oriented, though. The Apple IIe arrived in 1984 only when my Selectric typewriter went on the fritz and couldn't be economically repaired. That Apple was barely more than a glorified typewriter until about 1990, when I began to see the light after my fingers wore down to the bone punching and poking scanner keys.

Now, not only do computers control my scanners, but also the test equipment at my work bench, my security systems, and almost all of my communication and research resources!

I no longer waste gas, oil, and time driving to the public library to look up information or to check out books. I *own* libraries now, in my computers and on my CD-ROMs. Furthermore, I have instant connectivity to the libraries and other great information storehouses of the world.

Before you get a nasty case of hives at the idea of wrapping your brain around a computer, consider this: just a few years ago I was among the computer-illiterate!

Many of you call me a scanner guru, but now, to other groups, I have become more of a computer guru. I'm not sure that I deserve either title, but I did set out in 1991 to teach myself about computers. I met the enemy head-on, and conquered. Me! You can, too. And you must...

Radio is poised on the brink of change, and unless you change with it your days of enjoying it may be numbered. That's because radio has not changed much over the last few years, but everything else has, and the status quo can't last much longer. Broadcast, land mobile, and point-to-point radio, as we have known them for the last eighty years, are becoming less and less competitive with evolving new communication technologies, and the move is on.

I think that a combination of emerging computer control, digital encryption, efficient modulation methods, better communication media, and legislation are forcing radio as we know it to seek a new balance.

That result is likely to include less radio and more computer: computing makes it possible to use radio channels more efficiently. And the more radios there are, the more congested the channels become, so efficiency is critical because there is only so much spectrum. So computers and radios are getting married, and we're there for the wedding.

Relax, this book is not about computers; it's about the Ultimate Scanner. Computers just play a critical support role. Now, look at the handwriting on the wall.

Even some of my visually-challenged friends and associates can see it. For you, it's there in plain sight.

Bill

"Electric circuitry profoundly involves men with one another."

H. Marshall McLuhan

COMMUNICATING

Making Contact With Me (and the Rest of the Hobby)

That's what radio is all about, isn't it? Before we heat up our soldering irons and get into the world of hacking and chopping our scanners, let's talk about scannists helping each other.

COMMUNICATING WITH ME

Readers may recall "Operation Assist" from my *Scanner Modification Handbooks,* Volumes 1 and 2, in which I offered to help those having problems with their scanner modifications. That offer exploded in my face with a fireball of well-meant communication other than requests for technical assistance. The volume of mail and telephone calls got far out of hand, as I spent hours every day with hobby chit chat, giving advice for this, counseling for that, and neglecting the basics of running a business and a family. I had to fall back...

Except in the rarest of instances (and don't count on your smoking, melted-down, scanner being qualified), I can't provide hobby tech support by mail anymore – nor by voice telephone. In rare cases where a mail reply is the only possible way to get assistance with a modification, I will respond to questions that can be answered with a simple YES or NO, if a SASE and a loose extra stamp accompanies the request (foreign replies required a self-addressed envelope and two (2) IRC's). On the envelope where it can easily be seen, mark "OPERATION HELP," which will get it placed somewhere in the middle of the pile. If I can answer your questions with simple YES's and NO's, you'll hear from me.

Take serious time to prepare your questions to avoid answers that require a lengthy dissertation, research, and time. I simply cannot provide custom advice, custom problem diagnosis, custom instructions, etc., by mail or telephone, and that is all those two media offer: private, *custom,* one-on-one exchanges of ideas. However...

I want to help you address problems encountered with your scanner upgrade efforts, but compared to the past the communication methods must change. First of all, please don't waste your nickel trying to reach me by telephone. For three reasons I am not available for hobby talk by phone: (1) My work is too focused to permit the distraction of coming to the phone every few minutes "to answer a couple of questions." (2) The *spoken* word is an inferior medium for conveying technical information – there's no illustration, I might say something bass-ackwards and confuse you, or your ears might hear bass-ackwards. Or both. And, (3) I am hard of hearing. My ears were made into notch filters by things that went bang in and around Vietnam.

COMMUNICATION PATHS

Though I won't use the telephone for hobby chit-chat, here are several methods (in order of preference) by which you and I can communicate on matters from technical assistance to hobby chat to private confidences:

Hertzian Intercept BBS: (619) 578-9247, from 5:30pm-1:30pm – my personal BBS (see text)

FidoNet Public Forums: Any FidoNet BBS (see text)

Primary Internet e-mail: bcheek@cts.com

Another Internet address: bill.cheek@f731.n202.z1.fidonet.org – e-Mail

FidoNet address: 1:202/731 – Netmail or Echomail (see explanation in text)

CompuServe Address: 74107,1176 – e-Mail, but no Internet replies from this address

US Mail address: PO Box 262478, San Diego, CA 92196-2476

NOTE: I cannot respond to hobby questions by mail UNLESS questions are answerable by a simple YES or NO. The clearer you are in framing your questions, the higher the likelihood that you'll get useful and timely answers. One Self Addressed Stamped Envelope (SASE) must accompany such requests. No foreign SASE's or foreign postage; they're no good in the U.S.

My FAX number: (619) 578-9247 *after* 5:30pm but *before* 1:30pm, Pacific Time

NOTE: I cannot FAX replies to hobby questions and requests for assistance. My FAX is primarily for business purposes – to make sure I get information in a timely manner. Use it to SEND info on hot developments or to submit items for my monthly *World Scanner Report,* or even to prepare me for a question coming in on my BBS. But remember, the fax is generally a diode – because of cost, *fax information flows in one direction only.*

THE HERTZIAN INTERCEPT BBS

For several reasons, I like to help via my BBS: (1) It saves time. (2) It saves me money. (3) It saves hundreds of repetitions of the same replies to the same question. (4) My cotton-bale ears are no handicap in electronic communications. And, most importantly, (5) it allows me to render a valuable service to a wide cross-section of the Hobby Radio Community – and *that's* satisfying!

You see, the tech support areas of my BBS are public conferences where a single question and reply can be read by hundreds of other hobbyists! Don't give that much concern right now if you don't understand this part of the concept. When you need technical help, use your computer, modem, and terminal program to dial and connect with my BBS. If you don't have a modem or a computer... maybe it's time? If you do, then here is all you need to know to make a successful connect with my BBS at speeds up to 28,800 bps.

Set your terminal program for <u>8</u> data bits, <u>NO</u> parity, and <u>1</u> stop bit: "8N1." Even if you don't understand this, your terminal program will show you how to make the setting. Also set up for TTY emulation unless you know your system can support ANSI.

Set your modem initialization string to "auto-negotiate" the highest possible speed. This is AT&NØ for some modems, but check your manual. Otherwise, enable v.32, v.34, or v.42. Disable MNP-5. If you don't know about these things don't be concerned; most modems and terminal programs are smart enough to negotiate a good connection. Most modems today comply with the standard Hayes AT commands, and if yours does then the following applies, and your modem manual should have everything you need to decipher it.

Include in your modem init string the following commands: S7=9Ø S9=3Ø S10=3Ø. If your phone has "CALL WAITING" service, set your modem dial prefix to: *7Ø,. Here is a good init string for many high speed modems:

AT&F&C1&D2&NØS7=9ØS9=3ØS10=3Ø

Dial my BBS at: 619-578-9247, but *not* between 1:30–5:30pm, weekdays Pacific times, when the BBS is closed.

Once you connect, log in, and are presented with "The Opening Menu," my system will take you by the hand and guide you.

Your major benefit from using the Hertzian Intercept BBS is that I prepare and post most replies within 24 hours of receipt. Call one day and check back the next for a timely and pertinent reply.

Most replies are posted by noon.

E-MAIL

I am also accessible via E-Mail on the Internet, Compuserve, and FidoNet. I will rarely provide technical assistance over those media because of their one-on-one nature, which makes it tough to help as many people as possible given the limited constraints of time under which I work. Keep that in mind, and use the Hertzian Intercept BBS for questions and technical matters that can benefit others, too.

Here's one other benefit of a public message conference such as my BBS: there are times when I will either not know the answer to your question, or give an incorrect one. You can bet your sweet patooty that someone will jump in there with the right answer or a different point of view. The result helps all of us.

None of this is intended to discourage *all* mail contacts. To the contrary, I conduct much of my business by mail. But more importantly, I really appreciate it when people have something to offer *me* by way of new circuits, tips, concepts, ideas, etc. The mail is a way for me to keep on top of what people are doing, thinking, and discovering.

My mail box is always open where the contacts and exchanges are mutually beneficial. But when benefits are one-way, I have to use the Hertzian Intercept BBS and other public forums. Please cooperate.

If you don't have a computer and modem and aren't about to get one, for whatever reason, you'll not find me very sympathetic, but at least try to get someone with such facilities to contact me on your behalf if you need technical help.

There is yet another way we can communicate: computer conferencing! Several amateur computer networks provide hundreds of special-interest, topical conferences or forums whereby people from everywhere and anywhere communicate about their favorite subjects.

To access this wonderful medium, you need only a computer, a modem, and an appropriately affiliated BBS in your area. I will tell you about

something in the next few pages that may be more valuable to you in the long run than the rest of this book. Give it serious thought!

COMMUNICATING WITH THE REST OF THE WORLD

As you consider computer Bulletin Board Services (BBS's), let me share some inside scoop on a massive resource of ideas, information, and opinions on hundreds of subjects, including scanning and shortwave listening! I hope this section motivates you to put a computer on the list of tools that support your radio hobby. It might well become more useful and rewarding than some of your radio equipment!

You may wonder how you managed to play radio without a computer. The personal computer has opened doors to all areas of human pursuit thanks to automated information processing, and an enormous volume of instantly available data and information.

The five-person office of today does what it took fifty to do 25 years ago. Today's serious radio hobbyist, armed with a computer and a modem, is better prepared for a frontal assault on the airwaves than an entire radio intelligence detachment in Vietnam! There are many reasons, including rapidly advancing technology, but ACCESS to information is the focus of this argument.

You see, information exists everywhere, but getting to it can be worse than having your teeth pulled with a pair of rusty pliers. Even public libraries, traditional storehouses of information, are rarely convenient and accessible at the precise moment you need a bit of data.

On the other hand, a virtual treasure trove of information need be no more distant than your computer and only seconds away from your eyes and mind.

Consider how it might take several minutes to research a certain scanner frequency in *Police Call* and other directories but only a few seconds from your computer's memory banks.

"Okay," you ask, "a computer is dumb until it is programmed, so how do I get the data in the first place?"

A fair question. There are a number of ways to put information into your computer and there's no escaping the fact that the task can resemble that of assembling and maintaining a home library of books and files. I said "resemble." Actually, it's a lot different in action, requiring much less energy, time, space, and cost.

One of the most effortless and least costly resources of information for your computer files can be found in that public network of computer bulletin board systems called the FidoNet.

FIDO!

A few computer nerds, led by Tom Jennings in 1984, started a small message network among their personal computers. Word of their effort spread like wildfire. Their system evolved into a world wide network of 8,000 nodes by 1990, 14,000 in 1992, and over 33,000 participating BBS's with dozens in every metropolitan area, as of this writing.

FidoNet vaguely resembles Citizens Band and amateur radio in the sense that it provides a medium through which thousands of people communicate with others of like interests across city, state, country, geographical, and political borders, and even oceans, all from the comfort of the home or office.

If you have a telephone line, a computer, a modem, and software to run the communication link, then the cost to tap into this leviathan storehouse of information may be nearly zero.

You need only log on to any FidoNet BBS to be connected into this worldwide network. If that BBS is within your local calling area, there is usually no cost at all.

You see, the FidoNet is made up of amateur BBS's around the world, with almost 19,000 in the USA and Canada alone. Amateur? It is expressly forbidden to use the FidoNet for commercial purposes.

Therefore, if you can find a Fido BBS in your local calling area, chances are you won't have to spend a dime to link up with the world!

FidoNet SysOps are private citizens, and just like you and me are very dedicated to their hobby. They pay for their computer equipment and phone costs just like we dig into our pockets for radio equipment.

Most BBS's have FREE (or low cost) access and therefore, through them, you can connect with the world without making a major investment.

ECHO

Think of FidoNet as a CB radio with over 800 channels or "Echo Conferences," each focused on some special interest topic.

One "Echo" in which you will be keenly interested is called SCANRADIO, dedicated exclusively to VHF-UHF scanning. Another, called SHORTWAVE, focuses on Shortwave Listening (SWL) *and* VHF-UHF scanning.

Other "Echoes" are dedicated to ham radio, broadcast radio, satellite TV, knitting, coffee-lovers, law, medicine, arts, crafts, etc. There are Echoes for religion, politics, adult subjects, recreation, travel, computers and, of course, hundreds more.

Those in which we are interested are called SCANRADIO and SHORTWAVE.

No single FidoNet BBS carries all of the (800 or more) Echoes, so you might have to explore a few BBS's before you find one that has SCANRADIO and SHORTWAVE.

You might not find local BBS's that carry these Echoes, but don't despair; you have options. (1) call other Fido BBS's in nearby toll areas. If you call at night, tolls are lower and less painful to your budget, or (2) contact the System Operator (SysOp) of each BBS in your local calling area and ask if he/she will carry the SCANRADIO and SHORTWAVE Echoes for you, or help you find a BBS that does!

A primary objective of a FidoNet BBS is to carry Echoes that appeal to its patrons. The SysOps will usually be open-minded to your request. SysOps are supportive by definition, and pretty much know each other and which Echoes are carried by the various BBS's.

Here is a scenario that shows a working FidoNet Echo conference:

I log into my BBS every morning to read all the new shortwave and scanner messages that have come in during the preceding 24 hours (typically several hundred). When there is a message of interest to me, or one that needs my response, I'll usually compose my reply on the spot.

Throughout the day, my BBS electronically sends the day's traffic upstream to a "Hub," that in turn dumps the traffic from a number of nodes like mine further upstream to a "Host" (a server), that dumps this greater volume of traffic into a "Star."

The Stars then push all that traffic onto a link we call the "Backbone," that connects to the various "Servers," "Hosts," and "Hubs" and in turn, back down to the "Nodes."

Each Node can be programmed by the SysOp to carry just those topics that are of interest to his group. In my case, most of the topics are obvious.

So if I send out a message today, it will circulate throughout the worldwide system during the day and that night so that everyone who participates in the SHORTWAVE or SCANRADIO Echoes will see my message the following day or two.

If a reply is made at that time, I'll probably receive it in the next couple of days.

DON'T WORRY, BE HAPPY

If it sounds complicated, relax.

You don't really care how it happens. All you have to do is read the daily messages that interest you, and respond if and when you want to. It will come to you, after a few sessions, how easy it can be to interact with thousands of other radio hobbyists.

You will find people from all walks of life participating in the FidoNet conferences, including experts, dealers, and vendors, and "Who's Who" technical people right down to the greenest neophytes. They're all welcome!

Again, relax. Wear any clothes at all – or nothing. It's an informal setting where the newbie and the salty expert are on equal footing. Participation in the SHORTWAVE/SCANNER Echoes is a great way to pick up the inside scoop on everything in radio, from what's hot and what's not, to hints, tips, tricks, and answers to your most profound questions about everything from Antennas to Z-matchers.

In addition to the public message system, FidoNet also has a semi-private "NetMail" system that lets SysOps send E-Mail between themselves, off to the side and away from the public message areas.

Many SysOps give their users NetMail privileges, too; a great service. FidoNet's NetMail system is a lot like E-Mail in other information services; a handy, quick and easy way to communicate with others on a reasonably private basis.

Some SysOps restrict NetMail privileges, making it unavailable on your BBS. It's the SysOp's choice.

Less known, but extremely potent, is FidoNet's informal "library system" called the FREQ or "FileREQuest system." Most BBS's maintain large data file storage areas filled with everything from freeware and shareware computer programs to treasure troves of information on various subjects.

Since radio is a hobby and a pursuit of specialized interest, most BBS's don't stock radio related information in their File Sections unless the SysOp is a radio buff like us...

BUT, there are radio-exclusive specialty BBS's around the world that stock hundreds of megabytes worth of radio information on every subject you can think of, with product reviews, mods, and frequency lists.

If you know what to ask for and where it can be found, you might get your SysOp to obtain data for you using FileREQuest (FREQ). You can also get files directly, once you know how. Think of this file system as a huge "library" system that can be operated right from your keyboard.

If you just can't find a Fido BBS in your area, send us a SASE and a U.S. dollar to defray costs, and include your telephone Area Code. We will prepare a list of FidoNet BBS's in your Area Code, arranged in telephone number order so you can determine which are local from your phone. It is a good bet that you'll get 10 to 100 or more from which to choose! For example, the Michigan (313) Area Code has more than 150 Fido BBS's; my (619) area code has over 250!

This introduction has only scratched the surface of the FidoNet and how it can be used to enhance your hobby pleasure – the details will appear in *another* book – someday.

You just have to try it for yourself. You'll see. And if you have any trouble, let me know and I'll try to smooth the way for you. In summary, let me just say that the FidoNet and a computer can bring a *worldwide radio club* right onto your desktop along with a huge library of help and data.

Every morning, I rise to a steaming cup of fresh ground Colombian Supremo coffee and a roundtable discussion with radio enthusiasts around the world from The Netherlands, England, Germany, Australia, Canada, and all 50 of the United States.

Even as I awaken, a wealth of info and data lies at my fingertips. All this and much more can be at

YOUR fingertips, too! If this doesn't motivate you to join the FidoNet Radio Gang, tell me what will!

Did you think Fido is all we have?

FidoNet is small potatoes in comparison to the behemoth Internet! I'm not going to say much about the Internet because if you know about it, you're either all set or *(gasp!)* don't want anything to do with it. And, if you don't know about it, then the Internet is no place for the entry-level modemer to launch his first great Adventure.

You wouldn't start your football career at the 50-yard line, in a game between the Dallas Cowboys and the San Francisco 49'ers, now would you?

The FidoNet is a fine tool for neophytes and experts alike – you can quickly learn the ropes, and then it provides a level playing field. Start there and you'll go places, and one of those places (eventually) might be the Internet.

THE INFORMATION SUPERHIGHWAY

It's a popular buzzword, but with little practical meaning because the concept is so mind-boggling. Simply put, the Information Superhighway is the path to the Information Age. Its potential impact exceeds anything Humankind has yet experienced. Now is the time to rev up those data engines...

Computers, modems, FidoNet, and even the Internet are but back-alley tributaries to the street that leads to the boulevard that runs into the thoroughfare that feeds the Highway. You ain't seen anything yet, Bunky. But here's a teaser:

It's the best of several worlds. On the roof of my shop is a 2' diameter satellite dish antenna that focuses into a 0.8dB NF/55dB-gain Low Noise Block downconverter.

Out of the LNB runs 75' of RG-6 cable into my radio and computer lab where it connects to a nondescript el-cheapo satellite receiver. That's the radio part.

The special satellite receiver decodes a continuous data stream from the G4 satellite and sends it to a serial comm port on my computer, where the data is processed and made available for use.

That data stream consists of a wide variety of information, from weather maps and forecasts to "USA Today" to the latest shareware & freeware software to newsgroups from the Internet to all the domestic and international message conferences from the FidoNet, including the SCANRADIO and SHORTWAVE Echoes, and several other major networks.

And that's just one of the many onramps to the Highway.

MASSIVE INFORMATION OVERLOAD

As a matter of fact, as much as 100 megabytes (MB) of data and files come into my system daily. Some is radio information, my primary interest. Other data relates to computers and computing, my secondary interest. Some data is for my kids to use in their schoolwork.

I can't begin to overstress the value and need for computers to keep abreast of all the latest in our radio hobby! You might think your subscriptions to the *World Scanner Report* and maybe a few other magazines like *Popular Communications, Monitoring Times*, and a ham rag or two are sufficient. Sorry, my friend, but they are not even close to adequate if you take your radio seriously.

Our minds can only process and store so much information before overload pops our circuit breakers!

We need tools with which to process and manage ever-growing volumes of data. The computer and a modem are two of those tools! To be perfectly blunt about the whole matter, folks, I see an end to some paper/printed information in the future. Here is one reason why:

I have 45-50 CD-ROM data disks in my computer library which contain things like the entire FCC USA frequency database.

There's more than 70,000 freeware and shareware programs, several encyclopedias, history reference books, sounds, dictionaries, videos, music, fiction and non-fiction books, and other huge volumes of information.

It really is a lot like having a city library at my fingertips.

But what to do with it all?

That's where the computer enters the picture – do you see now? A massive library at our fingertips, *and* a method by which to access and correlate data from the tiniest piece of information to the most voluminous five-dimensional database!

A public library at your doorstep is one thing, but you still have to be able to use it! The personal computer offers both the library and the means by which to access it. A medium sackful of CD-ROM's can contain more information than the paper in many libraries!

WHY PAPER?

The sheer cost of paper, plus the cost of printing and storage, is another reason the Information Highway should become next century's replacement for paper. Next century? Of course! Society doesn't turn on a dime.

Our present system will last well into the 21st century, but mark my words, it will change, and the changes have already begun! Even now, many books are published on CD-ROM, or downloadable from online services! Never again will I buy a $500 encyclopedia. I have two on CD-ROM that cost less than $100 combined, and yearly upgrades are a lot less than that!

When someone asks me a question by mail or over a computer network, it might take a lot of time to research the information from books and papers.

If that information exists in database format in my CD-ROM library or on my hard drive, I can usually have the answer ready within seconds.

MAKING INFORMATION ACCESSIBLE

This is a good opportunity to offer not so much a critique of the present as a suggestion for the future. Let's start putting the meat of certain reference books, like frequency directories, on computer disk!

Already in my library are several books, most out of the computer industry, that came with a supporting floppy disk!

It is high time that data/information books like *The Worldwide Aeronautical Communications Frequency Directory, Top Secret Registry of US Government Radio Frequencies, Police Call*, et al., include a computer database compiling their information!

Here's why: when a certain frequency directory appeared for my review in my mail box one day, my first impression was, "Oh no, not another book to read!" And it lay in my in basket for several days before I opened it.

I don't have TIME to read and research books, for Pete's sake! When I need information, I want to

turn to a disk or CD-ROM, hit a few keys, and have it in hand....bzzzzzzzzaaaaaaap! Like *now!*

Bzzzzzzzzaaaaaaap.........the Information Age has dawned! Let's step to its beat! Ratttta-tat-tat-tat-tat... Ratttta-tat-tat-tat-tat... Get in step or be left behind!

INFORMATION SUPERHIGHWAY AND SCANNERS!

A computer and a modem are about the only way we can get together as a group at one time. It is being done, folks, and it's the biggest thing since radio itself, this computer communication business. I don't have a feel yet for the percentage of computerized monitoring posts, but I get a steady stream of mail from people who would rather fight than switch.

Every holdout will eventually stop holding out – and get that computer. But if your computerphobia continues after all that I have said, let me invite your attention to your VCR, your washing machine, your car, your TV and stereo system... and YOUR SCANNER, all of which contain microcomputers.

Get real... if you're holding out for any reason aside from religious belief or economic factors, then you're not being honest with yourself. In fact, you're *cheating* yourself!

JUNQUE WORKS!

You can get a clunker on which to sharpen your teeth for $200 or less. I bought an old NCR XT-clone with a 40-MB hard drive in late 1991 for $200.

It's still in use as a controller for my scanners, and though it's doubtful anyone would buy it for $50, it runs my CE-232 Scanner-Computer Interface and PRO-2006 just fine.

TOO OLD TO LEARN?

NO!

You're not too old to learn these new tricks, either. A number of the visitors to my BBS are sept- and octogenarians! One says he's so old he doesn't buy green bananas anymore.

Even if you don't welcome the trouble of learning something new, the pain of learning computers gets to be weirdly pleasant after a while. So, if you are holding out, you're missing out – and that's all I'll say on this matter as we drive ahead into the Information Age – dodging the roadkill on the Superhighway.

YES, YOU REALLY NEED A COMPUTER!

Now, the rest of this book is a monolog. It's me talking to you, and you're stuck with that. But throughout the book there is one message that should come across loud and clear, and you're in no position to argue. It's simple.

The computer age is here, and computers are an integral part of communication, and of the systems that achieve it. That includes your scanner, folks. Remember, at the other end there's a transmitter, and sure as shootin' it's either got computerized controls or is somehow managed with a computer interface.

It's time. Stop waiting for prices to come down. Get that computer, buy that modem, and get into the circuit, for two reasons. First, you will get better information, and more of it, and on a more timely basis, if you use the BBSs and other media that are available to you only with a computer.

Second, there's the little matter of whether or not you would enjoy having an Ultimate Scanner... Throughout this book you'll read the same message, over and over.

A CRITICAL PART OF EVERY ULTIMATE SCANNER IS A COMPUTER!

Ladies and Gentlemen, bite the bullet and start your computers! Without one you'll have to compromise, because – *by definition* – the Ultimate Scanner includes a computer...

Scanner Queen?
Behind every great man there's a woman... in this case, holding a microphone. This, my friends, is Cindy!

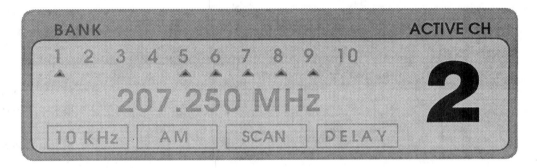

WHAT *IS* AN ULTIMATE SCANNER?

Hold on, now. When I tell you, you might not like the answer. It will possess enough of the following qualities to make your blood run cold and give your spouse a nasty disposition:

1. Goshawful costly – 5 figures, at least

2. Humonguously huge – 8-cu ft and up

3. Monstrously heavy – 100-lb plus

4. Butt-ugly – if your dog looked that bad, you'd shave his butt and teach 'im to walk backwards

5. Obnoxiously smelly – please don't ask

Really, you should determine for yourself the commodities, features, benefits, capabilities, looks, size, and economics that would, if you had them in your scanner, make life exceed your fondest dreams. Well, fantasies are over, so make a real-world list of the things you've only wished for in your scanner. When you can't add to that list anymore, you will have laid the groundwork for the Ultimate Scanner. The next step is to arm

yourself with my first two *Scanner Modification Handbooks* and perhaps the *World Scanner Report*. These publications will give you the warm-up exercises and preliminaries that it takes to go for the gusto.

But, yeah, I know... you want to learn what I think it takes to make up the Ultimate Scanner. First, you have to understand that it doesn't matter to me how costly, huge, heavy, ugly, and/or smelly it is. Those are incidental characteristics that have nothing to do with performance, and aren't factored into the equation when I set a goal. Performance and functionality count. Nothing else does.

You want the meanest, nastiest, most formidable scanner around? The one with the biggest teeth? I can assure you it's going to be big and ugly. For practical reasons, though, we will minimize the weight, cost, smell, and bad habits. Here are a few of the functionalities and features I demand of my front-line scanner.

COMPUTER CONTROL

I used to be good at hand-programming my PRO-2004 with its smooth, sloped, tactile-feedback keypad. I could get 400 channels programmed and running after only two or three hours' work. Sometimes, though, I made a mistake back in the first 40 channels and skipped an important frequency that belonged only there. (Gloom!) This forced me to choose between repeating the effort or accepting a flawed program. Nasty? Sure, but the alternative is to take enough time to avoid mistakes in the first place... *Hours!*

Yo! Hey! Scanning is supposed to be fun, right? Well, in this day and age, scanners with more than 50 channels that lack computer control are like outdoor potties, with corncobs, and Rears & Sawbuck catalogs. There's absolutely no excuse for such designs, but of the 400+ scanners produced to date, only a few have any excuse for a computer control port: the AR-3000, AR-2515, AR-2500, TR-4500, and MR-8100 and none of these are what I would call "good" computer control... they're more like afterthoughts. Each and every one of which I am aware has deficiencies in the implementation of the port or the accompanying software or both. I guess they're better than nothing, though... and at least those manufacturers tried. In many instances of computer-controlled radios, especially shortwave and ham, software is not included, period. Yup, out goes another $50-$500 for the software you absolutely gotta have.

I tip my hat to Electra Bearcat for their early 80's effort with the CompuScan 2100 (I think it was called). I never had one and I don't think it stayed on the market very long, but that contraption was designed from the ground up as a computer-controlled scanner. I believe it required a Commodore 64 to run it. Now there is a surge of interest in this old clunker around the computer networks as hobbyists try to buy one. If you have one, there is a market for it.

Uniden's only answer to the CompuScan after they bought out Electra Bearcat was the MR-8100 of a few years ago. It was designed more for the commercial market where apparently it was as warmly received as flies at a wedding. So the MR-8100 was dumped onto the hobby market where it generated little adrenaline.

The problem with the current crop of computer-interfaced radios is that they don't do anything much right out of the box except make you wish for more. As soon as you spend more money on hardware and software, then things start to happen... magically. Beware, what works with one interface on one radio might blow something up in another. Scanners are a different breed altogether. For the most part, if you want to interface one of the more popular scanners to a computer, it's going to take a 3rd party add-on package, of which several are floating around. Again, there's nothing compatible between them and they vary as night and day in what they can do and how they do it. This book is going to dedicate some space to showing how and what a computer-scanner interface should do. It's time for the manufacturers to wake up and give us what we want: a meaningful relationship (between the scanner and the computer).

ELEMENTARY INTERFACING

At a minimum, a computer interface should be able to AutoProgram the scanner's memory channels from a plain ASCII text file with the simplest of software. No proprietary formats; no sophisticated database managers; and yet the plain ASCII file should be in such a format as to be easily generated and read (exported and imported) by most any database manager or text editor, sophisticated or not. We're talking about a public-domain file format called "comma-delimited ASCII." Here is an example of the instruction that will program three channels of the PRO-2004/5/6 with the CE-232 Scanner/Computer Interface:

> **,38,158.970,nfm,D,L,**
>
> **,39,158.970,am,D,   ,**
>
> **,40,158.970,wfm,   ,L,**

Is anything there hard to understand? The first text line loads Channel 38 with the frequency 158.970 MHz, sets the NFM mode, sets the Delay function, and LocksOut the channel... the same program functions appear on the keyboard of the scanner! The second line does the same thing for channel 39, except selects the AM mode and does not LockOut the channel. The third line repeats the process for channel 40, but it sets the WFM mode without Delay, and LocksOut the channel. For details on this juicy subject, go to Chapter 8.

This was intended to give you a basic idea of how uncomplicated a computer interface's operation can be; black magic incantations are usually not required. A dead chicken at midnight might help a little bit, maybe...

A computer interface for the Ultimate Scanner should also be able to read data from the scanner and pass it to the computer for processing. In other words, a two-way street. The data generated by the scanner should consist, at least, of each variable that appears in the scanner's display: Channel, Frequency, custom settings of Delay, Lockout, Mode, Bank, etc., as well as Date, Time, and Duration of the logging. In other words, the computer interface should be able to AutoLog data from the scanner, and the computer should be equipped with a simple but powerful program to perform the task. I could go on and on here, but you get the idea....? Today's scanners need to be controllable from a computer, and the computer needs to be controlled... by you. So bite that bullet!

You've read a lot of accusations from me – pointing out the absence of computer competence and courage of some of my readers. If the shoe fits, wear it. If you're already aboard, however, think back to when you finally took that leap and bought your first TRS-80 (Level I) – and have pity on those I'm goading into taking the same step.

PROGRAMMABLE MEMORY

The Ultimate Scanner will have *programmable memory channels;* a lot of them. 400 is an absolute minimum and 1,000 isn't too many. Say *what?* Well, in San Diego County, where I make my home, I have identified over 20,000 active frequencies between 500 kHz and 1300 MHz. If your scanner is equipped with a computer interface, the number of memory channels is less important, but I still call 1,000 a minimum. Programming, whether by hand or by computer, isn't something you want to spend a lot of time doing, right? So the more memory channels in your scanner, the less programming you'll have to do. My TurboWhoppers are configured with 25,600 programmable channels. You'll see why (and how) later in this book.

Scanner memory bank organization is also important, but manufacturers just haven't caught on yet. The new PRO-2035 comes with 1,000 channels organized into ten banks of 100 each. Ridiculous! The 2,016 channels in the TR-4500 are organized into 62 banks; that's much better. Frankly, the Ultimate Scanner should have 1,000 channels organized as 100 banks of ten channels each. Don't hold your breath, though. Scan and

Search banks are controlled by the firmware in the CPU, which we can't alter, or even access. We can't do much about that, but the manufacturers can if we make enough noise.

The primary advantages of my 6,400 channel and 25,600 channel Extended Memory Mods is not the number of channels; rather, it is the flexibility of programming and organization. My 6,400-channel mods offer 16 blocks of 400 channels each, with 160 banks of 40 channels each. My 25,600-channel mods offer 64 blocks of 400 channels each, with 640 banks of 40 channels each. The number of organizational sub-levels between total number of channels in a scanner and each individual channel is an important logical separation to the human mind. Radio Shack's PRO-2035 with its 1,000 channels, 10 banks with 100 channels per bank is an operational failure. The PRO-2035's human interface is extremely dysfunctional, inefficient, and unfun.

The Ultimate Scanner's memory should be organized as 1,000 channels, 100 banks, 10 superbanks, 1 channel steps. See the 10:1 progression there? Because we have ten fingers to count on, we think and operate in decimal! The human mind is more efficient with such an organization to assist it. Mine is, anyway. How many fingers do *you* have?

KEYBOARD

Neither before nor after the PRO-2004 has there been a truly *efficient keyboard.* I thought the PRO-2005 and PRO-2006 keyboards were the utter pits until the PRO-2035 appeared with its keys haphazardly strewn all over the front panel. The sloping, tactile keypad of the PRO-2004 is the closest example of the keyboard that will appear on our Ultimate Scanner.

Manufacturers should pay a kinesthesiologist to design keyboards; someone who knows how the human wrist and fingers are constructed. For whatever it is worth to you dear Readers – my front-line TurboWhopper scanner is a PRO-2004, thanks partly to the efficient, visible, accessible keyboard, plus the next two qualities to be discussed.

METERS

S-meters (signal strength meters) belong on radios like gas gauges belong on cars. Most ham, CB, and shortwave radios come with S-meters; most scanners do not. I haven't the foggiest idea why not, so don't ask. But it sure wouldn't hurt to give your favorite scanner manufacturer a piece of your mind about the subject. Once again, here we have a bit of evidence that scanner manufacturers think we are stupid and don't know an S-meter from an odometer. Listen up: the single most important tool in my monitoring tactics aside from the receiver itself, is the S-meter. I wouldn't be without one! I've gone so far as to make S-meters for my handheld scanners! Let's look at a typical S-meter:

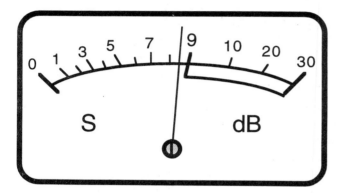

An S-meter is usually calibrated with markings similar to those shown. The markings between 0 and 9 are referred to as "S-units," while the marks above 9 are said to be "decibels above S-9." Each S-unit is usually scaled to be about 6 dB and S-9 is a reference, usually 100 μV, or sometimes 50 μV. This scheme of calibration and the associated markings aren't too important in the great scheme of things and we shall not dwell upon them at any greater length here. Instead, here is WHY an S-meter is important to the compleat scannist and The Ultimate Scanner:

In a word, an S-meter is an indicator of the relative strength of the incoming signal, after it has been processed by the receiver. Therefore, the S-meter can be used to evaluate the performance of the receiver, the coaxial cable, and even the antenna! Do you ever wonder if your antenna is working up to par? Without an S-meter, you may never know.

The predominant characteristic of an FM signal is clarity of the signal and lack of background noise. Basically, all VHF-UHF signals that register between 1 and 30 on the above S-meter will sound about the same. This is in stark contrast to AM

and SSB modes where clarity suffers and noise increases with weaker signals. You can't usually tell by ear, therefore, how well your receiver site is performing in the VHF-UHF bands because *if* the signal is received and demodulated, it will sound OK. With an S-meter, you can tell much more, and in a flash!

AN S-METER CAN CHECK THE WHOLE SYSTEM!

Suppose your present antenna is rusty, decrepit, and falling apart, but *seems* to be working okay. First, you monitor a NOAA weather station; maybe a couple of low band stations, a 450 MHz station, and several in the 800-1300 MHz range, writing down the S-meter reading of each. Now you put up your new antenna; run the same checks and measurements and the S-meter will tell you at a glance if there was improvement. Suppose the NOAA station registered S-8 before the change of antennas and halfway between S-8 and S-9 after, then you KNOW there was an improvement, and even if the station really sounds the same you'll soon see why the improvement is important.

The same principle applies when you change the coax cable: any differences will be visible. With some experience under your belt, you'll realize how the slightest physical changes in your station can make big differences in its performance. But now get this: you may hear no difference between S-8 and S-9 signals, nor between S-2 and S-3.

But if you do an improvement to boost an S-2 signal up to S-3, then signals that were previously *below* the threshold of detection at S-0 will be audible, loud and clear, at S-1. You just never know what you're missing until you make an improvement and hear things that were never there before. An S-meter affords a cheap and easy tool by which to evaluate your station's performance. But there's more!

It will also detect changes made at the remote transmitter. It will show how weather and seasons can affect radio transmission path characteristics. An S-meter is a sensory input from the world "out there" that helps personalize those cold, sterile, antiseptic signals.

Look at it this way: it takes all five human senses to get a good feel for an object or event, and a sixth sense doesn't hurt any. Radio affects only the auditory sense. The more sensors you have, the more personality and information will be found in the detected signals. An S-meter is a vital sensor for your monitoring warbag, and the more you use it, the more uses you'll discover for it than I have the time and space to tell you about here. The Ultimate Scanner must have an S-meter, no question about it. *Catch-22* is that most scanners don't come with 'em and only a few can be easily modified for an S-meter; they include the PRO-2004/5/6, PRO-43, and the new PRO-2035. Methods will be provided later for these and other scanners.

SHIELDING

Proper shielding is important to the compleat scannist now, but hopefully not in the future. Here's what I mean. All radios employ oscillators that can (and do) emit some of their energy as radio waves that escape the circuit board and pass through plastic cases. They're received by the antenna as self-interference, and as signals by the receivers of scanner-cops who might be passing through your neighborhood.

DETECTING A SCANNER

Preposterous, you say? Whoever heard of scanner-cops? *Yeah... right.... well...* anyway, the PRO-2004 was the last of the first-rate scanners to employ an all-metal case. When a metal case is connected to a True Earth Ground, shielding can be very effective, with minimal or no interference to adjacent receivers and less or no chance of detection by scanner cops who might be looking for contraband receivers. *Yeah... right.... well...* anyway, the PRO-2005, 2006, and 2035 successors have plastic cases through which RF emissions pass like water through a strainer. Most scanners now have plastic cases that make the unit much like a radio beacon, and does anyone really need to know you own a scanner? And if they think they do, would you want to advertise yours to them?

Gun owners don't put signs in their front lawns announcing the fact. Guns and scanners seem to have a lot in common these days, both from the perspective of governments as well as owners. Let me tell you a short story about governments, receivers, and citizens...

A country about 3,000 miles east of ours felt its citizens should beg permission to own and operate TV receivers and pay a stiff fee for the privilege. Some citizens disagreed, and failed to acquire the necessary permits. Not to be outdone and to collect his due, Caesar patrolled neighborhoods with sensitive detection equipment and identified homes where television receivers were being operated.

A check of license records identified those registered, with fees paid, and those which were not. Arrests were made; criminals created; and moneys collected or TV's confiscated. This really happened, and in a so-called free country, no less. You can only imagine, then, what things are like in not-so-free countries.

Well, if it ever becomes illegal to own a scanner in this country, you will have to either junk yours or ensure that *all* your receiving equipment is well shielded. You say it can't happen? Well, I say that government's first step is to limit their use. And that, fellow citizens, has already happened!

MECHANICAL ISSUES

Space and physical construction are very important to the contenders for the Ultimate Scanner. First, you have to accept as a given that no manufacturer will ever produce the Ultimate Scanner; only YOU will ever come close. Therefore, it is vital that your contender have a strong chassis with plenty of "real estate" on which to romp, stomp, hack, and stack things.

The PRO-2004 is a good example of this ruggedness; it has plenty of room in which to work. The PRO-2005 and PRO-2006 have adequate real estate, especially when the AC power supply is shifted to an external module, but they are neither as spacious nor as rugged as the PRO-2004. I have to underscore something about the PRO-2035: thanks to its microelectronics, there's almost enough real estate for a tennis match. Some of that comes at the expense of ruggedness, though. The metal frame is thinner and the plastic case weaker than its predecessors. Still, it will do... especially if you shield the case.

SPECIFICATIONS & PERFORMANCE

Performance of the Ultimate Scanner is hard to quantify by the hobbyist, because measurements at VHF and UHF frequencies cannot be made with your basic garden variety yardstick and DC voltmeter. If you buy a two-pound beefsteak, you can always take it home and weigh it to see if you got what you paid for. Therefore, instead of spouting a bunch of numbers that may or may not mean anything, and can't be proved by the casual hobbyist, I'll list some of the tangibles that should be offered by the 'engine' of your beast. Some of these 'tangibles' will be self-evident in published specs or in catalog descriptions, while others will have to be verified or determined using the service manual and instruments, or even by physical inspection.

TERMS

As this continues, you may encounter terms that are a bit alien. To reduce the number of queries on my BBS, I've put a glossary at the end of this book. To keep the book cost-effective, I've made that glossary modest. If you get stuck, remember: virtually every library has a technical dictionary...

FUNCTIONALITY AND FEATURES

Here are most of the things I demand in the Ultimate Scanner, and you should, too!

Bandpass filters in the RF preamplifier section (the more, the better) help reduce interference from bands other than the one in current use. The PRO-2004/5/6 series has seven bandpass filters: 25-40, 40-68, 68-108, 108-174, 174-280, 280-520, and 760-1300 MHz. That's one reason these scanners work so well.

Low-noise, high gain RF preamplifier section: hard to put a finger on, but a sensitivity spec of 0.5µV to produce 10 dB of "quieting" is fine. See the unit's specifications.

RF *and* IF Automatic Gain Control (AGC): hard to determine by measuring, but the service manual will tell.

Triple conversion superheterodyne, phase-locked-loop (PLL) controlled; usually found in the specs, though the term might be "triple-conversion synthesized," or something like that. This is critical to both sensitivity and the reduction of unwanted "birdies."

Double-balanced mixer between preamp and 1st IF section; identify in schematic.

Double balanced or balanced mixer between 1st and 2nd IF sections; identify in schematic.

Temperature Compensated Crystal Reference Oscillator (TCXO); identify in service manual.

Speed: 25-ch/sec scan; 50-steps/sec search, minimum; usually in the specifications.

Crystal or ceramic filters in each IF section; identify in schematic. Important because good filters *pass* desired signals, and *block* undesired ones.

Separate final IF sections for each of NFM, WFM, and AM modes; identify in service manual.

IF-derived SQUELCH and CPU-generated audio MUTE functions; identify in service manual.

The PRO-2004, PRO-2005, PRO-2006, and PRO-2035 generally meet these rigorous specs. Now we'll get into *external* controls and features, the most surely needed of which are:

User selectable controls for MODE (NFM, WFM, and AM); Search Steps (5, 12.5, 50 kHz).

Tape recorder output jack.

Automatic Tape Recorder Switch output jack (Carrier Operated Relay).

External DC power input jack.

External speaker jack.

Headphones jack.

Sound Squelch function: PRO-2004/5/6 and PRO-2035 only.

Center Tuning Indicator. See MOD-27 in my book, *Scanner Modification Manual*, Vol-2. Hereafter, if I just refer to Vol-1 and Vol-2, you'll know what I mean, right?

S-meter: MODs 25 and 26, Vol-2.

Data/Tone Squelch function: Chapter 6.

Adjustable (0-15 sec) Delay: MOD-29, Vol-2.

SSB Detector or BFO.

Programmable (per channel) RF attenuator in antenna circuit.

Programmable (per channel) CTCSS and DCS.

Manual tuning control – all displayed frequencies: PRO-2035.

Panel Lamp On/Dim/Off control.

The PRO-2004/5/6 and PRO-2035 meet the above minimums, or can be retrofitted (sometimes with modifications) to meet most of these needs.

There are exceptions.

FLOPPY DRIVE (?!?!)

I can go on and on, adding things and afterthoughts. Like, fer instance... why don't manufacturers add *floppy disk drives* to their better scanners? This would reduce the need to design high performance computer interfaces for the scanner, and it would definitely improve customer satisfaction. A disk drive doesn't cost much... $20 at the OEM-level, maybe? I'd happily pay $50 more for a scanner equipped with a floppy drive, especially if the disk could be read and the program files prepared by my computer.

"AutoProgramming" could and should be kept simple with basic delimited ASCII text to afford maximum compatibility among Apple, Atari, Commodore, and PC/compatible computers. With Commodore and Atari dropping from the scene, the compatibility issue for Macintosh and IBM/clones is the primary concern. No problemo in today's technology, when you consider those goofy LCD electronic typewriters with floppy disk drives for around $400.

So why can't we get a $400 scanner with a drive? I'll tell you why not... manufacturers think we don't know a floppy drive from a Sunday drive. Scanners are used mostly by 'Joe Consumer' hobbyists. Product demands from the business market seem to get more attention than consumer demands. Manufacturers employ professional marketers to talk and listen to the business community, but they rarely listen to consumers and hobbyists. We're stupid, remember?

I dream of a floppy drive in my Ultimate Scanner, but I'll be dreaming until hell freezes over because I don't know how to retrofit one. I do know how to fit a darned good computer interface to a few scanners, so this book has some reality to munch on rather than just whimsical wishes.

Frankly, I don't know HOW to get the attention of those dang manufacturers, and if I can't, you probably can't either. Therefore... we have to hack, cut, and chop our way into our scanners to make of them what we want. No one else is going to do it for us. If you can accept that, then you're a hacker.

SPECTRUM ANALYSIS

So, what else? A *spectrum analyzer*, maybe? Remember where I said we'd pay little attention to cost? Here's where we pay serious attention. Look at the $6,000 price tag on ICOM's R-9000

receiver with spectrum analyzer (SA). Sounds expensive? Well, once you look at the menu, it will seem cheap!

A spectrum analyzer can be important, depending on what the hobbyist is trying to do. This function is critical to the National Security Agency, and Fort Meade (MD) is loaded with them.

A spectrum analyzer provides a display of all received signals that comply with the operator's setup instructions. If you tell the SA to operate at 500 MHz ±10 MHz, it will display every detected signal from 490 to 510 MHz, with their relative signal strength. Useful? Depending on what you wish to do, it can be.

Some SAs are stand-alone instruments (Hewlett Packard, for instance, makes instruments at $50k or more), and others are configured as a card that fits within your PC and uses your PC for computing power and its monitor as a display.

USEFUL SAs

Grove Enterprises' add-on SDU-100 Spectrum Display Unit at ~$500 and up, with options, sets the bottom price in this field. Spectrum analysis just hasn't lit any fires on the hobby radio scene yet, most likely because of the cost: any decent SA is expensive.

The Ultimate Scanner can be configured with or for a spectrum analyzer, but such instruments are so pricey that I'll condense this topic till the numbers reach the hobby level. For those still interested in the function, at least four products fall more or less within the hobbyist's grasp.

Three of the four provide only modest performance, but might be suitable for those who insist on having some sort of spectrum display capability but want to conserve money. The fourth one offers serious quality, but at a price of $1,000-$3,000, depending on desired options.

You have to look long and hard at the idea of sticking a $3000 SA on a $400 scanner station, but a few potentially useful and "low-priced" resources are as follows:

Grove SDU-100

Grove Enterprises
PO Box 98
Brasstown, NC 28902-0098
(704) 837-9200

Poor Man's Spectrum Analyzer

> Science Workshop
> PO Box 310
> Bethpage, NY 11714
> (516) 731-7628

450 MHz Spectrum Analyzer

> A & A Engineering
> 2521 W. LaPalma; Unit K
> Anaheim, CA 92801
> (714) 952-2114

ITC SA500A Spectrum Analyzer

> Advantage Instruments Corp.
> 3817 S. Carson St. #818
> Carson, City, NV 89701
> (702) 885-0234 Fax: (702) 885-7600

BUYERS BEWARE: Such spectrum analyzers may or may not work with a given scanner or system configuration, and the buyer should learn a lot before making an investment. Contact the vendor's sales engineers to determine whether a product meets your needs and expectations.

DECODING — DECRYPTION CIRCUITRY AND SOFTWARE

Decryption of encrypted signals should be within the capability of the Ultimate Scanner, but the Electronics Communications Privacy Act of 1986 slaps the quietus on this subject.

It is against the law to decode coded signals unless those signals are to YOU, or you have permission by the sender to decode them. Yes, I know, you aren't the first to ask "How do I know if a signal is intended for me unless I first check it out?" I can't answer that, and I don't know how a judge would answer it; I can't afford a lawyer who might be wrong, and I'm not excited about finding out the hard way.

Besides, most signal encryption schemes fall into one of two categories. The first, called speech inversion, is so easy to decode that no one who truly needs security uses it anymore. The other, based upon some derivative of the infamous Digital Encryption Standard (DES), is nigh impossible to decrypt unless you can find some specialized Russian equipment on the surplus market. Because of the law and the extreme

difficulty of cryptanalysis and decryption, we'll not deal with the topic. But if you insist, you can find plenty of accessory equipment and software that will help you do it. Just check out the magazines that support our hobby.

At your own risk.

CONTINUOUS COVERAGE

The Ultimate Scanner should cover most of the range from 25 MHz to 1300 MHz, with no breaks at all. Unfortunately, a combination of the law and technology make this an increasingly touchy subject. My favorite scanners, the PRO-2004, PRO-2005, PRO-2006, and PRO-2035 have three segments deliberately deleted from the ideal continuous coverage:

520 to 760 MHz	UHF Television Band
824 to 851 MHz	Cellular Mobile Band
869 to 896 MHz	Cellular Base Band

It just happens that the 1st IF and PLL circuits use frequencies in the 520-760 MHz band, so even if reception were not blocked, that band would be unusable because of excessive spurious and "birdie" emissions.

Admittedly, I like to snoop around in this band because I suspect "bugs" and other clandestine signals can be found among those few and far between UHF TV channels. Why not? There are very few receivers that can access this no-man's band so I figure it's an attractive one to shady operatives and sensitive situations where discreet, short range, low power links are desired. *I'm right, by the way.*

A UHF TV receiver would not ordinarily detect these kinds of signals if care were exercised to transmit well away from active segments of the band, and separated from the standard audio carrier slots. It's simple to avoid detection between 520-760 MHz!

Some scanners *can* receive the UHF-TV band, but are known to be deficient in general performance and so I do not consider them contenders for our Ultimate Scanner.

You are, of course, free to do your own considering; you'll get no argument from me. It's just that those "other" scanners do not perform up to certain standards, and/or cannot be retrofitted with some of the modifications that are required to achieve Ultimate Scanner status.

The other two deliberately blocked bands (common to most 800 MHz scanners today) are the cellular mobile telephone (CMT) bands, detection of which is forbidden by the ECPA of 1986 and other legislation. The PRO-2004, PRO-2005, and PRO-2006, as well as a number of other scanners, *are* cellular-capable, despite the deliberate blocking of those bands at the factory. Clip a diode and you can listen to your favorite stockbroker or drug peddler.

Unfortunately, the federal Telephone Disclosure and Dispute Resolution Act (TDDRA) of 1994 (Public Law 102-556) forbids the importation and manufacture of receivers that can receive the CMT bands. Also forbidden are receivers that can be "easily retrofitted" to receive cellular signals! No more snip-a-diode/clip-a-resistor cellular-capable scanners for us, folks. In fact, the PRO-2035 is the first of the Ultimate Scanner contenders to hit the market that is *not* cellular capable. As I understand it, ICOM's world class receivers have the entire 800 MHz band permanently blocked. You won't even be able to monitor trunked transmissions!

Therefore, the ultimate contenders for Ultimate Scanner status may very well be limited to the PRO-2004, PRO-2005, and PRO-2006, if CMT capability is on your list of important criteria. Not that the so-called world class receivers were ever contenders in the first place... they are not, in my opinion, simply because they are NOT scanners! While most will "scan" a limited number of channels at some slow speed, they do not have the features and performance required of a true "scanner." Receivers by ICOM, Kenwood, and Yaesu are formidable, but they are not scanners and won't be treated at any length in this book.

CONTINUOUS TONE CODED SQUELCH SYSTEMS (CTCSS)

CTCSS was covered in Volume 2 of my *Scanner Modification Handbook*. It's simply a means by which a transmitted signal can control its own reception in properly equipped receivers. A special audio tone is added to a transmitted signal, and upon detection by the receiver the squelch is opened to allow the transmission to be heard.

CTCSS dwells in the off-center spotlight but certainly should have a place in the Ultimate Scanner, if it is practical to add it. CTCSS is not easily implemented as an add-on by the casual hobbyist because the required ICs have not been

developed for the after-market hobbyist. I have seen a few CTCSS products come and go, so if you're serious about this perhaps the components you need will be available. And perhaps not.

The only scanner radios (of which I am aware) that come factory or optionally equipped for CTCSS are the not-very-exciting Uniden BC-760XLT and BC-8500XLT. Radio Shack's 1995 catalog introduces a clone of the BC-8500XLT called the PRO-2036, which offers an optional CTCSS decoder.

Communications Specialists, Inc., at (800) 854-0547, is the foremost source of CTCSS products and expertise – you should contact them for the latest information. The model TS-32P CTCSS Tone Decoder & Encoder remains state of the art, and can be programmed by external addressing. If we spent serious time with it, I'm sure ways could be developed to incorporate CTCSS programming on a per-channel basis for the Ultimate Scanner. Again, the TS-32P module would be the heart of the project and only an external memory design would be required to implement it on a per-channel basis.

Some of you enterprising CE-232 Interface aficionados might contrive a way to let the computer do all this work for you. I'll have to leave this subject for another time, though, because there really isn't anything much new. Call Communications Specialists, Inc., for the latest technical scoop on CTCSS and stay tuned to the *World Scanner Report* for implementation news.

To a scannist, CTCSS is not very useful. You see, the technique was invented by professionals in the Land Mobile Radio services who didn't want to be bothered by any transmission unless it was aimed specifically at them. Today's two-way handheld radios include CTCSS so people don't have to listen to everything, but that's not the way it is in the scanning hobby.

Scannists generally want to hear fleas arguing over turf on a junkyard dog two counties over. For that reason, we dabble with CTCSS because it's an intriguing technology, but when a Decoder is added you hear *LESS,* not *MORE.* After a while, the sound of silence gets on your nerves and off goes the CTCSS...

DTMF

There are other sideshows down Ultimate Scanner highway that could take a half a book or more if I focused upon them. Take DTMF, the tone set used by your telephone. We hear DTMF tones on our scanners and sometimes wish we could decode them into numbers. DTMF decoders are advertised in the various radio magazines, but they're external add-ons, not an intrinsic part of the scanner.

The *World Scanner Report* featured a do-it-yourself DTMF decoder project in one of its back issues (the one that was discussed in Vol-2).

Speaking of which, HB Technologies (Spring Valley, CA), developers of the HB-16 DTMF Decoder, went out of business and gave us permission to print their HB-16 DTMF Decoder plans in the *World Scanner Report*. So check *Monitoring Times* and *Popular Communications* magazines for DTMF decoder ads; else roll your own. A nice concept, DTMF decoding, but definitely a sideshow, and definitely an add-on rather than an integrated scanner function. At least for now...

RECEIVING SIGNALS GENERATED 22,500 MILES AWAY

How about satellite reception? Sure, the Ultimate Scanner might be capable of satellite reception, but this is a specialized field that takes specialized tools and techniques.

There are several distinctly different kinds of satellite signals, each requiring its own strategy for detection, and none have become prominent on the hobby scene except for TVRO (TeleVision Receive Only). But *excuse me...* I don't watch television, and scanners can't receive C and Ku band signals anyway. For now, satellite communication is at relatively low power, and in bands that scanners cannot generally reach.

There's a lot of communication using high-power L-band, between 1.4 and 1.6 GHz, which a few receivers can hear directly or with a simple downconverter, and some new mobile satcom terminals. As examples, INMARSAT and the Westinghouse MET are using that range, but most of that is ordinary telephone conversations by people who can afford a private portable satcom terminal. Boring, right?

There's another sort of satellite communication you can hear if you already own a TVRO receiver and a satellite dish. This specialized mode of satcom that requires no modification to the scanner is called SCPC (Single Channel Per Carrier), a

method of packing upwards of a couple thousand voice or narrow band data channels into a single satellite transponder. Some long distance telephone carriers and corporations use SCPC as a low cost means of bypassing the telephone networks for their long distance communications needs.

TELEVISION RECEPTION

Those of you who have a TVRO receiver and dish can give try this experiment. Determine the IF output frequency of your satellite receiver – usually 70 MHz, but this can vary from one receiver to the next. It appears at the output to the descrambler unit, in most cases.

Point your dish at a satellite known to handle SCPC, select the appropriate transponder, and connect the 70 MHz IF signal to the antenna input connector on your scanner. Set your scanner to NFM mode, 12.5 kHz steps, and SEARCH the band from 55-85 MHz. If everything works you'll hear hundreds of signals, of which many are voice!

You have to answer the question: is this legal? For more data on satellite communications, contact Jeff Wallach, at the Dallas Remote Imaging Group BBS, (214) 394-7438.

BACK TO REALITY

So what is the Ultimate Scanner? Okay, I'll tell you what *I* think it is... It's a cost-effective, full-featured scanning receiver that can do all you want it to do at a performance level that meets or exceeds reasonable expectations. This is with the acknowledgment that manufacturers seem to think we are stupid and don't know what we want, and that we'll be satisfied with whatever they care to hand us. *Not!*

Ya' gotta start somewhere... The Ultimate Scanner begins with a full function scanner that provides space, power supply, and general opportunity for the hobbyist to add features and contrivances to satisfy every possible and practical monitoring urge. Here's some help...

WHAT DO YOU START WITH?

There's a lot more to the Ultimate Scanner than meets the eye... much more. The challenge starts with *turnips!* You can't get blood out of them.

Your cherished Snakebite XR-7265A scanner bought at a swap meet eleven years ago, won't appear on our list of contenders. Neither will that sporty Horsey-Cow HC-800GTZ. C'mon, folks... get with me. Ever since I wrote my first two scanner hack books, some complain that I didn't create magical "snip a diode/clip a resistor" mods for those revered Snakebite and Horsey-Cow scanners.

Whoaa there, hoss, I *DID* the research. There ain't a thing I can do for such scanners that wouldn't cost a lot more than a brand new, top-of-the-line modern scanner!

I continually get letters and e-mail from guys begging for me to develop some turbowhopper of a mod for their $89 bargain-basement, 16-channel, 2-band Widget that barely qualifies as a scanner in the first place. Hey, I'm not putting these instruments down; they have their place where there is a specific need to be fulfilled at the lowest possible cost. You don't find Honda Civics running in the Indianapolis 500, my dog can't compete in the Kentucky Derby, and your Snakebite doesn't make the starting line in the Ultimate Scanner race.

A candidate for the Horsey-Cow might be the Emergency Medical Technician who has to stay in touch with his dispatch center, even when off duty. For this dude, it makes no sense to spend $400 on a hobbyist scanner when an el-cheapo will work fine on the 450 MHz EMT frequency.

A drug peddler who wants to keep tabs on the local gendarmes doesn't need the Ultimate Scanner though he can probably afford to have an engineering team design one from scratch. Newbies to the hobby don't need a hot-dawg, rip-snorting, fire-breathing TurboWhopper.

These guys shouldn't even think about turning their Squeaky Sammies into the Ultimate Scanner. It can't be done.

Once and for all: I develop projects designed to make GOOD scanners BETTER, and they're for hobbyists – not for those who can support their job with a simple one channel receiver.

GREAT SPECIFICATIONS, BUT...

Let's take a look at a pair of nice scanners that ought to be natural lead-ins to Ultimate Scanner status, but aren't: the AOR AR-3000 and the Yupiteru MVT-7100.

The AR-3000 sports specifications that boggle the mind, goggle the eyes, and toggle the ears three ways from Sunday. It has everything: triple conversion, computer interface, S-meter, SSB, and a tuning control – this baby seems to have it all. That would be true except for the hefty price tag, limited distribution, inferior firmware, poor service manual, and the unresponsiveness of the USA distributor when I asked for technical information. The AR-3000 service manual (that I compiled on my own) is an incomplete composite of cutouts and photocopied pages sent to me by hobbyists over the years.

Based on the poor manual and the company's evident desire to keep secrets, there was no way my thousand bucks was going to find out if the AR-3000 was a worthy contender. You might say that I have a case of sour grapes...

Nooooooooo, that's not it. If it were, then some other engineer would be out there making a case for the AR-3000 to become the Ultimate Scanner. You don't see it happening, do you? But there's more: I talked with several owners of the AR-3000. None seemed ecstatic about their thousand-dollar scanner, and the average favorable comment was: "Oh, it's a very nice scanner, but..." There aren't many AR-3000's in circulation; not nearly enough to drum up any real interest in hacking it.

So if I bought one and invested my time and energy into it for a few hundred people, I'd end up eating out of the local soup kitchen mission. My decision was wise, in retrospect: the AR-3000 seems to be disappearing, and the former distributor carries another line of scanners now... impressive specifications, but the same attitude.

JUPITER

So what about the Yupiteru (it's really Jupiter, but there's no "J" in Japanese, and there's a final "u" at the end of many Nihon-go words). The MVT-7100 and its related brothers, sisters, and cousins are excellent, so what's wrong? Basically, they're illegal, that's what.

For reasons unknown to yours truly, Yupiteru created a whopper series of scanners that could cover from DC-to-daylight and do most everything but spoon feed you your dinner – and then chose *Europe* for their marketing playground.

Maybe these scanners couldn't meet the FCC's certification standards? Maybe Yupiteru thinks the USA doesn't have a serious scanner market? I don't know. But the bottom line is that Yupiteru scanners are not FCC certified and therefore are illegal to import into this country, and to sell.

Oh, sure, a few USA scannists bought Yupiterus from European distributors and then jumped onto the computer networks and information services to whoop and holler about their acquisitions. My first response to those who asked if I was going to get one was, "What about the Service Manual for these rigs?" So here it sits, boys and girls: a contraband radio cannot possibly contend as a starting point for the Ultimate Scanner project because it is doomed to very limited distribution. I can't pay a whole lot of attention to scanners to which no one else pays much attention.

WHAT DO I NEED TO SUPPORT A MODIFICATION PROJECT? DOCS!

Some people told me that the AR-3000 scanner could have become much more popular had I given it half the focus of the PRO-2004/5/6 series. Maybe, but I need more than hardware alone – consider the effort required to reverse engineer such a complex instrument!

If you think I'm ignoring a first class scanner, then before yelling at me tell the distributor that in addition to hardware, I must have a proper service manual and serious technical disclosure to support my projects.

TECHNICAL DOCUMENTATION

The common thread that eliminates many scanners from the competition for Ultimate Scanner status is painfully apparent: lack of service manual and technical data. I cannot put my effort into a high technology instrument without benefit and guidance of the documentation, which must contain at least the following:

Legible, professionally rendered, complete schematic diagram(s).

Assembly drawings of similar quality, showing part locations, ID, etc.

Complete wiring diagram(s) and interface data, of similar quality.

Parts list/bill of materials with part numbers, circuit symbols, and logistical information.

Functional block diagram.

Specifications and technical description of major circuitry.

Detailed alignment instructions.

Integrated circuit, transistor and other solid-state component pinouts, and functional diagrams.

Troubleshooting charts; key waveforms; typical voltage and resistance measurements.

If a service manual doesn't contain most of the above, there isn't a snowball's chance in a fast burning forest fire that I will mess with the equipment. If a manufacturer doesn't think enough of his products to professionally document them, then why should I invite certain trouble? I may fit a lot of adverse and perverse descriptions, but masochist? *Not!*

So that you will know how I judge a service manual, I will describe AOR's as inferior, Uniden's as adequate, and Radio Shack's as superior. ICOM, Kenwood, and Yaesu manuals are generally good to superior, but these are not just "scanners," are they?

POPULARITY

Here's another consideration: *popularity!* No, scanning is not exactly a popularity contest, but a serious contender must appeal to a significant part of the community and garner its support, and it must also generate a growing body of technical and operational knowledge collected by – and shared among – dedicated hobbyists. No one person can do ALL the work in this field. The development of a scanner hack usually involves several people, and preferably a lot of people.

Do you wonder why the PRO-2004, PRO-2005, and PRO-2006 achieved such popularity? Support of the product by the average consumer – *and* by the manufacturer – *and* by the serious hobbyists who hacked them and shared information.

Popularity means sales volume and satisfied owners. Popularity means size of the "aftermarket." Popularity means third party businesses that perceive opportunity to sell literature and develop accessories. How many books and aftermarket accessories are there for the AR-3000, and how many for the PRO-2004/5/6 series? I know of two third party products that support the AR-3000, but there must be hundreds for the PRO-2004/5/6 family.

Now do you see? It doesn't matter whether the chicken or the egg came first. What matters is that there are chickens *and* eggs; lots of both. It takes a good product that generates hobby support and third party activity...

The hobby generated a huge demand for the PRO-2004/5/6 series, but few buyers even knew about the AR-3000. That's not my fault; it's not your fault. It may not even be the fault of the AR-3000. Who cares? OK, if you are one of the AR-3000 minority, *you* will care. That's understandable; I sympathize, but I can't help you.

Your first step is to form an AR-3000 Users Group to gain some mass and then apply pressure on the distributor to produce a professional service manual. Then you have to convince an engineer or two that there is opportunity in the research and development for this fine rig. And that is where you will skin your knees. The engineer(s) may agree with you that it's the "best radio" ever produced. Then they will ask you how come more weren't sold. They lacked... *IT*. What's "IT?"

A LOOK AT RADIO SHACK

Radio Shack has the advantage of a store on most every street corner, but that won't swing the balance alone. I'd have to guesstimate that Radio Shack has brought over a hundred scanners to market since the early 70's, but less than 10% have been standouts. Sorry, but the PRO-2020 and PRO-30 together with about ninety others are... turnips. The advantage of over 7,000 outlets is nice, but that's not *IT*.

Radio Shack maintains a fantastic parts and consumer support facility in Fort Worth TX, called the National Parts Center, at (800) 442-2425. That's where you get your service manuals and repair parts for most any electronic product they ever sold. Parts and manuals are stocked for at least five years after a product goes off the market. Prices are reasonable, and delivery is quick and sure, provided you do the ordering yourself.

You may make a big mistake if you let a Radio Shack salesperson order a part or manual for you. You'll be asked a litany of questions starting with, "Isn't it an Owner's Manual you want?," to "What do you need with a Service Manual?," to "You're not going to work on your scanner, are you?," to "Would you like some batteries to go with that manual?"...and on and on and on.

Just order the dang thing yourself, *okay?*

But yes, Radio Shack's parts center *is* a great resource that certainly contributes to the advantage held by the PRO-2004/5/6 series. It's important, but even Radio Shack turnips enjoy the same support: so parts availability alone ain't *IT*.

WAY BACK THEN

A bit of history will show you what *"IT"* is. I was hacking scanners as far back as '81 or '82 when the PRO-2002 came out. I needed an S-meter for a professional requirement and of course, the machine didn't come with one.

So I hacked my way into the 2002 and made an S-meter. In the process, I found some now-forgotten diode (clip or add – I don't recall) that opened up the forbidden government band, 380-410 MHz! Wow! A bit more research produced a (clip or add) diode that allowed 800 MHz programming! Zounds!! Followed by gloom... the PRO-2002 lacked the necessary RF circuitry to actually *receive* 800 MHz signals, regardless of what the microprocessor told the RF circuit to do.

Back then, Citizens Band hacking was the hot topic, and it never occurred to me that there might be an interest in hacking scanners so I didn't even look. I still don't know if anyone else managed to hack 380-410 MHz out of their PRO-2002. I've been looking for that mod ever since (I never bothered to write it down and sold the rig five or six years ago) and nothing's turned up. Nice scanner, the PRO-2002, and it still rates high on my list because of the fluorescent display, accurate digital clock, and decent semi-sloped keyboard. The guts were nothing spectacular, but in its day it *was* a standout.

I hacked scanners a decade ago, and to the best of my knowledge I was alone. Then came 1986 and the now legendary PRO-2004. Armed with my knowledge of the PRO-2002's technology, and seeing similarities in the 2004, I hacked my way into it and discovered latent cellular capability, 100 extra channels, and a 25% speedup, all for free... nothing more arduous than clipping or adding diodes to the keyboard switch matrix.

I wrote those mods up into an article for *Popular Communications* magazine and before long those mods – and many others – appeared in other magazines. The revolution was born; others jumped onto the bandwagon. In 1988, an R. Roth, of Canada, offered a few typewritten and handdrawn pages of mods for the PRO-2004; Jerry Callam, of Ohio, started up a hacker newsletter, first called *The PRO-2004 News* and later, the *Realistic Scanner News*. Roth's mod sheets disappeared within the year and the *Realistic Scanner News* mysteriously died without explanation about a year after it started. One enterprise no sooner disappeared than two more were born, however. A Terry Vaura of Pennsylvania apparently was the first to contrive and/or publish a version of the 6,400-channel memory for the PRO-2004 in about April, 1988. About the same time, Tom McKee of Key Research, developed the now famous Search & Store Modules for the PRO-2004/5/6.

Several rudimentary computer interfaces had been developed for the PRO-2004 by 1991, and of course, my two *Scanner Modification Handbooks* became sensations in that period. When the PRO-2005 appeared in May, 1989, and the PRO-2006, a year later, it didn't hurt that their designs were virtual clones of the PRO-2004 with only minor additions and upgrades. *Monitoring Times* and *Popular Communications* magazines have regularly featured articles and hacks on the PRO-2004/5/6 since 1986.

Be patient... I'm coming to *IT*.

Even today, as of this writing, the PRO-2035 is a close relative to its three predecessors. If you're familiar with one, you're familiar with all four! For that matter, the PRO-43 shares some of the electronic design of these four. Meanwhile, the support of these better scanners continues to escalate now that worldwide computer network conferencing has caught on. We hackers and scannists communicate with each other around the globe on our favorite subjects almost like hams and CB'ers do. Questions stimulate thought; thoughts spark ideas; ideas ignite creative juices, the flow of which results in something being brought into reality.

IT!

It seems that *EVERY* successful scanner has generated an intense interactive hobby discussion!

That's what *"IT"* is, then: a synergy of thousands of people with a common interest, common goals, and the willingness and ability to communicate.

Radio Shack has nothing to do with it, though several of their scanners occupy honored seats.

The store on every corner, availability of parts, and good service manuals contribute a lot, but it's market synergy that creates the most successful scanners, and the candidates for Ultimate Scanner projects.

BACK TO THE FUTURE

While this unusual revolution about hacking and re-engineering scanners was launched with the PRO-2004 and perpetuated via the PRO-2005, 2006, and PRO-43, it leaked and overflowed onto the field occupied by all other scanners. The most common question from entry-level neophytes over the computer networks today goes something like,

"Hi! I heard that my SuperWhizBang CD-540YK Snakebite can be modified for 863,677 channels and coverage from 1 Hz to 645 GHz by cutting a trace and adding a resistor. The guy I heard it from doesn't remember the exact method, but he's certain it can be done. You know this one, don't you, Bill?"

The question is harmless enough, but it gets better when, after a few days, no one can answer the poor misguided fellow, and he comes back, all frosted over, chiding those who hold the secret to his Life's Dream and won't divulge it. Everyone nowadays seems to think they're sitting on gold in their lead scanners.

At the risk of sounding offensive, please listen to me when I claim that over 90% of all scanners are worth less than lead boat anchors in terms of getting anything more out of them than provided by the manufacturer's original design.

Most scanners, especially the modern ones, are just fine for the purposes for which they were intended and sold. When I call 'em turnips, I'm just saying that you better be satisfied with what you have; else peddle, pawn, or give 'em away and get yourself something that has some potential.

At the end of this chapter, I'll give you a list of scanners that I think are the contenders for Ultimate Scanner projects and those which have some potential for greatness if you dig in and sweat it out.

There is a distinction between those hackable contenders for the Ultimate Scanner and those which stand no chance. YOU must come to grips with this distinction because an understanding of it can save you a lot of grief and expense. The age of alchemy is gone; the Age of Enlightenment is here. Only a handful of scanners have any serious modification potential, and even fewer are contenders for the Ultimate Scanner throne.

I'll cover most to some extent in this book, but please don't get yourself all worked up into a snit because I didn't mention your Horsey-Cow HC-800GTZ.

WHO DO I WORK FOR?

Before we move on, I have to clear up one little misconception.

You may think I am on Radio Shack's payroll. ...*I wish.* I just praise, rant, and rave about a few of their better scanners. I'm a tell-it-like-it-is sort of dude, and I'll give credit to an enemy and scold a friend when they deserve it. Well, I don't like a lot of Radio Shack's stuff, but they market some mighty mean scanners, and they are convenient for parts, supplies, and support. On that note, we'll proceed so long as you don't accuse me of being on their payroll.

Basically, I don't like *any* of the manufacturers, not the big ones, anyway. I'm a former corporate president and CEO who knows what goes on up there in the headsheds. I don't mean anything sinister by that; just that their preoccupying interest is sales - sales - sales - *today.* Tomorrow will take care of itself.

Now that I am on a "sabbatical" and on the opposite end of things, I don't like how we're treated as customers.

TALKING TO THE INDUSTRY

It gripes me no end that there are so few effective channels by which we can communicate with businesses to let them know what we want in the products on which our hard earned money is spent. They'll say they're in touch with their markets, but how? Letters? Phone? *Ri--ght,* Ralph.

Try boogeying into your corner Radio Shack or Uniden store and tell them what you want in next year's scanner. Or call 'em up at their Headsheds and enjoy the interlude while they humor you.

You may spend hours working through the computerized telephone maze, only to leave your advice or want list on an answering machine with no tape.

SCANNER ECONOMICS

Let's do some simple math and see if the numbers converge on a reality... or at least a likelihood.

The Radio Shack catalog is a market barometer, and the current one dedicates about five pages solely to scanners and scanner accessories, with 18 models for sale! The catalog has 217 pages plus the index. Five out of 217 pages is a shade over 2% of the space. Is it reasonable, then, to guess that 2% of their annual sales derives from scanners and related accessories? Anyone have the latest Tandy Annual Report? ...in a minute.

Here's a second way to guess the size of this industry. Assume that there are over 7,000 Radio Shack stores, and that each sells four scanners per month (conservative estimate); that's 336,000 units per year. If the average sale is $150, that's annual scanner sales exceeding $50,000,000. The real numbers are probably higher, but the conservative figure is sufficient for this instant market analysis...

So how about Uniden? Let's be liberal and guess their sales are about equal to those of Radio Shack's; after all, a lot of Uniden product is sold by Radio Shack. The rest of the competition will be bundled in; so let's say it's also a $50M/year business.

Shooooey, that ain't hay, boys and girls. Now let's tackle some real numbers and check our work. Radio Shack's owner, Tandy, published its sales for the first nine months of 1994 at $3.1B, for a yearly rate of at least $4B. Wow! Their catalog devotes 2% of its space to scanners, and 2% of that $4B is $80,000,000. Our estimates look okay – or even conservative, don't they?

Therefore, a $100,000,000 USA scanner market is possible. OK, let's get real here: $100 million total comprises only a small part of Uniden's and Tandy's gross sales figures.

But the USA is about one-half of the world consumer electronics market, so one can guess the total global scanner business to be about $200 million.

That's just a medium profit-center to them, and it works fine as-is! From our end of the telescope, those numbers seem to justify effective lines of communication to cultivate this market.

But there's nothing like that. You can shout, but the only people listening are your fellow hobbyists.

OBSTACLES

I'm supporting the notion that if we want the Ultimate Scanner, we'll have to build it ourselves.

There are increasing obstacles, however. I've been told that Radio Shack has a policy to fire any employee who is into hacking scanners. Radio Shack is actively pasting a negative aura onto the mere concept of scanner hacking and those of us who do it.

For certain, neither I nor the hacking community have ever done anything to undermine the sales revenues of these corporations. Hacking our scanners is our business and it only serves to popularize the scanners that we select for our loving attentions.

I'm sure that a few more scanners than expected go back to the Service Centers for repair, but it cannot be an alarming number. This modern technology is very forgiving of error, and in all the trouble cases of which I am aware, the great majority of unfortunate hackers were able to straighten out their own messes, quickly and easily, with or without my help.

I know of less than a dozen cases where I referred the poor hacker to his nearest Service Center. And I know of only two basket cases that resulted from incompetent hacking. If the manufacturers worry about the potential for dramatically increased service calls, it's a false alarm. That's because in most cases the hacker will gladly pay for the service, thereby contributing to the profit margin of the Service Center. Warranty work will not be a problem with a properly written warranty in the first place, and many hackers wait out the major portion of the warranty period before ripping into the scanner's gizzard.

We're an opportunity and a source of revenue, even if you occasionally see evidence that the industry doesn't think much of hackers.

THE EXPECTED LAWYER STUFF, TRANSLATED TO ENGLISH

And now we have to put in a warning. Hacker books must have them, you know......

Radio receivers imported into – or manufactured for sale in – the United States are required by law to be "certified" by the FCC and labeled that certain technical standards have been met. This "certification" is more or less a blanket kind of thing, but it is based on the design and initial tests of production models of the receiver.

A manufacturer is permitted to place the "certification label" on the receivers after the FCC approves the design and test results, and may continue to place the label on all subsequently manufactured units without further red tape so long as the design and assembly are not changed or altered. When the design or construction of the receiver is changed, the certification process has to be done all over again.

How does this influence us hackers? Generally, it shouldn't, since there don't seem to be any certification rules as a contingency of ownership and operation. These rules are aimed at SALES of receivers. Therefore, it seems lawful enough to do whatever you want with your receiver after you've purchased it and before you go to sell it someday.

The manufacturer has met its obligations under the law, and as far as I am aware, no "modification" laws are imposed on the end user/operator. I suppose you could find yourself riding on the turnip truck if you did something to your scanner that made it emit such strong interference as to wipe out the neighborhood's television reception. Short of that, hacking your scanner is probably legit, though you might wish to consult with an attorney just to be on the safe side.

I am NOT an attorney and I am NOT telling you it is legal to hack your scanners. I just *think* it's okay, as long as it does not emit unlawful interference.

On the other hand, there may be a bit of a problem if and when you want to SELL your magnificent TurboWhopper Ultimate Scanner. Since you've modified the sucker from its original certified condition, the authorities just might deem that original certification to be null and void and thereby concoct ample reason to deposit your personage into the Federal slammer and your TurboWhopper into the Evidence Room. Sounds a little far-fetched, but far-fetched things like this can happen.

Just to clear my conscience (and stay out of trouble myself), I have to warn you to be aware of this potentially troublesome matter and advise you to consult with an attorney before you advertise a cellular-capable Ultimate Scanner for sale. Authorities do look at advertisements from time to time... especially radio authorities who, in their off hours, are probably about as interested in radio as you and me. Radio is one of those rare pursuits where it's fun to *both* work and play.

Remember that...

THE CONTENDERS, RUNNERS-UP, ALSO-RANS

And now, the moment arrives. I have to pick and choose among over 400 scanners ever made, looking for those that will get special treatment and focus in this book. Justice can be done only to a handful, for the many reasons already cited. The primary criteria for attention include the age, availability, and quality of the scanners. These criteria are, for the most part, objectively derived.

The only emotions possibly involved are toward those scanners where manufacturers or distributors were either uncooperative or where it was not possible to obtain quality service manuals.

With exception of the PRO-2004/5/6/2035 series (impeccable credentials and established quality), I do not buy scanners for personal review until I know my investment will be sound.

Manufacturers do not give or lend me scanners for review. Until they do, I have to BUY them, just like you do, at retail, in order to develop any substantial knowledge of them. I can't afford to buy more than a few and I won't buy just any scanner until I have a reasonable assurance that the purchase will be worthwhile.

Part of that knowledge comes from my extensive pre-reviews of the service manuals. Part comes from evaluating press releases and media attention on new market entries. Part comes from intuition and experience. And part comes from the user community which generally makes the best judgment of all.

The list that's about to come really wasn't picked so much by me as by YOU. My pick is really a consensus by the hobby; based upon our ability to support the best opportunities.

If your radio does not appear on the "good" list, please don't be offended; it is merely one of those rigs with which you will have to be happy pretty much as it is. There isn't really anything I can do to get your radio on the list. Turnips, remember? On the other hand, there is a LOT that can be done to most any half-way modern scanner, and a few things that can even be done to some turnips.

I'm not going to prepare detailed hack attacks for every scanner ever made. But there is a section that applies to most scanners and how to dissect them and identify those areas that can be modified or enhanced. You will receive generic instructions and a general plan for the hack attack. It will be up to you to apply this plan to your particular scanner. Remember, I can't cover them all.

MORE AND MORE CAVEATS

If your radio *is* on the list, don't do handsprings and somersaults; you might hurt yourself. Radios on this list might or might not be capable of all the performance you want. Also, I will not prepare a detailed hack attack for all these, either. As I develop a modification for a particular scanner, I will offer general tidbits on how to apply it to other scanners... if it can be done. Sometimes, a mod will be good only for two or three radios, sometimes just one, sometimes all *but* one. You know how it goes by now; we're at the mercy of the original design. One example is the group of extended memory modifications... I'll show the new techniques for one scanner, and those techniques are readily adaptable to the other dozen or so scanners that use the same kind of memory, and/or the same chip configuration.

If I showed them all, with every possible permutation, this book would outweigh your car.

SUMMARY

With this, my third scanner book, and a four-year publishing record with the *World Scanner Report,* I think I am in tune with the scanner community.

Still, there are some who can't be satisfied. Like the angry fellow in late 1994 who bought one of my first two books (published respectively in 1989 and 1991), and was incensed that his PRO-43 (introduced in 1993) was not covered in them. That dude came after me with both barrels.

My goal for this book is to concentrate on a few widely accepted radios in the pursuit of the Ultimate Scanner and at the same time, convey a variety of modifications for several scanners so as many people as possible can benefit from the Hacking Experience.

This is your adventure, so STOP! LOOK! LISTEN! Get prepared mentally, physically, emotionally.

Develop an attitude; gather some patience; pack your sack; stash your trash; open up your mind and let your fantasies unwind.......

ULTIMATE SCANNER STARTING POINTS, TABLETOP UNITS

Radio Shack	PRO-2004, 2005, ⁺2006, ⁺2035
AOR	AR-3000A*, AR-8000A*
Other	TR-2400*, TR-4500*

⁺ *Author's choice of best of the best*

RUNNERS-UP

Radio Shack	PRO-2032, 2036, 2037, 2026
Uniden	BC-760, 890, 8500, 9000* XLT
AOR	AR-2500*, 2515*
Other	Shinwa SR-002, Regency R-1600, ICOM R-100*, Kenwood RZ-1*

NON-CONTENDERS NOW, BUT IN THEIR TIME?

Radio Shack	PRO 2039, 2030, 2027, 2022, 2003, 2002
Uniden	BC-855, 800, 590 XLT
AOR	AR-950*
Other	JIL SX-400

ULTIMATE HANDHELD SCANNERS

Radio Shack	⁺PRO-43
Uniden	BC-2500 XLT
AOR	AR-1000XC*, 1500*, 8000*
Yupiteru	MVT*
ICOM	R-1

⁺ *Author's choice of best of the best*

ULTIMATE HANDHELD SCANNERS – RUNNERS-UP

Radio Shack	§PRO-43a, 39, 37, 34, 46, 51, 62
Uniden	BC-200, 100, *220 XLT*, SC-150B*
Regency	R-4030, 4020

§ *non-cellular replacement for original PRO-43*

...throughout, wherever you see an asterisk *:

I, and my fellow hobbyists who share information with me, don't know a lot about these radios other than published specs.

That's due to recent entry, no technical support, lack of cooperation by manufacturer and distributor, etc. They therefore cannot be treated comprehensively in this book, and are listed only because of apparent good technical specifications.

WHO'S GRE?

The PRO-2004, PRO-2005, PRO-2006, PRO-2035, and PRO-43, manufactured by General Research Electronics (GRE, of course) in Japan for Radio Shack, are superbly crafted scanners, readily available on the new and/or used markets as of this writing.

The PRO-2035 is the non-cellular-capable replacement for the PRO-2006, but makes up for that deficiency with an overwhelming number of brand new features and powerful capabilities.

FEATURES AND CAPABILITIES

The PRO-2035's lack of cellular capability and the possibility only of a 1-way computer interface certainly helps the PRO-2004, PRO-2005, and PRO-2006 retain the market's interest. They are not outdated at all! All four share much the same design, with the first three being almost clones of each other. The PRO-2006 and the PRO-2004 are much alike, though the 2006 is advanced in the speed, squelch, and selectivity departments.

The PRO-2004 can be modified to 2006 standards in all ways but speed – and maybe that too, though I confess I haven't tried. The PRO-2004 hit the streets in September, 1986, and was replaced by the PRO-2005 in May, 1989, after which followed the PRO-2006 in May, 1990.

The PRO-2035 shoved the PRO-2006 off the shelves in September, 1994.

Each of these four has special merits over the others such that I can hardly rate them against each other. All are "separate but equal" in my opinion, just like my children, the exception being the PRO-2005 which has almost no technical advancement over the PRO-2004, and which otherwise was downgraded from the PRO-2004 to a plastic case with an inferior keyboard. I see no reason to settle for a PRO-2005 unless you already have one. You're not stuck; it's just not your best starting point.

FAVORITES

My personal favorite remains the PRO-2004 followed by the PRO-2006 and then the PRO-2035 with the PRO-2005 bringing up the rear of the winners list. For you dear readers, I suggest a different rating structure, in this order: PRO-2035, -2006, -2004, and -2005. I have to put my own feelings aside for the greater good, your good, and so I'll emphasize virgin newness for wannabe and novice hackers. The PRO-2035 will remain new and on the shelves for some time; the rest are relegated to "used" status now, and unless you know what you're doing, the used-market is always risky. If you are technically savvy, you can go by my preferences, though most likely you'll have your own. If you really need a guide in a big way, then you can buy the PRO-2035 with a clear conscience, despite my teeth-gnashing.

Us old-timers generally resist new stuff, you see. You can think for yourself. Now let's chat about each of these contenders.

To help you make a good decision as to where to start, and what to start with, here's some insider stuff.

PRO-2004

Be careful with the PRO-2004 because early in its production life (early 1987), there was a run of units with defective solder joints! Apparently, the production wave soldering machine slowly drifted out of whack before the problem was discovered and corrected.

The result was that a few hundred PRO-2004's passed quality control in the plant, but failed some time thereafter. Radio Shack's warranty program caught quite a few, but some units performed flawlessly until well after the warranty had expired.

Symptoms of the problem include intermittent operation at first, and finally, total failure. The failure mode was often exacerbated by ambient and internal temperature excursions. (Solder metal expands and contracts with temperature changes.)

These defective PRO-2004's ran well at cooler temperatures, but as the units warmed up, operation turned erratic and then failed and often stayed failed until cooled down. Between warranty and after-warranty repairs, I would think most of these defectives have been remedied by now.

I repaired quite a few between 1987 and 1993. The stream seems to have diminished now with the remaining defectives probably having been junked for parts or stowed away in garages and on closet shelves.

This highlights a slight risk in buying a used PRO-2004 now. Check it out thoroughly before committing to the deal. If it continues to function after a thorough warm-up, I'd guess it will perform well in the months and years ahead, but troubleshooting and correcting defective solder joints is not an easy task, and will be expensive, if professionally done.

There is no known common failure mode in these defective PRO-2004's; the bad solder joints can be anywhere in the unit, and I have seen some units require several repair cycles before all the defective joints were found and resoldered. Fix one bad joint today, but another could pop up tomorrow, see?

I do not know of any comparable failure modes in the PRO-2005, PRO-2006, and PRO-2035. If you find one working, there is every reason to believe it will stay working. So now you understand why I rank these scanners a little differently, depending on whether the list is for you or for me.

I can fix 'em, but have to assume you can't.

VIVE LA DIFFERENCE!

There were two distinctly different productions of the PRO-2004, by the way, and the defective solder-joint problem seems limited to the first. There's both an easy and a pain-in-the-butt way to tell the difference between the two runs.

The hard way is to pop the metal case off the scanner; turn the unit upside down, and pry off the compartment cover to the Logic/CPU board, PC-3. Inside will be a large 64-pin DIP chip, the CPU. Early units had the chip number "GRE-0327" and later ones were marked "GRE-0327A."

The easiest way to tell is possible ONLY after the scanner has been modified for cellular capability. Early models with the 0327 chip will Limit and Direct SEARCH in 12.5 kHz steps between 868.950-870 MHz; and the normal 30 kHz steps between 870-890 MHz.

The 12.5-kHz step appears again between 891-894 MHz. Units with the 0327A chip will search the entire CMT bands in the proper 30 kHz steps. The chip has nothing to do with the defective solder joint problem, but if you're buying a PRO-2004 from someone, and it has the 0327A chip, your concerns can be lessened. On the other hand, it's always possible that the 0327 chip was swapped out for the 0327A, so examine the unit closely, if you can.

Caveat emptor!

THE FIRST MODIFICATION!

This prompts the first Ultimate Scanner mod in this book! If you have one of those early PRO-2004's that otherwise works okay, you can upgrade it to the later version by exchanging the GRE-0327 chip with the newer GRE-0327A chip, available from Tandy National Parts Center at (800) 442-2425. Order for catalog #20-119, GRE-0327A, circuit symbol IC-503.

Disconnect all power; remove the Memory Retention Battery; remove the seven screws from around the perimeter of PC-3; disconnect ONLY the one cable and connector CN-501 from the left-rear area of PC-3. The board can then flip up, forward, and over to allow easy access to the solder side of the board.

Removing that 64-pin DIP chip is not the easiest chore in the world, but can be done if you're patient and persistent and use a solder sucker and desoldering wick. Also, I hope you have plenty of time to do it right!

You may have to cut some pins away from the chip on the component side, especially those that are soldered to both sides of the board. That's okay, because you really won't need the old chip anymore.

Once you have it out, there is no good reason to solder the new one in! Instead, solder in a 64-pin DIP socket with 0.07" spacing.

Then plug your new CPU chip into the socket! Cheap insurance against blowing the new CPU with excessive heat or mishandling. Also, it will be a snap to replace if ever the new CPU blows for any reason.

If your PRO-2004 otherwise runs well, there may be no reason to rush into this hack, but I don't know how long Tandy will stock the replacement 0327A chip so it may be wise to get one before too long. No manufacturer stocks parts for off-market products forever, most being for about five years after the model goes off sale.

While you're at it, there are a couple of other parts you might want to stock up for a contingency. The first is the electroluminescent panel backlight for the (liquid crystal) display.

For some reason, these darned things wear out and need periodic replacement. The part number is GE-86D-6011. You might also want to lay in a spare front panel assembly and keypad overlay, part numbers GA-86D-6385 and GE-86D-6358 respectively. These latter three items, EL Panel, Front Panel, and Keypad Overlay will make your PRO-2004 look brand new which might enhance its sale if you're looking to peddle yours.

ANOTHER 2004 HACK

We haven't gotten to the real modification section yet, but I will highlight one more possible upgrade for the PRO-2004 for those daring and foolhardy souls willing to try anything. Besides, if you totally blow your unit trying this, you won't even need the rest of the book.

I haven't done it myself, nor do I know of anyone who has, but I suspect (and other expert hackers don't disagree) that a PRO-2006 CPU might be made to replace the one in the PRO-2004! The PRO-2006 CPU is a 72-pin, more or less square, surface-mount (SMT) equivalent of the PRO-2004's 64-pin DIP CPU.

Comparing the two service manuals, it can be seen that each of the two CPUs have the same number of exactly matching *functional* pins at 62 each. The PRO-2004's CPU has two "n/c" (no connection) pins while the PRO-2006's has ten "n/c" pins.

The process would entail laying the 2006's CPU atop a 64-pin machine-pin IC socket or header and with point-to-point wiring, connecting each of the surface-mount chip pins to the corresponding pin of the DIP header or socket.

Good luck... and as always, LET ME KNOW! This is how our body of knowledge grows.

THE 2004 DIODE MATRIX

Next, the diode matrix of the 2004 has to be rearranged to match that of the 2006. Again, comparison of service manuals is required. I'm not going to spell out the details here, since if you're ballsy enough to try this job, you're sufficiently astute to have already noted the remaining minor differences between the two switch matrices. Naturally, you'll exchange the 2004's CX-501 at 7.37 MHz with one from the 2006 at 12 MHz.

Microsurgery is definitely required for this job and with the cost of a 2006 CPU in the neighborhood of $50, this is not a job for the faint-of-heart nor those to whom disaster might cause a heart attack. So, if you're gutsy and had a recent physical, get out your blowtorch and crowbar!

There is plenty of risk here, and if the project is successful the rewards might be worth it only to the most dedicated hobbyist who leaves no stone unturned. Benefits of the updated firmware of the 2006's CPU over the 2004's really boil down to a max speed boost from 20-ch/sec to 30-ch/sec, diode speedups already considered.

If this job is successful, then modifying squelch (Chapter 6) and selectivity (I'm working on it!) will give you a PRO-2006 in PRO-2004's clothing; clearly the best of two worlds.

2004 SUMMARY

Summarizing the PRO-2004, it's an excellent scanner that either has all the specs and capabilities of the PRO-2006 or that can be brought up to most specs with relative ease.

The PRO-2004 is unique, without peer, given rugged construction, metal cabinet, sloped front panel, large display, and a smooth, tactile keyboard on which (after some practice) your fingers can really fly!

The PRO-2004 has plenty of real estate for modifications and add-ons. The downside is its age and slight potential for solder joint problems. If you can live with that, then the PRO-2004 is as competitive as any and better than most, and clearly qualifies as a foundation for the Ultimate Scanner. I see used PRO-2004's continually appear on the market for between $25 and $150 with about $75 typical and reasonable. Professionally hacked and upgraded PRO-2004's command much higher prices, though.

PRO-2005

The PRO-2005 is little more than a repackaged PRO-2004. The AM section sports a ceramic IF filter for better aero band selectivity than its predecessor; otherwise, its entire electronics layout was changed for the new chassis and case that were to become standard in the product line.

The front panel is nearly vertical and the keypad reduced in size and refitted with discrete buttons, making operation more of a chore, especially for southpaws and for those with large hands. The display is functionally the same as that of the PRO-2004, but smaller and harder to view.

Still... if you have one of these units, it might be easier to upgrade to 2006 specs than the PRO-2004, with a simple squelch modification and replacement of the stock CPU with one from the PRO-2006; a drop-in replacement. By "drop-in," I mean pin-for-pin replaceable.

Unsoldering those 72-pins without damaging the Logic/CPU board is easier said than done, but I have done it. Of course, CX-501 at 7.37 MHz needs to be replaced with the 12 MHz version from the PRO-2006. The keyboard matrix needs to be made to match that of the PRO-2006, but you'll know what to do there if you're capable of replacing the CPU.

Another possible way to upgrade to PRO-2006 specs is to replace the entire Logic/CPU Board with one from the 2006. The expense of this at just under $200 is probably not worth it just to get 30-ch/sec. Also, Radio Shack Service Centers and Tandy National Parts will not ordinarily sell you an entire board.

I mention this only because I have heard of it being done. I've tried to get boards and they won't sell them to me. The 2005 had such a short market-life you don't see too many used ones on the market. Prices vary wildly, but I'd not pay more than about $50 for a clean one.

Summarizing the PRO-2005, it's a PRO-2004 with missing advantages, but it is a good unit. If you already have a PRO-2005, then use it. You're sitting on a machine with potential to manipulate it into the Ultimate Scanner of your dreams.

PRO-2006

For many of you, this is the best there is! The scanner market was sound asleep when the PRO-2004 was introduced in 1986, and by the time people woke up the 2004 had been replaced by the 2005 – which lasted but a year.

The PRO-2006 was introduced during a period when the scanner market literally exploded and went through the roof. It stayed on sale for four years of a boom market, and I would guess there are maybe a quarter-million or more of them "out there" now.

If your scanner budget is tight, hang loose because more and more of these will appear on the used market in the months and years ahead. Expect prices to range between $125 and $300 through 1996.

Beware that a change of faceplates on a 2005 with one for a PRO-2006 can conceal the scanner's identity. It's not foolproof, but check the label on the rear chassis before buying a used "PRO-2006." Better to pop the top cover and look for "TP-2" on the main receiver board. In the PRO-2006, TP-2 is near T-6 and D-33 while in the PRO-2005, TP-2 is located next to IC-2, Pin 9, and CN-4.

There are other ways to tell the difference between a bogus PRO-2006 and a real one, but the foregoing is about the quickest, easiest, and most certain.

I know about this scam of dressing up a PRO-2005 in 2006's clothing, thanks to a fellow who had requested assistance from me about a modification on his 2006. I asked him to take a measurement at TP-2, but he reported back that it didn't exist! Huh? Later he wrote to proclaim that I must have been mixed up... "TP-2 was located by IC-2!" Whooooaaa there, Hoss... *brakes! Screech! Halt!* Turns out he had just bought his scanner from a Radio Shack store... it came with a box, front panel, rear label, and owner's manual for a PRO-2006, but TP-2 was located by IC-2!

That's a PRO-2005, boys and girls, no two ways about it. Some double and triple checks confirmed it, so I referred the fellow to his local Radio Shack District Manager and never heard from him again.

I have since determined that it is relatively easy to remove that label on the rear chassis and replace it. Exchanges of the front panel are a piece of cake. Scan speed is not a very good indicator of which scanner it is, because a couple of speedup mods can push the PRO-2005 close to 2006 specs.

So let buyers of used PRO-2006's beware – there is enough difference between the two that if you pay attention, you can prevent the possible scam.

TELLING THE DIFFERENCE

There were two distinctly different productions of the PRO-2006, by the way, but there is no functional difference between the PRO-2006 and the PRO-2006A, distinguishable by either of two methods.

The PRO-2006A is noted by its "Light" switch on the front panel and the catalog number of 20-145A on the real panel label.

The PRO-2006 is distinguished by the "Dimmer" switch on the front panel and the catalog number of 20-145 on the rear panel label. The first two years of the PRO-2006 had the dimmer switch which brightened or dimmed the blue LCD backlight, while the last two years of PRO-2006's had the "Light" switch which just turned the backlight on and off. That is the only difference between the two units, and it is not significant.

I suppose of the two, the better is the 2006A, because keeping the backlight turned off when not needed will prolong its life somewhat. That's splitting hairs!

The PRO-2006 is a righteous scanner with a ton of performance and an ounce of drawbacks. Drawbacks are but two: the unrecoverable gap between 520-760 MHz, and the poorly designed keyboard.

Any other shortcomings are common to most all scanners, for the most part and need not be dwelt upon here. Performance is rock solid, with good sensitivity, good selectivity, immunity to image frequency interference and most other forms of pseudo interference including intermod and strong-signal overload.

Of course, the PRO-2004/5 and 2035 share this advantage for the most part, too. The PRO-2006 is highly modifiable, exceptionally forgiving of error, and will be supported by Tandy National Parts for the next several years. The PRO-2006 is the latest, newest, and most potent of all widely available scanners to go onto the used market. There just isn't anything much really bad to say against the PRO-2006, so it's right up there as one of the best choices as a pathway to the Ultimate Scanner.

PRO-2035

I have this new scanner in my paws, hot off the assembly line, but there's not much I can say here, yet. It's good, and we're off to a great start, but the BBS needs input from all you hackers so we can really get going on this one.

I can highlight some ups and downs about the PRO-2035 here, based on my experience with it so far. For the latest on this fine unit, including the continuing saga of specific modifications for it and worldwide user experience, you'll need to take out a subscription to the *World Scanner Report* where we'll keep it current and under continued development.

EVOLUTION

The PRO-2035 is very much like its ancestors, the PRO-2004/5/6, in its fundamental design. There are differences, but they are mostly enhancements rather than fundamental changes.

The first major difference I saw was a new Master Reference Oscillator, X-301, in the PLL section in the shielded compartment just behind the tuning knob. This one is 12 MHz in contrast to the 10 MHz version used in the PRO-2004/5/6. Otherwise, the PLL section is similar to that of its predecessors.

Another difference that jumped up and bit me on the nose was an apparent lack of a Memory Retention Battery, but then I found it, a 3-volt "button" type lithium cell soldered in place on the main receiver board! This is going to pose problems for the casual "Joe" who doesn't know a soldering iron from a tire iron.

We hackers will manage nicely, since Radio Shack will probably stock these batteries for one thing and replacing it will be a piece of cake to those who know how.

The harder-to-replace Memory Retention Battery might suggest that Radio Shack thinks it won't need replacement very often. I'm not sure I see how that can be since for all intents and purposes, the memory chip is about the same as that of its predecessors, which we all know can drain a 9-volt battery in a year or so.

We'll see...

MEMORY

The PRO-2035 uses not a 2k x 8 SRAM (16k) like its predecessors, but an 8k x 8 (64k) S-RAM. Therefore, my standard memory mods will work well without deviation from procedure. A 32k x 8 SRAM will provide 4,000 channels while a 128k x 8 SRAM will yield 16,000 channels. See the modification section for the latest variants of how my MOD-16 Extended Memory will be possible for the PRO-2035. 4,000-16,000 channels should suffice for most needs, eh?

THE BOARDS AND DISPLAY

The PRO-2035 has only two printed circuit boards, both much easier to access and hack than those of the PRO-2004/5/6. The Main Receiver board is out in the wide-open spaces, top and bottom, so that removal will rarely if ever be necessary.

You can get to most everything here! The Logic/CPU board is also easier to access with no soldered-down shields nor cramped quarters as in the PRO-2005/6.

It's hard to beat the ease of access to the Logic/CPU board in the PRO-2004, but the PRO-2035 comes close.

The PRO-2035 does not have a separate LCD driver chip like the PRO-2004/5/6, which means that it's located in the CPU chip where we can't access it. That precludes a full adaptation of the CE-232 Interface to this rig. A one-way interface using the CE-232 for AutoProgramming and Keyboard Controlling from the PC has been successfully implemented, but the data acquisition side seems improbable without the ability to access the serial data and serial clock lines between the CPU and LCD driver.

The trouble-prone electroluminescent backlight panel (EL Panel) of the PRO-2004/5/6 series has finally given way to a modern concept: light emitting diodes! The PRO-2035's LCD Display is illuminated from the rear by nine bright yellow-green LEDs to produce an adequate contrast with a rather sick color. I guess blue LEDs are still too expensive for Radio Shack's blood, but if you don't like the sick green, it may be possible to change LED's for a back-light color of choice.

MORE COMPARISONS

In terms of hardware, I see very little that can be called "new" in the PRO-2035 with exception of the "TUNING" knob and its related functions. This means that most of the feature differences are a matter of firmware that's permanently programmed into the CPU. Firmware features are a problem to us hackers because it makes the receiver more and more like a computer that's dependent on the quality of its software as to what can be done with it.

Well, modern software is really hard, if not impossible, to hack. Uniden has long relied on firmware to make its scanners seem so attractive, but when you start trading off hardware for software, there is always a loss of quality. This is especially applicable to both computers and radios, because it's the hardware that determines quality while software or firmware determines what and how much you can use that hardware.

Well, the PRO-2035 seems not to have lost much of the hardware sported by its predecessors and at the same time, it gained a lot of firmware. In the final analysis, it is probably the best overall receiver so far in the series, but it may well be the last of the best, too, if the move to firmware is any indicator.

The PRO-2035 is definitely a hands-on scanner in the sense that its new features of channel and frequency management are controlled from the unappealing keyboard. That is to say that you can move frequencies around from channel to channel or even move whole groups of frequencies at one time by keyboard manipulations... a nice touch.

But that's "firmware" for you.

Even the TUNING knob is more a matter of firmware than hardware. Knobs are knobs, and this one goes straight to the CPU if that tells you anything. When you control a CPU, then you're controlling the firmware, or exactly what the manufacturer wants you to control, and nothing more. Understand? Comprende? Savvy? Wakaremasuka?

Just keep in mind when you look at flashy features on an as-yet unreleased, six ounce, micro-sized SuperWhizBang that it consists of a case and a chip, so you cannot get to the guts of it. The more discrete components, the easier it is to hack. The more highly integrated (fewer chips and inaccessible programming, or firmware), the tougher.

Fortunately, the PRO-2035 retains much the same electronic design as its predecessors, which means, firmware or no firmware, there will be a lot we can do to polish this baby: S-meter, Center-Tune Meter, Extended Delay, Automatic Tape Recorder Switch, Extended Memory, and much more.

Given time, this unit *will* evolve!

SUMMARY OF THE WINNERS

Any of the PRO-2004/5/6 and PRO-2035 units will make a fine cornerstone for the Ultimate Scanner of your dreams.

It's a tossup as to the best of the best and I won't make that choice for you. Each has advantages over the others, but the PRO-2005 is slightly behind the front runners since it is a repackaged PRO-2004, and misses a few niceties.

The PRO-2035 offers distinct advantages if ultra-modern features and utmost basic performance are at the top of your list.

On the other hand, if cellular capability and full two-way computer interface potential are at the top of your list, then you will select between the PRO-2004 and PRO-2006.

AND NOW THE REST OF THE PACK...

Sorry, but AOR and their complementary or competing (dunno which) TR-series scanners will only be casually mentioned, for previously stated reasons. They are premium, high quality scanners, and for some operators, may indeed be the Ultimate Scanner. Great specs, super performance, but...

They have good performance out of the box. It's just that you're on your own when it comes to modifying these rigs; I can't get enough information to help you with them.

And regardless of how good they are, they are missing *IT!* There's just not enough hobbyist discussion and experimentation to generate the synergy that makes a product successful.

ULTIMATE SCANNER RUNNERS-UP...

The PRO-2037 with its triple conversion and 'hyperscan' may be among the best of this bunch, but with limited coverage and other ho-hum features, it won't climb higher. The PRO-2026, Uniden BC-760XLT, and Regency R-1600 are clones of each other, though the PRO-2026 has different firmware and internals.

Nice scanners for the most part, but lacking in the more critical performance features demanded by the compleat scannist.

The BC-760XLT was long Uniden's flagship until eased aside by the BC-8500XLT. It's capable of some decent hacks including cellular and extended memory to 6,400-channels or more. Also capable of CTCSS operations with Uniden's optional add-on module (but you're paying MORE for SILENCE!).

There were two productions of the BC-760XLT, the early one prior to 1988 that sported a Motorola-type antenna connector; and the later version, with a BNC connector. The guts of the two were markedly different as well, which explains the different cellular restoration procedures.

The R1600 is a clone of the later BC-760XLT but is not seen around much. Uniden bought out Regency a few years ago and probably continued to make a few scanners under that name to appease Regency loyalists for a while. The BC-890XLT was a decent scanner, but overpriced and there's little that can be done with this rig. Lots of built-in (inaccessible) firmware; no guts.

The BC-8500 and 9000XLT lead Uniden's line of quality scanners, with no close contenders in terms of performance, features, and modifiability. While they are indeed feature-rich, the BC-8500 and 9000 do not contend with the Ultimate Scanner contenders because they are not cellular capable, cannot be interfaced to a computer and typical of the Uniden line, though anything can happen when we thoroughly evaluate the new 9000.

They are nice looking scanners loaded with highly integrated chips and firmware, packed into a mostly empty cavity.

There isn't anything much you can do to Uniden scanners, including the top-of-the-liners. Uniden receivers are fabbed with proprietary chips and modules (flatpacking, as we say in the trade), with high levels of integration. While this makes for good performance:price ratios, cheap assembly, and good reliability, there are tradeoffs in access and modifiability. Here it is again: when you cannot access the circuitry between two functions integrated into a single chip, you lose options!

If you never remove the cases of your scanners, then the BC-9000XLT is worth a second look on your shopping list. It is the best they've managed to date. You'll see later where there's not a lot we can do to it. When it comes to modifiability, the BC-8500 and 9000 are very nice... *turnips*.

Radio Shack's PRO-2036 looks suspiciously like the Uniden BC-8500XLT, and is probably a clone with Radio Shack custom-specified firmware.

More and more of Radio Shack's scanners are of Uniden origin, so this is a distinct probability. If so... *yawn*... except for its optional CTCSS capability if that's important to you.

Uniden has now released its 9000XLT, a considerable improvement over the 8500-series, but no cigar! As-is, it is a very good scanner with excellent performance (low noise, high sensitivity, fast switching/seeking, etc.), but for us hackers it's a problem since, like its Uniden predecessor, it's highly integrated.

NON-CONTENDERS BUT QUALITY (IN THEIR TIME)

These scanners are all nice... or once were... in their time. There is nothing about them now to warrant a lot of attention. Some are new or current market models, but all on this list have old technology in them or they are highly integrated and inaccessible, or use high levels of integration without accessible ROMs or data paths.

There are a few things that can be done to these scanners, so watch for them in the modification section just ahead. Don't get mad because I don't rate them highly. Sorry, but they're (nice) turnips.

ULTIMATE HANDHELD SCANNERS

My choice of the Ultimate Handheld Scanner may seem arbitrary and capricious to some extent, but to my way of thinking there's a solid foundation. The PRO-43 (not sold anymore) was one helluva handheld that shared some of the electronic architecture of the PRO-2004/5/6 and 2035. The actual receiver diagrams appear startlingly similar.

The PRO-43 offers quality not available in any other handheld scanner. Now I will readily concede that the AR-1000XC, AR-1500, and the new AR-8000, not to mention the ICOM R-1 and the Yupiteru MVT-7100 all offer greater coverage and more features than the PRO-43. Take that to the bank. If you are a shortwave listener and a scannist, but can have only one radio, then one of these may be better for you than the PRO-43. If so, I don't mind.

Just be forewarned that the ICOM R-1 and the AR-1000 are not "user friendly." The ICOM R-1 has a major design flaw in its relatively simple receiver section that admits massive interference and birdies. Incidentally, it has a superb service manual, but there is little that can be done to this unit because it's so tightly packed and integrated. Buy an R-1 and you have to be happy with it as it is. Nice radio, except for its birdie/interference problem.

And just try to get a service manual for any of the Yupi or AR radios. The AR-1000XC is a nice radio, and they make other good ones, but without technical support and disclosure it's an also-ran in the Ultimate Scanner race.

BACK TO THE 43

The original PRO-43 is backed by a great service manual and has a triple conversion, double-balanced mixer receiver that's free from most interference. It has wide coverage and is cellular restorable. The 54-88 MHz band is recoverable, too! No big deal since most of that band is the VHF-Lo TV area, but there can be a lot of interesting action in the little known 72-76 MHz utility band, which is otherwise blocked until you restore it.

Beware the new PRO-43A sold after April, 1994: so far, we haven't found a way to get that extra coverage. Consider it a *different* scanner!

There's a bit more in the PRO-43 that can be extracted including a great S-meter function, an audio improvement or two, and even a nice memory expansion. Cramped quarters and skimpy real estate conspire to limit the things that can be done to the PRO-43 or any other handheld for that matter, though a LOT can be done if you tack on an external box to hold all the extra goodies.

Most people aren't that willing, and so I don't consider handhelds to be serious contenders for the Ultimate Scanner, per se. If there were such a contender, the PRO-43 would be one because it can also be adapted to work with the CE-232 Interface for AutoProgramming and keyboard control from the computer!

Believe me, it's not fun to sit there and hand-program in 200-channels at a whack on that tiny keyboard, or do any serious operating from it.

But hook the PRO-43 to a computer, plug a decent antenna into that jack, and it's as good as just about any tabletop units.

Even in handheld scanners, computer interface is a well defined need. By the way, I know a dedicated scannist who designed a functional one-way programmer interface for his AR-1000XC, so for you dedicated AOR fans, there may be your ticket to the Ultimate Handheld Scanner . Otherwise, my choice is the PRO-43......the early model; NOT the later one described below.

ULTIMATE HANDHELD SCANNERS — RUNNERS-UP

The PRO-43A is a runner-up because production was altered to meet the requirements of the TDDRA law that forbids "easily modified cellular capable" scanners. A new CPU and a slightly redesigned Logic/CPU board in this unit makes recovery of the cellular and 54-88 MHz bands impossible. All PRO-43's sold after April, 1994, are the "A" version. If there is the "Radio Shack" logo on the front case of the PRO-43, you can let your suspicions rise, whereas if the logo is "Realistic," modifiability is a safe bet.

There is also a date code hidden in the PRO-43's battery compartment, but it will be helpful only if it hasn't been removed. It has been pretty well established that PRO-43's with a date code of 2A4 and earlier are modifiable, 3A4 may or may not be, and 4A4 and later are definitely not modifiable. An "A" prefix in the serial number means it has the newer CPU and is the most reliable indicator that modifiability is very limited.

Words to the wise....

Beware acquisitions of later PRO-43's if cellular and 54-88 MHz are on your list of important capabilities. Otherwise, the PRO-43A is a potent and high performance handheld scanner.

MORE RUNNERS-UP

Also on the list of runners-up in the handheld category are the still-useful oldies/goodies of the past, including the PRO-34 and PRO-37 which are electronic clones of the PRO-2022 base scanner! (Betcha didn't know that.) Lay their schematic diagrams side by side and you can hardly tell the difference. Therefore, what can be done to one can be done to the other two.

These aren't what you could call 'great' radios, but they can be made a lot better than what came out of the box.

The PRO-39 is a "come and gone" handheld that had some potential, but just didn't last long. The PRO-46/51/62 are johnny-come-lately's with nothing exciting about them other than decent memory and speed.

The time-honored Uniden BC-200XLT and BC-100XLT are on this list with good reason; they're good radios but not much can be done to them.

I don't know about the newer Uniden Sportcat and BC-220XLT but their specs are impressive enough to give them a mention.

As usual, beware Uniden with lots of features packed into an empty case, as highly integrated circuitry means that you and I cannot reach it!

By the way, the Regency 4030 and 4020 are clones of the BC-200XLT and BC-100XLT, respectively. Not many are around, but they're the same rigs.

WRAPPING UP and MOVING ON

My aim for this section was a broad overview of the Ultimate Scanner Contenders, and those that have no chance. To those astute scannists whose positions were already established before ever opening this book, I apologize for the 'waste' of space. I think, however, that I was able to convey a lot of useful information about scanners and what they're made of.

The Ultimate Scanner will reach audiences never before touched by this type of book, so it was important to chat a little about features and differences from one scanner or brand to the next.

You never know who's going to pick up this book, and we want it to help as many people as possible.

Let's now continue the Great Adventure. Ladies and Gentlemen: light up your gasoline torches, rev up your attitudes and patience, on your mark... get set...

Let's Go!

A portion of my Shack.
**Believe it or not, every dial, knob, LED, and meter has a function!
The computers are mostly behind me...**

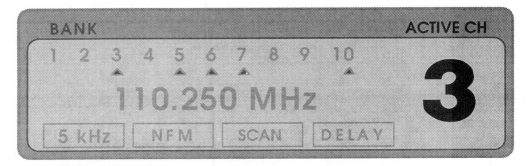

BANK

1 2 3 4 5 6 7 8 9 10

110.250 MHz

ACTIVE CH

3

5 kHz | NFM | SCAN | DELAY

GENERAL MODIFICATION TIPS, HINTS, and KINKS

This chapter will slip a few general purpose tidbits and tools into your warbag. Having The Right Stuff on hand will improve confidence as you plan and begin the metamorphosis of "Squeaky Sammy" into the boss-hawg Ultimate Scanner.

I'll throw in a few minor projects just to get your knife sharp, and perhaps to teach you technique and patience before you attack the main job.

PROPERLY HACKING YOUR SCANNER

"Properly" is a real issue, because I've noticed a rash of mis-hacked scanners coming across my bench. For the first couple of years after my *Scanner Modification Handbooks* came out, I was pleasantly surprised at the few mis-hacks and serious errors. Frankly, I prepared for a flood, but the trickle lulled me into a false sense of security.

It's a new generation now; maybe the "CB Butcher Brigade" has found its way onto the scanner scene.

I've seen a lot of shoddy work lately, so it's time to review the basics. Several common factors are worth your attention.

While fundamental techniques and principles of scanner hacking have not appreciably changed since I wrote my first two books, there have been a few refinements and perhaps a new trick or two. Again, as emphasized throughout this book, I am not going to repeat everything from my previous books.

The Ultimate Scanner is a continuation; an evolution; an advancement above and beyond the turf on which the earlier books cavort.

If you are a beginner in the fine arts of scanner re-engineering, my first two books will help you on the Path of Enlightenment. They contain mods, projects, ideas, tips, tricks, hints, and kinks that will only coincidentally be covered in this third volume of exotic lore. No matter your status as a scanner hacker, if you don't have my first two books, you'll need them sooner or later.

Now don't get frosted at this *new concept*, either. I have letters from readers who wanted to find everything for their scanner in one package, and they were steamed at "having to buy both books!" They'll be livid when they see *The Ultimate Scanner!*

But I could make them a lot madder, if I tried.

We could do one book, just as they asked. We'd stuff twice as much information into it, at twice the size and twice or three times the cost, and it wouldn't be very timely.

What we decided to do is a *new* and cost-effective book that adds to the body of knowledge. This is my third effort on scanner re-engineering. I don't know of any way around the dilemma. If scanner hacking is among your interests, then you're just going to have to settle in for the long haul and prepare for serial efforts. Forgive me, please...

You may want to consider a subscription to my monthly scanner hacking newsletter, the *World Scanner Report,* which keeps the body of knowledge current, updated, error-corrected, *and* charts new territory in the world of re-engineering scanner receivers.

Armed with my first two books, and now, *The Ultimate Scanner*, and with the *World Scanner Report* as well, you'll be well prepared for a TurboWhopper of an adventure. If your budget (time or money) won't permit doing everything at once, that's fine. You will find plenty here to chew. Managing the ol' budget is a part of the *patience* you'll find me talking about in this book.

Consider logging onto my computer bulletin board, the *Hertzian Intercept BBS,* where there is a wealth of technical information, frequency data, and distilled experience – from me and from hobbyists around the world. I am personally available on the BBS for many forms of tech support and consultations, including plain old chit-chatting. Please see Chapter 1 for detailed information about connecting with BBS's and associating with scannists the world over! A valuable resource, indeed...

GET THE SERVICE MANUAL FOR YOUR SCANNER!

Emphasized throughout my first two books, the service manual for your scanner is mandatory before you do much more than pop the case. You will create needless problems for yourself without

one, and I will not be sympathetic when I hear you "lost yours" or never had one to begin with. You cannot be helped and you cannot build an Ultimate Scanner without a service manual. And don't whine that you can't read such a manual; sure you can! If you're going to hack, you'll learn. Get the manual! Here's where:

Radio Shack scanners	(800)	442-2425
Uniden/Regency/Bearcat	(317)	842-1036
ACE/AOR scanners	(317)	849-3570
ICOM radios	(206)	454-7619
Kenwood radios	(213)	639-9000
Yaesu radios	(213)	404-2700

PREPARE A PLAN!

Else suffer expensive or frustrating consequences. You should have a Plan behind your attack on the innards of your beloved scanner. Scanners have limited space in which to work and to house new widgets. If you randomly and haphazardly install things now, imagine the havoc and constipation that can reign after you've done bunches of mods with no forethought as to what should go first and what should go last. This planning process is a lot like packing the trunk of your car for an extended road trip. Some things won't require access except in an emergency, while other things will require frequent access.

I can't plan your hacking adventures – it's *you* who's best qualified to do that. But someone better do it, or *else!*

What do I mean by "Plan?" *Harrumph!* I know you better than you know yourself. See, if you sneak into your scanner and pull off a mod successfully, it won't be long before you're sticking something else in there. And then again! And again. You won't be able to resist!

If you don't take this into account from the very start, then your scanner is going to get cluttered and boogered up before you know it. And then, what if trouble arises with some real hairy mod? Well, your troubleshooting and diagnosis efforts will be severely hampered for one thing, and if you later draw a blank and ask me to service the unit for you, *I won't do it!*

There's just no way that I can work free. And your budget can't handle 8-16 hours of my fumbling around wondering what you did, where, and how. So keep notes...

Maybe your first investment should be a dollar notebook, because you'll have to document everything you do, making reference to the original source of information, sketching wiring layouts, showing color coded wire, and more. That notebook might keep you sane, later.

Keep things neat, and prepare for the future. The objective is to tuck away each and every mod as if there will be a hundred more to follow. Dress all wiring cleanly and neatly and out of the way. Wire bundles should he routed around the perimeter of the scanner, for the most part. Little circuit boards can be soldered to the metal sides of the scanner. The power transformer can be removed to create more room for the larger mods, and besides, it's better to power the scanner from an external DC power supply anyway, because it runs cooler and makes things last longer. These principles are expanded in detail just ahead, so hang loose.

Except for very high speed circuitry, digital modifications are not critical with respect to wire length. Two exceptions are extended memory modifications, and mods that connect to the keyboard matrix of the scanner. In these two exceptions, keep the wire runs short. Otherwise, digital mods can be installed almost anywhere.

RF mods need short wire leads, and audio mods require little attention to wire length, though these leads are higher-power and should never be cabled with RF and digital wiring. Another rule of thumb is that all ground wires should be as short as possible, while DC power leads can be of any length.

Hobbyists tend to be impatient and hurried in their work. Force yourself to slow down; do things one step at a time, and make each step as perfect as possible before proceeding to the next.

PATIENCE

I know... "patience, my ass, I want to kill something."

The problem is that without patience it will be your scanner that gets killed. Be forewarned, I now avoid servicing mis-hacked scanners. I tried it for a few years and after a severe combined attack of ulcers, hives, boils, cysts, zits, psoriasis, hair loss, and St. Vitus Dance, not to mention a tenure in the local alms-houses

(homeless missions and soup kitchens), I had to give it up. My doctor, accountant, and family will not allow me to service hacker-blown scanners. Well, let's put it this way: the price starts at twice the cost of a new scanner and goes up from there, depending on the degree of damage and whether or not I have to open the case. Catch my drift?

Really, the percentage of mis-hacked scanners remains very low, and I want it to stay that way. With something over 30 years experience behind me, I can tell you flat out that *patience* is a critical ingredient to the scanner hacker. Lack of skill certainly can contribute to abysmal failure, but lack of patience *causes* it. So what is this thing called "patience"?

Patience is the guiding light that oversees the following steps of hacking and re-engineering:

Planning: Objectives, materials, procedures.

Acquisition: Parts, materials, tools, supplies, *service manuals,* test equipment.

Process Review: Ensuring that all needed materials and instructions are on hand and ready to go, and a sort of rehearsal.

Execution: The job itself.

Work Review: Detailed checking of every step, with remedial action where necessary.

Documentation: Drawings, test results, etc.

Testing and Quality Assurance: Checks of solder joints, layout, mechanical integrity, out-of and in-scanner tests; evaluation of results.

Acceptance: Remedial action to correct any deficiency.

Not that you have to make a big deal out of each of the above steps (it won't hurt if you do), but if you are patient, you will not do anything before you're ready for it.

That means having all required parts and materials on hand, preparing a plan, and being familiar with what you're about to do, before ever popping the case of the scanner. It also means documenting your work, so errors can be found and later mods added without frustration.

IMPATIENCE

Let's talk about impatience. If you launch a frontal assault on your scanner at 6 PM, expecting to enjoy the benefits of the hack-attack by 8 PM, then you are headed for trouble. When you rush to be done by a certain time, you're imposing limits and begging for mishap.

Impatience prompts compromise when the right stuff isn't on hand, and there's no room for compromise in the Ultimate Scanner. Impatience is not stopping and going to bed at 1am when you've been at it all day, thinking the job would only be a "couple of hours." Impatience is failing to put the scanner aside for a while to get away from it all when something isn't going right. Impatience is sticking that mod in there and firing up the scanner without first checking all your work for solder globs and wiring errors.

Impatience is saying to yourself you've checked everything when you buried the dang widget in there without testing it outside the scanner first.

TROUBLE

Here is one of the most frequent ways I'm asked to help troubleshoot a mis-hack. ..... "*I've checked everything three times and it don't work...*"

My usual reply for that one is "*Okay, check it a fourth time – but this time, check everything.*" My definition of "*everything*" is E-V-E-R-Y-T-H-I-N-G, not S-O-M-E-T-H-I-N-G. I guess those words sound a lot alike and confuse people.

My mods generally work the first time out, if you make no errors. So you think I'm saying here that I make no errors? *Hah!* Far from it.

I make more than you do, which is why I am an expert on errors. You just don't get to see mine – by the time my mods appear in print, you can bet your sweet patooty they've been checked and field-tested by others. If an error goes undetected, we will publish its correction in the *World Scanner Report* and over the computer networks for the widest possible dissemination.

You should not assume I made an error when your mod doesn't work and there are unturned stones in your backtrail.

When I'm asked for technical assistance, my first line of guidance is to be certain that YOU kicked over all the rocks. If you are impatient, there will be many unturned stones in your backtrail and I will find them, believe me, including all the critters and vermin that set up housekeeping underneath.

Speaking of which, I have to tell you a little story from a couple of years ago when a fellow sent me a PRO-2005 to diagnose and repair. As I opened the shipping box, an odd odor wafted up from the scanner. It wasn't a familiar odor either, kind of pungent and rank. My first guess was that something had burned up.

Electronic components have odors all their own when they go up in smoke, and I've been around long enough to recognize nearly everything that can cook in an electronic circuit. But this stink was really *strange!*

I popped the case of the scanner and was greeted by a massive scurrying, and the pitter-patter of little feet. I don't mean to overstate this, but my heart sorta stopped and blood chilled in my veins, As about a thousand "*cucarachas*" scattered helter-skelter all over my workbench. All work stopped, and we set off bug-bombs throughout the house and shop. We went out to dinner and the movies that night while the insecticide did its work.

Believe me, my patience was tested that day. After a good cleaning (soaking in alcohol), the fellow's PRO-2005 worked thereafter – once I got the bugs out of it. Another of those lessons of life, I guess.

Anyway, make a solid commitment to planning, quality, and especially to patience. Not only is the result worth it, without it the penalty is high.

SOLDERING TECHNIQUES

Good soldering is neither an art nor a science, but a manual skill mixed with a little horse sense and the right tools. Since mistakes here (1) are common, (2) become evident later – usually at the worst time, (3) disguise themselves as component failure, and (4) are easy to prevent with the right approach, I'll spend a few minutes on the subject.

While too much heat can fry a component, a little excess heat is better than too little heat! Low heat can produce cold solder joints.

If they don't cause a fault now, they will later, usually at a most inopportune moment. Your soldering pencil should be rated at 25-to-50 watts. (*I'm not advocating use of welding torches, though.*)

The tip of the soldering iron should be "iron clad," *not copper*. After it's up to temperature, the tip should be wiped on a wet sponge before and after every solder connection to keep it clean – avoid oxide buildup. Immediately prior to making a solder joint, apply a dab of solder to the tip and then touch the tip to the connection to transfer heat to the lead or component. Wait for a second or two and then apply solder to the connection, NOT to the tip of the iron. Then pull away the solder, but leave the soldering tip on the joint for another second before removing it.

After the joint has cooled, it should be bright and shiny; not gray and wrinkled, and it should flow smoothly (a "fillet") to the surfaces of the materials being soldered. Solder, at the right temperature, will also flow into the heated joint to make a permanent connection.

HOOKUP WIRE

This is an often overlooked subject. You should use only good quality, small gauge, stranded, and very flexible hookup wire for your scanner hacking projects. This eliminates most of Radio Shack "battery cables" which they call hookup wire. The insulation drips like melted candle wax and the wires are much too stiff and rigid for our needs.

Radio Shack once had great wire, though it's been discontinued for several years. Still, a few stores may have some in stock, and you should lay in a supply if you can find any. But it's not what you think it is! We're talking about their "Computer LAN cable," #278-776 (25-cond) and #278-775 (9-cond). Don't ask me why they called it LAN cable; I don't think they knew either.

You have to strip off the outer gray insulation and then remove the braided and foil shields, but what's left is some of the finest color-coded hookup wires you ever saw in your life! This stuff is so great you'll wonder how you ever did without it. It's very flexible, strong, and easily handled in most circumstances. I don't know of replacements for these long discontinued cables. I laid in a monstrous supply when they were discontinued and haven't run out yet. No, I will not sell or give any of it away.

Teflon? The temperatures in our scanners don't need teflon insulation, and it's a bear to strip and work with, but teflon insulation identifies some of the best quality wires on the market. To use it, you have to find a high-quality stripping tool.

I cannot over emphasize the use of good quality hook up wire in your hacking adventures. Use ONLY the general type of stuff described above.

If your local Radio Shacks are out of the good stuff, go to your local electronics supply house and ask to see their multi-conductor, shielded parallel cable or shielded serial cable.

SERIOUS TOOLS, SERIOUS HACKING

When did those new-fangled "hot glue" guns and glue sticks come out? Maybe 15-20 years ago? Yeah, well I ignored them with a passion until a couple of years ago when Ali, my lovely daughter, tapped me on the shoulder while I was hard at work one day, and asked if I'd like to try her hot glue gun. Now mind you, I had no use for "hot glue" because of a long love affair with super glues and epoxy resins. What could be better?

Later, curiosity got the better of me. I plugged in that stupid-looking glue gun, rammed a .50-caliber stick into the magazine, and commenced to fire away at the first thing that moved.

The gun has lousy range, so I missed the dog. Out oozed a gob of liquid plastic with the consistency of molasses in a winter blizzard, that landed smack-dab on the carpet of my workbench! The stuff is *still* embedded there! But I learned, and now use "hot glue" for most everything, no holds barred! And so should you! Here's the deal:

First, we're not really talking about "hot glue." Maybe there is such a thing, but what I'm referring to is really a type of plastic. The refill package uses terms like "hot melt adhesive" and "glue sticks," but the stuff is really a plastic.

A little glop of the stuff makes a great anchor for a wire bundle or a small circuit board. And I can think of a host of insulating and other anchoring uses. I use it to make "molded plastic" connectors; to hold loose things down, to reinforce weakness, to hold LEDs in place, and sometimes just for sticking things together.

Hot glue is an excellent insulator for exposed solder joints, wire splices, and electrical conductors that might short out against something.

I would not use hot glue as an insulator for high voltage applications (>50V) without first talking to the manufacturer about dielectric characteristics at high voltages.

You won't find anything more utilitarian and useful for low voltage (5 and 12 volt) hobby needs, though. Tiny applications of hot glue can be fairly easily removed where permanency is not desired, say as anchors for wire bundles, and small circuit boards. Another great application for hot glue is as "injection plastic." How many utility patch cables have you made over the years to save a few bucks? You'd do it more if they weren't so prone to failure, right? Most failures of homemade audio, RF, and computing cables occur in or at the connector.

After you've made up a cable and checked that it's flawless, assemble the connector and its shell. Then, squirt hot glue plastic into the shell, binding everything together, for ultra reliability!

I'm not sure there is a limit to the practical application of a hot glue gun, and you'll soon agree. I now use two different models; one is a larger type that uses glue sticks 4" long and about $1/2$" diameter. This type is great for bulk needs such as moldings and insulated surfaces for printed circuit boards. Then there is a dainty, petite type with slim glue sticks 2" long, for situations that need fine control and less glue.

You'll need a separate glue gun for each size, but if you can have only one or the other, get the smaller size for most bench uses.

There's no trick to using a hot glue gun – just squeeze the trigger (or push the rear of the glue stick) and out comes a hot stream of liquid plastic, the rate of which is proportional to the amount of squeeze or push. When not in use, the hot glue gun seems relatively safe, but you should devise a holder for it to point straight up so as to minimize leakage of the hot plastic. This will also help prevent the hot tip from touching your benchtop and causing a hazard.

Safety first – always!

Apply the hot glue with the nozzle as close as possible to the point of contact. Adhesion is enhanced if the point of application is warmed to the same temperature as the glue.

In other words, adhesion can be inferior if the hot glue is applied to a cold surface. I use a soldering gun and sometimes a butane device to preheat larger metal surfaces for best adhesion. Now let's find more great uses for the hot glop!

PIN-LINE SOCKETS (and PLUGS)!

One of the slickest assets in the experimenter's shop is called a "pin-line" strip or "pin-line" socket. Radio Shack doesn't have them, so a universal reference is difficult, but DigiKey's *"Pin-Line Sockets with 'break' feature,"* part number A-208, is one example.

Hosfelt Electronics' *"Machine Pin SIP Sockets,"* part number 21-161 or 21-234 is another. Mouser Electronics offers their *"SIP Breakaway IC Sockets,"* part number 151-5530. All three of these suppliers have a variety of pin-line sockets in various configurations and pin-counts, so get their catalogs if you want to shop for the best "deals" for your needs.

Imagine, if you will, a precision machined IC socket cut apart so that you have two strips. One of these strips resembles what we're talking about by way of pin-line sockets. The neat thing about them is that the male plug part mates perfectly with the female socket part. Because they are so small, the most immediate experimenter's application is that of a miniature, quick-disconnect plug and socket combination.

Pin-line sockets are available in strips of as many as 56 pins each, and can be cut or broken apart for a desired lesser number. Suppose, for example, you had a pair of wires in your scanner that you wanted to quickly and easily disconnect from some special modification board you had installed. An excellent application!

Cut the two wires, and solder the four cut ends, one pair to the male ends of a pin-line pair, and the other pair to the female ends of a pin-line pair. In this fashion, the plugs for one pair of wires will mate with the sockets of the other pair. Quick and dirty; neat and functional; and extremely low profile.

You won't easily find a connector that's smaller, handier, more functional, or less expensive!

See *Figure 3-1* for views of two styles of pin-line sockets, and *Figure 3-2* for how they can be easily pressed into duty as plug and socket connectors!

Figure 3-1: Pin-line sockets

Spacing between pins is 0.1", center-to-center ($^1/_{10}$")

Figure 3-2: Pin-line socket/plug connector

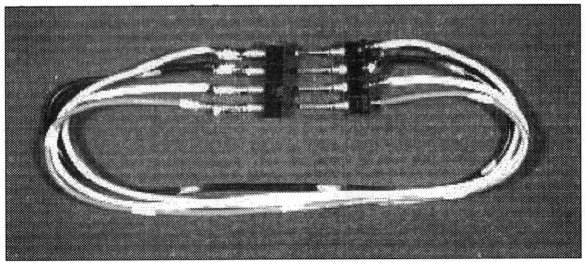

Left: *Socket*　　　Right: *Plug*　　　Both: *made from pin-line strips*

Pin-line sockets are machined to precision tolerances, usually (in U.S. products) spaced precisely 0.1" apart, center to center, like the holes in "perf board" and "vector board."

They're useful as IC-sockets in experimenter projects when you happen to be short of a socket or two! Just break apart a strip of whatever number of pins you need into two equal strips to match the IC and position them on the board for an instant IC socket!

Drill 1-mm diameter holes in the perf board or circuit board surface for a snug fit of the upper body (fat parts) of the male pins. Three adjacent pin-line sockets make a great socket for TO-92-style transistors. The machined plug and socket offers a better electrical contact than conventional spring contact sockets.

MAKESHIFT IC SOCKETS

Some conventional IC sockets fail for no reason other than poor electrical contact. I have never seen pin-line sockets fail in that manner – you're looking at high reliability connections here! Another use I have found for pin-line sockets is as a wire splice, but with a difference.

For instance, you may know that a lot of modification procedures call for the soldering of a wire or a component lead to a pin of an IC

somewhere in the radio. Instead of that, I first solder the male end of a pin-line socket to the IC-pin and then use the exposed socket to accept either a male pin with its socket soldered to the end of a wire, or sometimes a component lead will plug into the socket for a nice fit, and allow for an easy disconnect when the need arises.

HI-REL MOLDED CONNECTORS

When you mix hot glue with pin-line sockets, you're looking at one heck of a molded-connector possibility! Talk about reliability! Just solder your pin-line sockets to a wire bundle and after examination and tests for errors, squirt some hot glue between and around the soldered points of contact so that the metal is insulated and all wire-to-pin connections are separated by a layer of the plastic molding glue.

The results may not look great, but you can't get a more reliable connector for the size and cost. *Figure 3-3* shows the same plug and socket combination as in *Figure 3-2*, but molded with the hot glue plastic into a permanent, long-lived connector.

Aside from the reliability factor, a primary advantage of pin-line sockets made into quick-disconnect connectors is the small size! Great for mod jobs in very small radios!

Figure 3-3:   Molded socket/plug connector using pin-line hardware and hot-melt glue

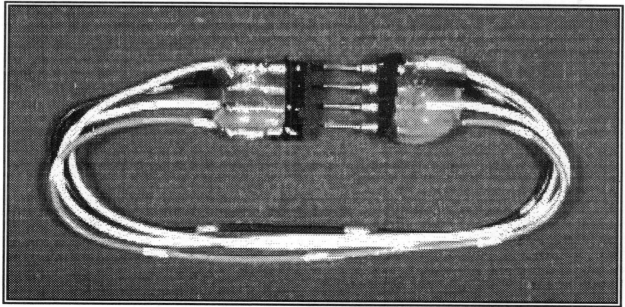

Just a little *glop* will do - nothing fancy needed!

NOTE: Clearly, such "home made" connectors would not be used in manufacturing, but in the R & D lab they're fine. A handful of pin-line sockets and a hot glue gun are mighty inexpensive "breadboard" items when the perfect solution isn't in the supply room! If you need to get on with your design, pin-line sockets and hot-melt glue might make a difference, both in the schedule and in the budget!

Hot glue and pin-line sockets have become absolutely vital around my shop, where a lot of work is related to some form of R & D or testing and evaluation. I often need to stick things in somewhere for a quick observation and then pop them back out for revision or redesign. Time and reliability are critical in my work, and I just can't be bothered with a lot of wire splicing, soldering and desoldering, etc.

Pin-line sockets and hot glue have boosted the quality and efficiency of my work and reduced much of the drudgery and monotony. Give these two items a trial run on your bench and watch the quality of your work and time go upscale! Many thanks to Ken Wells of Kwajalein, Marshall Islands, for the tip on pin-line sockets a few years ago. Ken also introduced me to high-reliability machine-pin IC sockets, without which I'd never again function! And thanks to my daughter, Ali, for the hot glue idea!

DENTAL TOOLS FOR SCANNER HACKING !

My better tools rarely come from electronic stores! Parts, yes. Solder, yes. A hundred other things, yes. Tools, usually not! Most of my hand tools come from dental supply houses now.

Yes, they cost more, but it's a pleasure to work with fine steel; sharp cutting edges that don't dull on the first slice or the 50th; magnifiers that magnify without distortion; tweezers that don't lose their "tweeze" after a few grips; and hemostats (clamps) that glide through the varied uses put to them. Fine tools enhance and promote fine work.

Dental tools are expensive, but you won't need a boatload at the onset. I would recommend three to start, and you'll go from there on your own. My favorite is a toss-up between the 4" Hu-Friedy R3 German stainless steel 606K curved hemostats, and a 6" G. Hartzell and Son "Carbon 44-20" chisel tipped plaque scraper. My #3 is a weird pair of short bladed scissors that can cut sheet metal! The scissors are 3" long overall, with 0.5" cutting edges. The leverage is fantastic, and these scissors can cut and trim the chrome metal shield on the back of the PRO-2005/6 Logic/CPU board like a piece of paper, and without removing it!

Next favorite on my list is a magnifier lens that clips onto my spectacles for hands-free, high magnification work. Immediately thereafter are a power screwdriver and Radio Shack's Nibbling Tool, #64-823.

Beyond these six tools, the first four of which come from a dental supply house, the rest of my regular hand tools are about as generic as they come – and yours can be, too. Radio Shack's diagonal cutting pliers, #64-1813 are pretty good when they're new and sharp, but they'll get dull cutting butter. *Figure 3-4* shows most of these tools and more. The main point here is to pay a visit to your local dental supply and use your imagination; open up your mind and let your fantasies unwind to find excellent electronic uses for some of that goshawful stainless steel that hurts so much when it runs amok in your chops!

Dental plaque scrapers make great circuit trace cutters as well as scorers for raw printed circuit board. I used to saw my PCB's to size, but now, I just lay out a carpenter's square on the circuit board and score it a few times with a curved, pointed plaque scraper, and then snap the board along the score for a clean cut! Thanks to the plaque scraper, it's kind of like glass-cutting – efficient, clean, and quick.

THE RIGHT TOOLS & MATERIALS

They're critical to good hacking! For Pete's sake, throw away those rolls of black electrical tape and duct tape. Same for cellophane and masking tapes.

Yuk! Sometimes, *Scotch 810 Magic Tape* can be useful for wrapping wire bundles, but better still are cable ties, heat shrinkable tubing, and short lengths of bundling "spaghetti."

Anything is better than tape! *Never* use tape to insulate. You can bet your bottom dollar the stuff will come undone when you least expect it! Tape is uncouth around the Ultimate Scanner!

Figure 3-4: Useful hacker tools

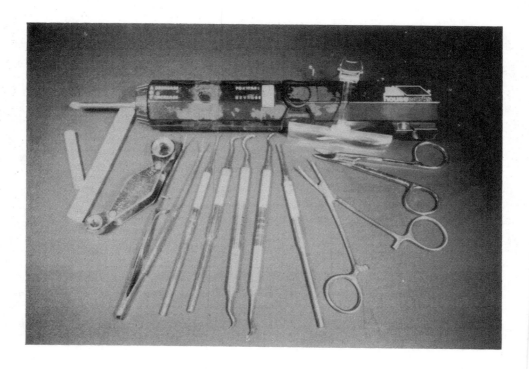

Top: Power screwdriver and clip-on magnifier. *Left-to-right:* small hot-glue stick, large hot-glue stick, jeweler's loupe, locking dental tweezers, five types of plaque scrapers, curved hemostats, and dental scissors that can cut sheet metal! *Not pictured:* welding torch, crowbar, sledgehammer, aspirin.

Tools... a good subject. Yes, I have a few bucks invested in good tools of the trade but you know what? I use less than a hundred bucks worth for 95% of my needs.

The following is what I call a good, functional tool kit for hacking and chopping scanners. A lot of Radio Shack's stuff I don't like, but this list will do a good job for you.

It's provided to help you inventory and assess your needs. Not everything here is essential to success of your hacking projects, depending on your skills and desire for aesthetics and quality. Radio Shack catalog numbers are given ONLY for your convenience; better prices and quality may be available elsewhere.

Items marked with a * are advisable and very useful. ! means almost essential. You decide.

Now here's the crazy thing about it all. You can take or leave my list of tools, stuff, and widgets! It's not going to make or break you as a hacker.

There's something else that I can't really give you directly; only awaken you to it: *ATTITUDE!* An ounce of the right attitude will go farther than a kilobuck worth of tools.

You've got to PLAN your hack attack, stick to a methodology, and be patient. Yes, you have to be prepared with the right tools and materials, but putting attitude and patience at the top of the list will help the rest of the list take care of itself.

If you are a novice hacker, don't outsmart me and take shortcuts. Follow along for a while and get used to the taste of success. I may seem to take the long way around at times, but it's with the BIG PICTURE in mind.

Table 3-1: Recommended/useful materials, tools, and supplies

Pri	Check	Description	Radio Shack Catalog# (if appropriate)
*	__	Electric drill, 3/8", w/bits to 3/8"	Anywhere
!	__	Diagonal cutting pliers, small	64-1841
	__	Locking longnose pliers	64-1864
	__	Adjustable wrench, 4" (small)	Anywhere
*	__	Precision flatblade screwdrivers	64-1948
*	__	Precision crosspoint screwdrivers	64-1962
!	__	Mini forceps....................................	64-1910
!	__	Nibbling tool	64-823
!	__	Lighted magnifier	63-848
	__	Screwdrivers, assorted........................	64-1823
*	__	Needle file set	64-1985
*	__	Knife set	64-1801
*	__	Hot glue gun and glue sticks	Anywhere
*	__	Soldering pencil holder/cleaner	64-2078
!	__	Soldering pencil base unit	64-2080
!	__	Soldering element	64-2082
!	__	Soldering tips	64-2089 and 64-2074
*	__	Desoldering tool	64-2098
!	__	Pocket penlight	61-2626
!	__	Disposable butane lighter	Anywhere
!	__	Silver bearing solder	64-013
	__	Micro-mini solder	64-005
*	__	Desoldering braid	64-2090
*	__	"Helping Hands" project holder	64-2093 (Best)
*	__	Mini-vise project holder.......................	64-2094 (Good)
	__	Cleaner/degreaser solvent	64-3322
*	__	Rosin flux remover............................	64-3324
	__	Double-sided tape	64-2344
	__	Velcro (hook and loop) strips	64-2345
	__	Epoxy resin	64-2313
*	__	Super glue	64-2308
	__	Silicone rubber sealant	64-2314
	__	Precision lubricator	64-2301 *continues...*

Tools and materials, continued...

	__	Standoffs w/screws	276-195
	__	Perf board stock	276-1395
	__	Machine screws	64-3010, 3011, and 3012
	__	Machine nuts	64-3017, 3018, and 3019
	__	Flat washers	64-3022
	__	Grommets	64-3025
*	__	Wire ties	278-1632
!	__	Heat shrinkable tubing	278-1627
*	__	Digital Volt/Ohm/Milliammeter (VOM) (several choices work fine)	22-194, -184, -185, -188, -167, -186
		Dynamite, for difficult cases	Your neighborhood terrorist.

HOW TO PREPARE AND INSTALL MODIFICATION CIRCUITRY

I favor the easy ways of doing things when possible. In my early days of hacking I installed many a SuperWhizBang modification with painstaking effort to make the thing LOOK good, and able to withstand earthquakes and atom bombs. I don't do that anymore; it's a waste of time and energy.

Well, let me qualify that... when I do a hack for hire, I'll spend more time on its aesthetics and cosmetics than I do for my own. That's expected. But, there is a difference between doing your own work and work for someone else.

When I develop and test my mods, it is important that I have easy access to them, both for adjustment and fine-tuning and for removal/re-installation. When I do a job for someone else, there is not going to be any readjustment and relocation, so I do it right the first time, based on my experience.

Your efforts are almost always going to be R & D, so it's better to make it easy on yourself regarding ease of access to your hacks. Nothing is worse than to bury the results of a 12-hour effort deep into the gizzard of your scanner, only to find that it doesn't work as it should, or it does fine until we develop an improvement that requires it to come back out for more work. I guarantee that you won't bother to polish your work if it's difficult to access and service! Unless we know a certain mod is as good as it's ever going to be, let's make it easy on ourselves and dispense with rigid professional techniques and conduct ourselves more like what we really are: R & D shops. This implies certain ways of doing things that would never be employed on the assembly line or by a pro-shop. That's okay!

HOMEBREW MECHANICALS

First, I do ALL my initial developments on "perf-board" with simple point-to-point wiring. There is no sense in making a custom printed circuit board only to learn it needs a layout change to work properly.

Use a perf-board (Radio Shack #276-1394, 1395, or 1396). Design your circuit layout on paper and cut the perf-board slightly larger than anticipated size, stuff in the parts, add the wiring and soldering, and let it go at that.

Rarely do I advocate installing homebrew circuit boards with standoffs, spacers, nuts, and bolts. That's just too much trouble, for one thing, and for another, it's hard to install things that way and still leave plenty of room for other mods. Besides, have you ever drilled a hole in your favorite scanner only to have the bit suddenly break through and run amok around the circuit board? No? Good... and you don't want to, either.

Even if you're careful, what about minuscule drill shavings and metal dust? For hackers, there is a better way.

Feast your eyeballs on *Figure 3-5* to learn how small modification circuit boards can be easily installed in a scanner housing. Most base scanner chassis employ a metal frame around the circuit boards and other hardware. Even though the case slips over or bolts down to this frame, there is always a little space on the outside, bottom, and top edges of the frame.

Circuit boards installed as shown in *Figure 3-5* are held rigid to this frame by the stiff, #18 copper wire that's soldered to this metal frame and to the circuit board. The #18 wire should be tightly looped over the top edge of the frame before it is soldered to the inside surface.

If you look closely, this #18 wire also loops though holes in the circuit board and should be soldered on both sides of the board to make it stable and immovable. This wire should also be connected to the circuit board's ground traces.

If there is any danger of the bottom side of your mod circuit board touching something on the chassis or main receiver board below it, then insulate the bottom of this board with some hot glue, or even a sheet of acetate or plastic cut to size and held underneath with silicone rubber or hot glue. A single 18-ga "mounting" and ground wire will suffice for most home-brew circuits of about 2-square inches or less. Larger boards might fare better with two or more of these mounting wires, depending. Extra won't hurt, but one is usually sufficient.

This method of installing modification circuit boards is relatively permanent, yet easily undone if ever needed. It allows maximum utilization of the space inside the scanner and facilitates easy, clean routing of wires from the board to destination points within the scanner.

Figure 3-5: Small circuit board installation

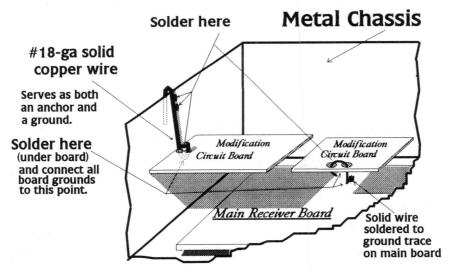

Metal Chassis

Solder here

#18-ga solid copper wire

Serves as both an anchor and a ground.

Solder here (under board) and connect all board grounds to this point.

Modification Circuit Board

Modification Circuit Board

Main Receiver Board

Solid wire soldered to ground trace on main board

The rest of this chapter approaches the nitty-gritty with some warm-up exercises and preparatory adventures. Don't skip anything – hot stuff ahead.

REMOVE THE AC POWER SUPPLY FROM YOUR SCANNER!

First and foremost, I suggest removing any AC power supply from the scanner, including transformer and power cord – for two reasons:

(1) to create more "real estate" for present and future modifications and (2) to remove the single greatest generator of HEAT within the scanner. At their best, AC power supplies are not what you could call *efficient*. This simply means that if a scanner is specified to require 20 watts of power on which to operate, it's virtually all dissipated as heat, with the majority of it in the power supply. As the power transformer heats up, it will warm up the scanner around it!

Heat is *Shiva,* the *Great Destroyer* (of electronics). Minimize or remove heat for greatly extended operating life of components!

The PRO-2004/5/6/2035 series of scanners get quite warm after only a short period of operation. If you don't believe me, touch the top case of your scanner after it's been on for a while.

No, it won't burn you, but it will be considerably warmer than room temperature. Nearly all of that heat comes from the power supply! Remove the power transformer for dramatically reduced heat accumulation and to gain hackable real estate at the same time!

It is easy to non-destructively test my hypothesis regarding excess heat caused by AC operation in the PRO-2004/5/6 scanners. These scanners have a DC power jack on the rear panel. Connect a 10-to-15 volt, 500 mA source of DC to this jack, center-tip positive (+) and shell negative (−).

Run the scanner continuously for 24 hours and you'll not feel significant warmth. Then feel the DC adapter or power supply that you're using to power the scanner! It may be warm, but that's OK; the heat is escaping into the atmosphere, not into your beloved scanner! DC power adapters and supplies are a dime a dozen. Here's how to remove the AC supply in the PRO-2004/5/6/2035 and, generically, other scanners:

PRO-2004/5/6: Unplug the AC cord from the wall! Remove the case of the scanner. Cut the AC power cord on both sides of its entry point through the real panel. Use a pair of pliers or diagonal cutters to squeeze and remove the plastic feed-thru clamp for the AC cord. This leaves a hole in the rear panel that might become useful later. For now, cover this hole on both inside and outside with tape or a pressure-sensitive label to block the entry of bugs, dust, and kids' fingers. Cut resistor R-801 (inside the clear plastic sleeve) from its attachment to the AC lead that goes to the power transformer and then cut it away from its soldered termination on the side chassis.

Flip the scanner over for access to the top area and cut the two blue transformer leads that go to the main receiver board about 0.25˝ above their solder points on the main receiver board, so that you can tell where they go should you ever want to reinstall the AC power supply.

Loosen and remove the two nuts and bolts that hold the power transformer, T-801, to the side wall of the chassis, and carefully lift it out of the

scanner. This transformer offers possibilities for a general purpose power supply as shown in my Vol-2. I wouldn't use it to power the scanner, even externally, because it is underrated for seriously hacked scanners. You'll want to power your PRO-2004/5/6 with something rated at 12VDC @ 1 amp or more.

The DC Power jack on the rear of the PRO-2004/5/6 takes the same size coaxial power plug as what's on the end of Radio Shack's *#270-1533, "Standard 12-VDC Fused Cord."* In fact, you can buy this ready-made cable, cut off the cigar-lighter plug, and use the cable and coaxial power plug between your external DC power supply and the scanner!

The important thing here is to get the right size coaxial power plug to mate with the DC power jack on the rear of the scanner, and be sure it is correctly connected: center-tip positive (+) and shell negative (-). Add an in-line fuse of 1 or 2 amp rating to put a polish (and a bit of safety) into the project!

ALL PRO-2004/5/6 NOTE

There is one other thing you ought to do while the scanner is open, if you're in the mood. Inside the scanner, just in front of the DC power jack, is a series limiter resistor, (PRO-2004 calls it R-256, 1Ω, 0.5 W. PRO-2005/6 have R-249, 1Ω, 0.5W. PRO-2035 has R-223, 1Ω, 0.5W)

The function of these current-limiting resistors is to act as fuses, and they DO BURN OUT when the scanner has been extensively modified and then powered with an external DC supply.

The resistor is rated at 1 ohm at a half watt.

Power equals current squared times the resistance. Therefore, 707 mA will hit the maximum rating of the resistor as shown in the following relationships. Actually, this is pushing it a bit, because I have seen these resistors burn out in unmodified scanners with a current of around a half amp (500 mA).

When a modified scanner is powered by external DC, this resistor tends to run hot, and I suppose the elevated heat eventually takes its toll. It doesn't take much to solve the problem before it happens.

This will help, both now and in similar situations when a bit of math is required. Make a separate note of it and keep it handy...

$$P = I^2 R$$

$$I = \sqrt{\frac{P}{R}}$$

$$I = \sqrt{\frac{.5}{1}}$$

$$I = \sqrt{.5}$$

$$I = 0.707 \, amp$$

If you're smart right about now, you'll take one of three options: (1) solder a jumper wire around this series limiter resistor to bypass it from the circuit; or (2) solder another 1Ω, 0.5-watt resistor in parallel with it, or (3) replace the stock R-256 or R-249 with a larger 1Ω, 2W resistor. Any of these three options will effectively eliminate this area as a potential trouble spot.

Choose one. I favor Option 1, which is easily done by crushing the resistor with a pair of dikes and then soldering a jumper wire between the exposed leads. This eliminates the need to remove the main receiver board as might be necessary with either of the other two options.

Take your choice, but do something with this resistor before it fails at exactly the wrong time. You know Murphy's Law as well as I do...

DC POWER FOR OTHER SCANNERS

If your scanner has an external DC power jack, then follow the guidelines given above for the PRO-2004/5/6/2035 scanners. If your scanner does not have a DC power jack, and many don't, you can still remove the AC power supply and run on external DC with only a little more work. Here's how (and why):

Modern scanners employ internal voltage regulators to control the necessary voltages for various portions of the scanner circuit. These voltage regulators, typically +5V and +8V, are fed with some higher DC level, usually 12V, but it doesn't really matter.

You see, voltage regulators are uncaring about the feed levels so long as it's a few volts above the intended output. A +5V regulator, for example, will produce a nice and stable +5V for any input of +7.5V or greater.

It is pretty much standard for +12V to be the main feed to the scanner's voltage regulators so all you have to do is find that +12V feed point on the output of the scanner's AC power supply and you're in business.

Figure 3-6: Typical AC/DC power supply for most base scanners

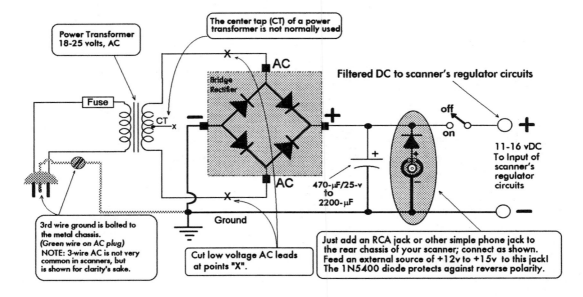

Remember one thing, however. If your wall-plug tranny produces too high a voltage, and the regulator has to reduce it to the required working voltage, there's a potential problem (pun intended).

For instance, reducing 24V to 5V (a 19V drop) in a 100mA circuit dissipates almost 2W, which might be outside the capacity of your voltage regulation circuit. Stay conservative unless you know exactly what you're doing

Using *Figure 3-6* as a guide, follow the AC power cord into the scanner. You'll see where it runs into the primary side (high voltage side) of a power transformer. The secondary (low voltage side) of the transformer will have two or three leads going to the main circuit board.

Somewhere in the immediate vicinity of these low voltage leads will be a bridge rectifier and a healthy-sized filter capacitor, usually 470µF or larger.

If you measure the voltage at the (+) leg of the filter capacitor, you should see somewhere between +11 and +16 volts.

That's where you will tie an external DC feed after removing the AC power supply. The best way is to install a convenient phone jack on the rear panel – I prefer simple RCA phone jacks. Solder the *anode* of a 1N5400 diode to the center lug of the jack. Solder the *cathode* of the diode to a point on the output of the bridge rectifier, and connect the feed to the On/Off switch of the scanner.

If the chassis of the scanner is ground, then you're done; if the power jack is installed in a plastic panel, solder a wire from the shell of the new jack to any convenient scanner ground.

TEST EQUIPMENT

Things change. The cost of a given function has really dropped since I wrote my first books, and new capabilities such as virtual instruments (RF cards that use the PC as a platform) have hit the market. It gets easier every day...

Radio Shack has added new multimeters to their arsenal, including an upgraded version of their benchtop model, #22-175. Another model I really like is their #22-182 Multimeter with PC Interface! The 1995 model is #22-168.

Indeed, a simple connection to a serial port (COM1 or COM2) on your computer allows

automated measurements and data acquisition! Great software comes with this meter, including the necessary serial cable to connect to your PC/compatible computer! Automated operation consists of flexible setups and variable periodicity of measurements with outputs logged to a plain ASCII text file for subsequent use as desired.

Two fields of data are outputed to the text file: time of measurement and value of measurement. The two data fields are delimited (separated) by a goofy ASCII character (decimal 028, hex 1C), between the columns of time and data.

Why Radio Shack didn't use either a tab or a comma for the delimiter is beyond me, but fortunately most text editors and word processors have a quick replace function by which this character can be replaced with a comma.

I mention this because a database manager makes quick work of processing volumes of accumulated data, but that ASCII 028 character will first have to be replaced with a comma in order to import the raw file into a database. Radio Shack's Multimeter with PC Interface (#22-182) is great for taking hands-free, automated measurements while you're busy with other things.

My personal experience is with the 1994 model, but I've looked at the 1995 software and found it to be a work of art! It's backwards compatible with earlier hardware, and supports Windows.

FREQUENCY COUNTERS

Radio Shack recently added a handheld frequency counter to their arsenal, but don't go running down there to buy one. Salt away your hundred bucks and check out what you can get from Optoelectronics or StarTech. You'll get a much better counter for the same or only a little more money.

Speaking of which, hobbyists can really be weird when it comes to gizmos and gadgets. A lot of people now think you can just lug around a frequency counter and lock onto all sorts of frequencies. Those who believe that are wrong...

A frequency counter will not lock onto and display a frequency unless it can get enough signal to trigger the counting circuits, which will be usually be somewhere between 10mV and 100mV.

In a word, that means you have to be pretty close to the transmitter, no matter how powerful it is, in order to get a lock for a stable readout.

Typical ranges, in actual practice, come to about 20-40 feet for handheld transceivers used by security guards and stadium ushers to 50 feet or so for mobile radios. Even base radios won't trigger a conventional counter beyond 100-300'. With a lot of work, plenty of experience, and some extra time on your hands, you can build up a specialized antenna and wideband preamp to feed the input of your counter to extend its range.

Unfortunately, if you buy a frequency counter to pull secret frequencies right out of the air, you'll be disillusioned. Frequency counters have their place, sure enough, but usually in the lab or shop for direct measurements, *in-circuit*. The more astute and experienced hobbyists will have good uses for them, but save your money until you know what you're doing.

Besides all that... a frequency counter does not necessarily read out the exact frequency of a signal. Much depends on the accuracy and stability of the counter's internal circuits. Most hundred-dollar counters are neither accurate nor stable. If you try to adjust the master oscillator of a receiver or transmitter using a cheap frequency counter as a readout, you'll probably do more harm than good. See just ahead under *Precision Frequency Standards*.

ADD A HOLD FUNCTION TO THE RADIO SHACK RF FREQUENCY COUNTER

Get the service manual for Radio Shack's Frequency Counter (by calling 800-442-2428), and follow these directions.

Locate TP 17 – in the schematic, it's pin one of U3, connected to +5V thru a 47k resistor. On the circuit board, TP17 is on the display side, just right of the lower-right corner of the IC.

Grounds are about 1/4 inch below and to the right of the three non-tinned points in the large area of metal. TP17 is the tinned pad next to a chip resistor marked '473' for 47k.

Rig a momentary push button switch that, when pushed, grounds TP17 thru a 1k resistor (you never can tell) and it works just fine!

Drill a small hole to mount the switch just above the plastic depression to permit access to the button with your right thumb. A small toggle switch will fit if you want to HOLD readings indefinitely.

Now let's make some useful test equipment for shop and shack.

RF DETECTOR PROBE FOR YOUR MULTIMETER

Here's a slick little project for dedicated radioists, from hams to CB'ers; from SWL's to scannists; and from engineers to technicians on a budget. The keyword here is *b-u-d-g-e-t*.

Electronic test equipment can be very expensive but my RF VOLTAGE PROBE will cost very little, if anything.

You might already have everything you need lying around your shack. So what's an RF voltage probe? Take a look at *Figure 3-7*. That's a simple one, and a very handy tool

Figure 3-7: RF detector probe – schematic

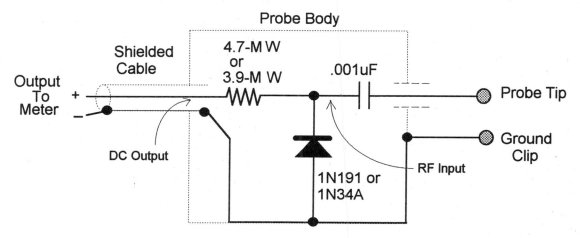

Figure 3-8: RF detector probe – mechanical layout

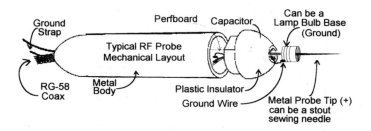

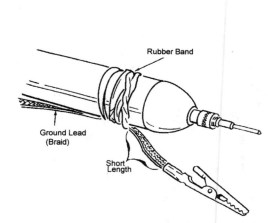

In a word, an RF probe is a "detector"; a simple circuit that samples radio frequency energy and converts it to a DC level that's proportional to the amplitude of the original RF signal. What's neat is that the output of this RF probe can be measured with almost any high impedance voltmeter!

GOOD ENOUGH??

Unless you have to take measurements down to the millivolt, my simple RF probe will satisfy virtually all needs, even of professionals, who rarely need more than an indication of RF and not so much absolute values. RF voltages can be extremely difficult to measure by the hobbyist, and the process usually requires costly equipment.

Yet, we're going to crash some barriers with old technology – an old circuit, and a slick way of putting it all together! *Figure 3-7* shows the schematic diagram of the detector. *Figure 3-8* depicts the mechanical solution.

This project gets really convenient if you convert the body and light bulb of a pocket penlight, typically Radio Shack's #61-2626. The only part of this flashlight not used is the push-button end, and the internal spring "guts" of the penlight.

The metal body of the penlight serves as a shielded housing for the detector circuit and something to grasp when making measurements.

If you use the penlight as the basic building block, then first remove the push-button end and the spring inside. It will just push out through the tube if you apply a little force. Next, unscrew the lamp bulb from the white plastic head and

carefully break the glass and clean out the shell without damaging the threaded brass base.

As the probe tip, get a stout sewing needle or something comparable and solder it to the center conductor of the bulb's threaded base from inside the shell, so the point sticks out in the same direction as the glass formerly did.

Fill in the hollow base of the bulb around the needle with epoxy or hot glue to give mechanical strength to the assembly. Screw it back into the plastic head. Finish up that part of the operation by filling in the rest of the white plastic head with either epoxy or hot glue.

Then solder one shortened lead of a 0.001 µF capacitor to the outside (back side) of the center conductor of the bulb's threaded base. It might be wise to solder the lamp shell to the metal ring that holds it inside the white plastic head. Also solder a short ground wire to the lamp shell and let it hang free for the time being.

Build the simple detector circuit in *Figure 3-7* on a narrow piece of perf board that can slide down inside the metal tube. Insert a 3' section of RG-58 or RG-59 coax into the hole left by removal of the push button.

Prepare the end of that coax so that the center conductor can be soldered to the back end of the resistor (DC OUTPUT) and the shield of the coax to the ground on the board. Solder the free end of the 0.001 µF capacitor to the junction of the diode cathode and the front end of the resistor (RF INPUT). Solder the free hanging ground wire from the lamp's shell (above) to the ground trace on the perf board.

ASSEMBLY

Carefully slide the whole assembly into the tube and gently screw the white head into the metal tube. On the distant end of the coax, install a connector to mate with the matching connector of your high impedance voltmeter. It's usually a dual-banana plug, but this can vary from one meter to the next. That's up to you.

Assembly of the RF probe is not particularly critical, but if you plan on measuring RF much above 25 MHz or so, you should keep leads very short, especially those of the capacitor, diode, and the front end of the resistor. Nothing is very important from the back end of the resistor down through the coax.

If you want your RF probe to be more accurate, then use a precision (1%) resistor. Check the specs of your meter; most have an input impedance of either 10 MΩ or 11 MΩ. If 10 MΩ, use a 3.9 MΩ resistor. If your meter has 11 MΩ input impedance, then select a 4.7 MΩ resistor. If your meter has some oddball input impedance other than 10 MΩ or 11 MΩ, then select a resistor approximately 35% - 45% of that value. Nothing to it, actually. The resistor converts the peak-to-peak value of the RF signal to a DC RMS value, generally more useful than P-P. *RMS equals 0.707 times P-P, and P-P voltage equals 1.414 times RMS voltage.*

Connect your RF probe to any high input impedance DC voltmeter – that's virtually ALL digital voltmeters, by the way. The output voltage of the probe is at a positive DC level, and the voltmeter should be set accordingly.

The RF probe can be used as a signal tracer and gain analyzer, as well as an RF voltage measuring device. It can also be used as a general purpose RF detector for emissions up to around 100MHz or so, and it's great for hidden transmitter hunts and debugging operations!

Its sensitivity will be enhanced with an "antenna" connected to the probe tip, if you're sampling signals from the air. You can also connect an antenna to the input of a wideband RF preamp and then sample the output of the preamp with the RF probe for even greater sensitivity! When a preamp is used for this purpose, it would be well to connect a 50Ω resistor across the preamp's output to simulate the 50Ω input of a receiver. Because this probe is designed primarily for RF applications, signals below 10,000 Hz will read low. Forget the RF probe and use the AC section of the voltmeter for frequencies below 10 kHz.

APPLICATION EXAMPLE

If your receiver is not functioning properly, the RF probe can be used as a signal tracer. First, connect the probe to the output of the last IF. stage and note the amount of RF energy present tere. If no indication, move the probe back to the input of the last IF stage and observe the meter again. If still no indication, move the probe to the output of the previous IF stage and, if necessary, keep going forward toward the RF input in this step-by-step manner.

When RF energy first appears, look for a problem in the following circuit. Local oscillator operation can also be checked, by touching the probe to the oscillator.

The probe sensitivity is limited by the sensitivity of the voltmeter, so it is unlikely that you will obtain satisfactory measurements in the RF and mixer stages of a receiver where signals are in the microvolt range.

The RF probe will be good for signals of a couple millivolts (0.002V) up to the break-down voltage of the diode (30V). Use this procedure to check RF or IF amplifier gain. Write down the readings obtained and divide the output voltage by the input voltage.

The answer you obtain will be the gain of the stage or stages. RF voltages from transmitters can also be measured, if the ratings of the diode are not exceeded.

30 volts P-P will be about maximum for a single diode. If your needs for an RF probe include transmitters above 15 watts, then use two or more diodes in series to extend the ratings. One diode is good for 15 watts RF, two for 70 watts, and three for 150 watts.

Nope – that's no error. Remember the math regarding the relationship between voltage and power? Depending on the voltage rating of the 0.001 μF capacitor, high DC voltages can be safely connected to the probe as long as the superimposed RF voltage does not exceed the RF voltage limit of about 30V P-P per diode.

For measurements in circuits where the RF frequency is lower than 25 MHz, the ground lead length and position are not too critical.

For measurements of higher frequency signals, the frequency response of the probe can be maintained "flat" by securing the ground lead firmly to the probe body with a rubber band. This provides a short length ground return with low inductance.

The RF probe is an indispensable tool around the serious monitoring shack. It can also be useful as a "bug" detector, but you'd want to practice up using it for that purpose to determine its limitations and exceptions.

A short length of wire on the probe tip will serve as an antenna to detect RF fields from bugs and low power transmitters, but practice with it using a cordless telephone to determine range and sensitivity.

OSCILLATORS, SIGNAL GENERATORS

Signal generators are costly, and cumbersome to lug around. You can, however, roll your own into a cubic inch or less for next to nothing provided you don't mind a lack of frills, a little work, modest performance, and serious ugliness.

The gizmo I have in mind is a basic crystal oscillator that will accept almost any type of quartz crystal over a very wide range of frequencies. A handful of crystals will yield a perfectly functional signal generator that can be used to evaluate the performance of shortwave and scanning receivers, as well as antennas. The oscillator can be the emitting device for hidden transmitter hunts. Add a few extras for an FM wireless microphone.

An oscillator does the same thing as a guitar string when plucked; or a piano string when struck: it oscillates or vibrates at a precise and relatively stable, consistent rate.

Like musical strings, an oscillator can be tuned or adjusted. Unlike musical strings which vibrate at audio rates, our oscillator vibrates at radio frequencies, from maybe as low as a few hundred kHz to 100 MHz or higher.

Our oscillator will be coarse-tuned or "adjusted" by choice of the crystal. Each crystal can be "trimmed" or finely tuned by means of a small trimmer capacitor. There's nothing much to it; a crystal, a transistor, and a few parts.

One benefit of the cheap oscillator in *Figure 3-9* is that not only will it put out a healthy signal on the fundamental frequency, but also plenty of harmonics up to the 8th to 10th or thereabouts.

Normally this is not good; signal generators are supposed to produce just the frequency to which they are tuned, but ours is so simple (on purpose) that it puts out eight or more odd and even multiples of the crystal frequency.

Then, depending on the type of crystal, it might also put out subharmonics of the crystal frequency as well! Again, this "*shoddy*" operation is not normally considered good, but for our purposes, it means a number of test signals will exist in the output at the same time. That means you can test your shortwave receiver and scanner across fairly wide bandwidths without changing crystals.

BUILDING YOUR OSCILLATOR

Construction of the test oscillator is not critical, but for best operation with the most harmonics, all components should be close together with short interconnecting wiring. The test oscillator is powered by 9V, but the supply can probably vary from as low as 5V to as high as 12V or a little more. Just be aware that the frequency will change as the voltage changes, which is not good even for our test purposes.

For portable operations and transmitter hunts (they're a lot of fun... ever try one?), I prefer to power my test oscillators with two 9V batteries, in series for 18V, and fed to a 78L09 or LM-317T regulator to set the voltage to a regulated 9 volts. I'll leave the oscillator's power to you, but my design is 9V.

WARNING: Depending on how you configure and use the test oscillator, its operation could be illegal. The FCC imposes a limit on the effective radiated power, which involves both amplification and antenna configuration.

Regulations tend to change periodically, so check first before you go hog wild with sophisticated antennas and power-increasing design techniques. The transistor can self-destruct if you draw too much power from the oscillator.

Caveats out of the way, let's build it and have some fun.

Refer to *Figure 3-9*: perf board assembly, with point-to-point wiring and soldered connections, is fine. A crystal socket facilitates easy swap of crystals as desired. That's how the fundamental frequency is set, of course.

A socket for the transistor is nice in the event you destroy one during setups and alignment.

THE MECHANICALS

The assembled board should be installed in a small metal box for shielding and isolation from sudden temperature changes. The metal box always should be grounded to the ground traces on the board.

A BNC jack can be installed almost anywhere convenient on the box to facilitate the connection of an antenna, which should not be longer than about 10" to keep operation legal. If you live near me, make that a maximum of 5″ or so.

Use a DC adapter, and a corresponding DC jack to input power. Install battery clips to hold the one or two 9V batteries for portable operations. The trimmer capacitor can be most any mini-tunable type with a maximum of not more than 100-200 pF and a minimum of 10-15pF or so.

ADDING VOICE

If you need a low power voice transmitter, the trimmer capacitor can be substituted with a varactor diode. It is beyond the scope of this section to dwell on how to choose the best varactor diode, but they are cheap enough that trial and error of a few will produce a nice sounding voice transmitter.

Add a 470μH (micro-Henry) RF choke to the junction of the crystal and the varactor diode and feed a preamplified audio signal to the other end of the choke. The output will be narrow-band FM, so this unit might make a nice wireless microphone if you use ingenious mechanical packaging.

The peak-to-peak value of the modulating audio signal will determine the FM deviation of the carrier, and something on the order of 1V P-P, will probably be required.

This means the audio signal should come from a gain-adjustable preamplifier so you can set the FM deviation to about ±3 kHz.

USING IT

The oscillator is great for testing and evaluating antennas, too! A portable version a hundred feet from the antenna under test will produce a real-life signal without bothering a soul anywhere else.

The antenna can then be trimmed, tuned, and adjusted for optimum performance on the desired frequency using your receiver and S-meter as visual/aural feedback instruments.

The Low-Cost All-Purpose Oscillator emits a range of signals as multiples of the crystal frequency. For example, if you select a 20 MHz crystal, you can expect to find signals at 20, 40, 60, 80, 100, 120, 140, and possibly even 160 MHz and above, but all at 20 MHz intervals (they are *harmonics,* right?).

You might also find subharmonics at 10, 5, and 2.5 MHz. "Overtone" crystals like those used in older CB radios demonstrate this characteristic. The once-popular 23 MHz and 37 MHz series work great.

So, you see, the Low-Cost All Purpose Test Oscillator makes a handy instrument for your bench. This simple, low-cost, design is good for other things, too...

OSCILLATOR PRANKS

I heard this story from the golden days of CB in the late '70s. The "good guys" in Springfield, Missouri, whipped up one of these oscillators and carefully tuned it to a "bad guy's" home channel. The "bad guy" called himself "Cookie Monster," but everyone else called 'im "Turkey Monster." You catch my drift here...

The gizmo was sealed into a jar with a fistful of batteries to last several weeks, and a 2-3 ft antenna wire was fed through the lid. The jar was buried 50 yards from Turkey Monster's house, and the antenna snaked under leaves and grass, so that for weeks, the poor fellow was unable to hear anything on his favorite channel, thanks to the dead carrier.

The oscillator has many uses, obviously. Put it to good use, and test *your* receivers with it; not those of other people.

Unless they *really* deserve it...

Figure 3-9: All-purpose test oscillator

NOTES:

1. The crystal is not critical, but probably should not be lower than 1 MHz, nor higher than 50 MHz.

2. An optimum value may be as high as 1100-ohms. Use of a 2-k trimpot is suggested to determine best value.

3. An optimum value may be as low as 4000 ohms. Use of a 100-k trimpot is suggested to determine best value.

4. The trimmer capacitor should have as wide of a "swing" or tuning ratio, max to min, as possible. The high end will not adversely affect the oscillator's operation, but oscillations may stop as the trimmer is adjusted toward the minimum end of the range.

5. Ground traces and connections are shown in heavy black lines. All grounds are interconnected.

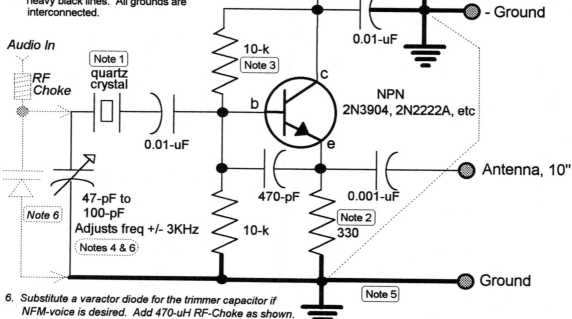

6. *Substitute a varactor diode for the trimmer capacitor if NFM-voice is desired. Add 470-uH RF-Choke as shown.*

PRECISION FREQUENCY STANDARDS ...YOU MAY ALREADY OWN ONE!

If you own a PRO-2004, PRO-2005, or a PRO-2006, then you're sitting on a precision frequency standard, so you may as well put it to use to upgrade the capabilities of your shop and shack!

Everything in RF today is crystal-based, and the accuracy of the crystal determines the performance of the communication channel, so it's important to have a good, stable, and accurate reference in your shack. There's one inside each of those units...

If you don't own one of these scanners, I'll show you how to *make* a precision frequency standard similar to the one inside them!

A SPECIAL ADJUSTMENT IN THE PRO-2004/5/6

To date, we have paid lots of attention to the "brains" (CPU) of the PRO-2004/5/6, but nothing has been said about its Reference Oscillator. It's a sorta secret, but I'll show you where to look.

Referring to *Figure 3-10,* open your PRO-2004/5/6 Service Manual to the schematic diagram for the **PLL Section**.

Hunt up IC-301 (PRO-2004) or IC-302 (PRO-2005/6). Next find Pin 1 of that chip, an MC145158. Follow the trace from Pin 1 and it will run directly to a nondescript little gizmo called "X-301."

I'll bet you never noticed it before, or dismissed it as unimportant. The Service Manual pays it no attention and pretty much leads you to believe that it is just a 10 MHz crystal. It's not mentioned in the *Alignment Instructions*, either.

Oh, but this little puppy is more than just a crystal, measuring 18mm x 8mm x 10mm high. X-301 contains a crystal, a transistor, and a few other components and is marked TEW or TX-1824, with various suffix letters. X-301 has a little hole on top of its metal housing, sealed with a small square of clear tape.

Inside that hole is an ADJUSTMENT! For Pete's sake, LEAVE IT ALONE until you learn what it's for, what it takes to tweak it, *and what will happen if you screw it up.*

Figure 3-10: X-301 in the PRO-2005/6

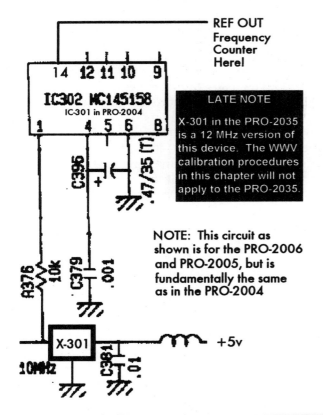

REF OUT
Frequency Counter Here!

LATE NOTE
X-301 in the PRO-2035 is a 12 MHz version of this device. The WWV calibration procedures in this chapter will not apply to the PRO-2035.

NOTE: This circuit as shown is for the PRO-2006 and PRO-2005, but is fundamentally the same as in the PRO-2004

THE SYSTEM CLOCK

You know how important the scanner's CPU is? Well, X-301 is just as important if not more so. A brain without a heart is about as useful as feathers on a lizard. X-301 is the system "ticker" but we're not supposed to know about it for good reason! X-301 is the Master Reference Oscillator for the

scanner. It's vital to run at exactly 10.000000 MHz give or take maybe 10 Hz (1ppm, or one part per million).

THE MAGIC SCREW

That's what the ADJUSTMENT is for and there is absolutely NO WAY to correctly adjust it without the proper tools and equipment.

I wouldn't even tell you about X-301 except for a wonderful use for it that I'll get into a bit later. But since I have mentioned X-301, then I'm obliged to tell the whole story, so bear with me.

X-301 has to run at an exact frequency or else the scanner won't tune properly; kind of like the timing of your car's ignition. That 10 MHz does a number of thing in your scanner, one of which is to get multiplied up to around 600 MHz for use as the first IF injection frequency. So a 20 Hz error at 10 MHz, multiplied by 60 becomes a 1200 Hz error at 600 MHz.

Not bad, but not good either. The fine razor's edge of your scanner's performance can be lost with errors in excess of 10 Hz. At errors of 40 Hz or more, it's sunk!

Now here is WHY Radio Shack doesn't tell us about that adjustment. Say you have a frequency counter *(aimlessly adjust X-301 without one, and you're hopelessly mired)*. With one, you're dangerous! A frequency counter has its own time base, or crystal reference, and if it's to be useful in this situation that counter's time base must be more accurate than the scanner's reference you're trying to adjust. Few are.

Your frequency counter is no more accurate than its time base, which in most hobby grade counters is pretty sloppy, and that's true for some inexpensive counters, too. I'm saying that you can't trust your frequency counter to be as accurate as required for X-301 adjustments. In fact, X-301 is probably more accurate and stable than most frequency counters you're likely to own as a hobbyist!

Let's put it this way: I have several frequency counters; some good and some so-so, and I don't trust any of 'em without first checking its calibration.

That's because the time base in each one can drift throughout the course of a day, and is different when it's first turned on than it is when it's been running for a while.

Your counter drifts, too, and probably worse than mine. Even if your frequency counter is within 20 Hz at 10 MHz (that's two parts per million), it's worthless for adjusting X-301!

ADJUSTING X-301

Now I am going to undo almost everything I just said by showing you HOW to adjust X-301. There are some restrictions. Read 'em and heed 'em. First, the tool necessary to adjust X-301 can't be found just anywhere. In fact, I don't know where to find the PROPER tool.

The adjustment in there is a little weird, but the #4 flat-blade screwdriver in Radio Shack's Precision Screwdriver Set, #64-1948, will get the job done if you're gentle and careful.

Nothing else will work that I know of without damaging the adjustment head of X-301, and if you do that, you're dead in the water.

WWV — TAX MONEY AT WORK!

Now that you're armed with the right tool, here's how to bring the United States National Bureau of Standards into your shack. You'll need a shortwave receiver capable of receiving WWV at 10 MHz. As you may know, WWV in Colorado and WWVH in Hawaii each broadcast a 10 MHz standard frequency along with Time of Day and other standard parameters.

We'll use their 10 MHz RF carrier because it is certified to be accurate to within one part in 10^{11}. We will use the most accurate radio frequency in the world to calibrate X-301. You can't beat that with a stick!

Now tune in WWV or WWVH at 10 MHz and make sure you get a fairly decent signal. At certain times of the day, it may fade or be hard to detect. If so, wait for a better time, because you have to have a stable, clean WWV signal.

A *little* noise won't hurt, but you better be able to hear the voice announcements each minute and the tones in between the minutes.

Assuming that you have a decent WWV signal available, pop the case on your scanner and locate the PLL sub-chassis on the bottom side of the PRO-2004/5/6. Pop the cover off the shielded compartment that contains X-301 and take a moment to familiarize yourself with everything

you need to know. Identify X-301 and the 16-pin MC145158 chip.

See *Figure 3-11* where X-301 for the PRO-2004, and its surrounding circuit, are shown in great detail. It closely resembles X-301's circuit in the PRO-2005/6. The MC145158 chip is IC-302 in the PRO-2005/6 and IC-301 in the PRO-2004. Then locate Pin 14 of the chip, the buffered (isolated) 10 MHz output of X-301. Interesting (and useful) that the Pin 14 Reference Output is not used by the scanner. Therefore we can use it without affecting anything in the scanner!

With your SW receiver tuned to WWV at 10 MHz, touch the end of a short 6-12" insulated wire to Pin 14 of the MC145158 chip. Immediately you'll note a different sound out of the nearby shortwave receiver! That's because the 10 MHz signal from X-301 will radiate from the wire and be picked by the SWL receiver, and mixed with the WWV signal.

It will be helpful if your receiver has an S-meter for a visual indication of what's happening, too. We will use this "sound" and the S-meter, if your SW receiver has one, to adjust X-301 more accurately than any frequency counter reliably could!!!! If the signal from X-301 totally overrides WWV's signal on your receiver, cut a few inches off the wire that touches Pin 14. The idea is to be able to hear (and see) both WWV and X-301's signals at the same time at about the same strength, give or take a little.

BEAT FREQUENCIES

Now, pause for a moment to get a clear picture of what we're about to do.

Get someone to gently whistle a very steady tone at about 1 kHz, and then you do the same. Have the other person hold their tone very steady while YOU adjust yours to match theirs. As your tone comes close to the other's, you'll "hear" a flutter or warble, which will slow down the closer the tones get to matching, and which will speed up the farther away they get from a match.

That flutter is a "beat frequency," or the difference between the two tones. If your tone exactly matches the other, there will be no warble or flutter and the two tones will "sync" in an indescribable sort of a way. You'll see what I mean with a little practice. This process is called "zero beating" or "heterodyning."

Back to WWV, the scanner, and X-301... WWV transmits a *very* high quality 10 MHz signal, and X-301 generates ("transmits") a signal pretty close to that, but not as close to a perfect 10 MHz. You will "hear" the difference between the two by listening to the receiver as the wire is touched to Pin 14 of the MC145158 chip. If your SW receiver has an S-meter, so much the better: watch it as you listen to the sound.

TUNING

Peel away one corner of the tape that covers the hole in X-301. Gently tweak X-301 a fraction of a turn in one direction; instantly you'll hear a difference out of the SW receiver. If you went the "wrong" way, that difference will "speed up," if you went the right way, it will "slow down."

If you're watching an S-Meter, it will jiggle faster when you tweak X-301 the "wrong" way and slower in the "right" direction. Now tweak X-301 in the "right" direction slowly, and a bit at a time, while listening to the SW receiver.

When you get X-301's frequency to match WWV, you'll know it. The "effects" will slow down to zero. Tweak X-301 back and forth a few times to see what I mean. You just kind of "rock" it in until things are right. It's tough to describe, but you'll know when it's right. And, when it is, X-301 will be within 1 or 2 Hz of WWV's 10 MHz. That's your objective; to get it "right on."

During this process, you might occasionally remove the wire from Pin 14 to adjust your hearing to pure WWV. Then touch the wire to Pin 14 again and you'll "sense" any differences. The whole process takes only a few seconds after you understand what to do, what to listen for, and what to watch for on the S-Meter. It isn't mystical or difficult, it's just harder to describe than to do.

After you become comfortable with this procedure, you can use it whenever a WWV 10 MHz signal is available to keep tabs on the condition of X-301. That's when you will be pleasantly surprised! It will rarely need readjustment!

At the beginning of this section, I spoke of accuracy and stability. X-301 is a precision Temperature Compensated Crystal Oscillator (TCXO) which will rarely if ever drift out of tolerance. Once adjusted, a TCXO tends to stay adjusted. I would be surprised if it needed readjustment more than once every few months, to tell you the truth, and even then...??

Whenever you check X-301, count the number of beats or warbles per second and if less than 5, don't bother with the readjustment. 5 Hz off is no big deal. That's the neat thing about X-301, which takes us next to the "wonderful little use for it" that I mentioned earlier.

USE YOUR PRO-2004/5/6 AS A PRECISION FREQUENCY STANDARD

NOTE: Even if you don't have a SW receiver with which to verify and adjust X-301 per the above procedure, you can still perform the following modification with high confidence that the 10 MHz output will be within 20 Hz of exactly 10 MHz. That's pretty close tolerance!

Trim all but about 1/8" of the leads of a 0.01 µF disk capacitor and carefully solder one of the leads to Pin 14 of the MC145158 chip. To the other leg of the cap, solder the center conductor of a section of mini coax cable such as RG-177/U (impedance doesn't matter), and I suppose you could use RG-58, though it's a bit bulky for this purpose. Solder the shield of this coax to the side wall of the metal compartment that houses X-301. Route the coax to the rear of the scanner's chassis and install a BNC jack RS #278-105. Solder the center conductor of the coax to the center pin of the BNC jack, and the shield of the coax to the metal chassis or to the BNC ground lug, if it has one.

Now trim a notch or hole in the cover of X-301's metal shield compartment so the cover can fit back on over the coax.

YOUR OWN PRECISION TIME BASE

Congratulations!

Now you have a precision 10 MHz signal that can be used for anything from calibrating frequency counters to just periodically checking X-301 against WWV without having to take apart the scanner! To calibrate a frequency counter, first do the WWV "zero-beat" test to make sure that X-301 is pretty close, within 5 Hz is great. Then connect the counter to the 10 MHz BNC jack and adjust the counter's internal calibration trimmer so that it reads 10.00000 MHz. Check both X-301 and your counter periodically, and you'll soon learn how drifty the counter can be. You'll also learn

Figure 3-11: Precision frequency standard

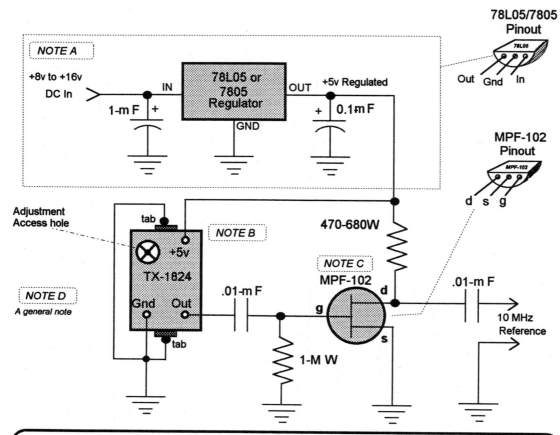

NOTES:

A. Voltage regulator circuit not required if other source of +5v regulated DC is available

B. Bottom view of the TX-1824 is shown; metal case tabs to be grounded.

C. N-channel JFET; not critical; idea is to isolate the output of the TX-1824 from the external world.

D. All parts available from Radio Shack; wiring not critical, but all leads should be kept as short as possible and assembly should be installed in a metal shielded box with a BNC output connector for best results. Add other enhancements as desired including On/Off switch, LED, power jacks, etc.

how rock-solid X-301 is; a space-age miracle of accuracy and stability.

The 10 MHz output jack can provide your shop, shack, or station with a new dimension in precision and confidence in the accuracy of your equipment.

I have evaluated X-301 in every PRO-2004/5/6 that has crossed my bench since 1986, and in all that time the worst case of inaccuracy ever noted was about 40 Hz, and that unit had problems! The rest have been within 20 Hz and most within 10 Hz. Therefore, even if you have no method or

desire to adjust X-301, you can still use the above modification as a standard frequency output for a variety of purposes!

You see, it is safe to assume that X-301 is within 20 Hz of 10 MHz and possibly a lot closer.

I have been evaluating a spare X-301 that I installed in a small metal box and keep powered up, night and day. I check it several times a day against WWV, and so far, it has not drifted more than 4 Hz. Most of the time, it stays within 1 or 2 Hz of WWV, despite daily ambient temperature excursions of 20-30° in my shop.

So why did I tell you all this? Maybe I ought to have my head examined, because a perfectly fine scanner can get boogered up by indiscriminate monkeying around. On the other hand, the neat things about X-301 are just too valuable to keep to myself. Everyone trusts frequency counters these days like babies trust their Mamas, but that's the wrong thing to do.

A frequency counter is no more accurate than its time base, and most in the hobbyist's price range are no closer than 200-500 Hz, with 100 Hz near the best until price jumps sky-high.

Hobby counters are typically specified to have a time base accuracy of 1ppm when they leave the factory. Manufacturers rarely mention DRIFT in their literature. So you can see why a frequency counter is no good for adjusting X-301, but if I hadn't told you, then sooner or later you'd have discovered X-301 all by yourself and that little hole would have whispered, *"Adjust me, adjust me!"*

And you would have grabbed your trusty frequency counter and gone to town... and to oblivion. Now there's hope, because you can adjust X-301 correctly and at the same time, calibrate your frequency counter for other precision needs!

Now it's project time, especially for those who don't own a PRO-2004/5/6 scanner.

LOOK OUT! While the new PRO-2035 is almost a clone of the PRO-2004/5/6, its time base, or version of X301, is at 12.000000 MHz, not 10.000000 MHz.

You cannot use WWV to calibrate it using the technique this section describes for the PRO-2004/5/6. See the next section for alternatives.

ASSEMBLE YOUR OWN PRECISION FREQUENCY STANDARD

Use a stand-alone X-301 mounted in a metal (temperature controlled?) box with a BNC jack output! First call Tandy National Parts at (800) 442-2425 and order a replacement X-301.

Tell the order-taker that you have a PRO-2006 (cat #20-145A) and that you need Part #TX1824G-3, identified as X-301 on the schematic diagram. A few days later, and you'll be well on the way to turning your shack into a mini-calibration lab!

The new X-301 has three pins on it: +5V, Gnd, and 10 MHz Out. Make certain you understand which is which before moving forward.

You'll need a few other components and a metal box, preferably sealable, to complete the project. Refer to *Figure 3-11* for the schematic, simple wiring plan, and the needed parts. The circuit is simple and self explanatory, but I'll add that a J-FET transistor (MPF-102), or similar is necessary to isolate the critical TX1824 module from the things you may connect to it.

The impedance between the drain and the gate of a J-FET is extremely high, such that if you were to short the output terminals of the cheap J-FET, absolutely nothing would happen to the more expensive oscillator module. Also, connecting things directly to the output of the TX-1824 could cause the frequency to drift a little. Oscillators are like that. The J-FET is cheap insurance.

GENERAL PURPOSE RF PREAMP — THE WBA-6

It's not often the home brewer can concoct an incredibly useful gizmo with almost embarrassing ease, but I've got a hot dawg for everyone, from confirmed couch potatoes to dedicated field techs.

The WBA-6 Low Noise, Wideband, RF Preamplifier will suit a variety of non-critical needs for amplification of RF signals from below 1 MHz to beyond 2000 MHz, with a noise figure of 3dB or less. Flip ahead to *Figure 3-12* for the gain curve of this useful gadget, which is +20dB at 1 MHz, +23dB at 250 MHz, +12dB at 1 GHz, and +6dB at 2.5 GHz.

Gain remains above +9dB out to 2 GHz. There may even be useful gain well below 1 MHz, but it's not specified by the manufacturer of the monolithic IC. So what's all the ruckus about this circuit?

Radio hobbyists need to amplify radio signals between DC and Daylight, not only for receivers but also for test and measurement applications including frequency counters, RF and bug detectors, signal generators, oscilloscopes, RF voltmeters, and more.

GAIN

First, we need a basic understanding of amplifiers. Hobbyists tend to think in terms of pure, raw, unadulterated, rip-snorting, fire-breathing *GAIN*. Well, it would be nice *if gain could be* "unadulterated," but unfortunately, we live in a real world. Basically, gain is a multiplication of signal strength and, preferably, to the *exclusion of undesired signals.*

This is very difficult to achieve when the amplifier is to be what we call "wideband," because within that "wide" band reside potential undesired signals.

Unfortunately, a wideband amplifier amplifies ALL signals within its passband, so those are not the kind of undesirable signals of which we speak in this context. Instead, we're talking about nasty signals like internally generated *noise, intermodulation,* and *cross-modulation* products. These funky signals are controllable, but control comes at a price in the real world.

Think of inter/cross-mod products as pseudo-signals, or signals that do not exist outside the device. They're generated by interaction of discrete (single frequency) signals within the circuit, and appear as sum and difference signals.

Think of noise as it really is; random and chaotic energy, like static, that covers up or obliterates desirable signals. Amplifiers should be designed for *low noise* and *high dynamic range* to maximize the benefits of GAIN, but it's easier said than done.

Modern technology has come a long way, however, and we can make use of it to home-brew a general purpose, low noise, wideband preamplifier for radio signals from way below 1 MHz to well over 1 GHz.

Thanks to the cheap, simple MAR-6 monolithic amplifier chip from Mini-Circuits Labs, Inc., which is specified to have a performance range from DC to 2 GHz.

DYNAMIC RANGE

The dynamic range of the MAR-6 device is defined by the *"1dB compression point,"* which is +2dBm. This is a ratio of the maximum gain of the device where incoming signals are compressed by 1dB to the minimum discernible signal level. +2dBm isn't especially great, but what do you want for a few bucks?

The MAR-6, as used in our WBA-6, will do nicely as an experimenter's general purpose RF preamp. You're gonna love it!

NOISE FIGURE

Noise figure is a very important specification of an amplifier. Imagine 100dB of gain with 100dB of noise. *(Arrrgh ☹!)* Obviously, the lower the noise figure, the better.

As a rule of thumb, anything below 5dB can be considered to be relatively low noise, but for receiver applications the lower the better.

The noise figure for a typical commercial receiver, including scanners, is 2dB or less with the real pro stuff coming in under 0.5dB. The MAR-6 device in our Low Noise, Wideband Preamplifier has a Noise Figure of 3.0dB, which is *"useful; not great."* I tried the WBA-6 preamp with my PRO-2004, PRO-2006, and PRO-43 scanners, and with a Yaesu FRG-7700 shortwave receiver. It definitely made a difference on weak signals, and found some that couldn't be heard without it.

Like most preamplifiers, it added pseudo-signals of its own, but this is acceptable for most hobby situations. I also used my WBA-6 as a preamp for a hand-held frequency counter and a handheld RF (bug) detector, where it really stood out!

RESULTS

If you use a frequency counter to determine frequencies used by security guards, stadium ushers and such, you'll find that the WBA-6 can double or triple the effective range!

If a walkie-talkie triggers your frequency counter from 20 feet away, the WBA-6 might increase the range to 40 feet or more (and double the range equals four times the power). The WBA-6 also lends itself as an oscilloscope and RF voltmeter preamplifier where circuit signals might be just a bit too weak to detect.

BUILDING IT — FOLLOW BASIC RULES

Okay, let's get down to brass tacks and build this jim-dandy, all-purpose RF preamplifier. You'll need only a few parts, as shown in *Table 3-2.*

Remember that I said this project was going to be easy? It is, but you can't just slop it together and expect to enjoy the benefits of low noise and high gain over a wide bandwidth.

Electronic design and construction techniques are "anything goes" between DC and a few hundred kHz. Up to about 30 MHz or so, only the basic RF techniques are required. Then, between 30 MHz and 300 MHz, things can get touchy if you don't choose the right components and pay close attention to how they are laid out.

Above 300 MHz (UHF), there simply is no choice but to follow established guidelines for component and circuit designs for which there is almost no room for error. UHF frequencies just don't behave like HF and below. VHF is a middle zone where sometimes the old ways are okay, and sometimes not. The WBA-6, however, can perform up to 2 GHz and beyond, so special care must be exercised in its construction if you hope for lots of wideband gain with a low noise figure!

COP-OUT

Comes first, THE EASY WAY! Electronic Rainbow, Inc. offers the WBA-6 as a kit of all required parts, including precision printed circuit board.

The kit comes with good instructions to assemble, install, and operate. See *Table 3-2* to find sources for the WBA-6 Kit or for the discrete parts if you want to roll your own. You can fabricate your own WBA-6 from the diagrams and guidance offered here if you are handy with assembly and know something about the parts for VHF-UHF circuits; otherwise, the kit is your best bet.

CIRCUIT BOARD

Fabrication of the little printed circuit board will be the most difficult part of this job, and only because VHF-UHF circuits don't tolerate much sloppiness or deviation from specs. Therefore, you should get the WBA-6 Kit from Electronic Rainbow, Inc., if you aren't comfortable doing the PC board yourself.

You will need a double-sided PC board that measures about 20 x 30 mm. All the traces and foils are lines or rectangles, so the standard etching process might not be as good as a sharp utility blade (Xacto™ Knife) to slice through the copper foil; remove the unwanted copper strips by hand.

That dental plaque scraper is a good tool for working the copper foil off the board after it has been scored/patterned with the knife.

Figure 3-13 will present the simple schematic diagram and *Figure 3-14* shows the foil pattern,

parts placement, and important dimensions of the PC board. *Figure 3-15* is a photo of Rainbow's WBA-6 printed circuit board.

After the PC board has been bought or made, and properly prepared, the rest of the job is a snap. Position and solder the components as shown in *Figure 3-14*. The MAR-6 amplifier chip has a dot next to one of the leads, to identify the INPUT pin, so check that when you solder it in place and the other three leads will be positioned just right.

Use as little solder and heat as possible, but enough of each to flow smoothly and evenly. The choke, L-1, is a ferrite core slipped over a short length of solid hookup wire.

You don't want to use a regular coil type of choke here, which doesn't work well at VHF and UHF frequencies. A 20 μH chip-style choke *might* work here, if specified for UHF frequencies, and if you can find one. Otherwise, use the specified ferrite bead slipped over a piece of solid hookup wire and keep the leads SHORT! Other than that, assembly of the PCB is straightforward so long as you use chip-type capacitors and resistors. Remember, we are anxious to achieve high gain over a wide band, with low noise.

MECHANICALS

The WBA-6 amplifier board should be installed inside a metal enclosure: the smaller, the better. BNC chassis-mount connectors should be installed on opposite ends of the enclosure at points closest to the RF Input and Output points on the WBA-6. You don't want any more lead length between the BNC connectors and the WBA-6 than is absolutely necessary. The RF Out end of the box should be fitted with a *male BNC chassis jack* to facilitate easy connection to scanners, frequency counters, etc. without the need for an adapter.

You can use a female BNC jack at each end if more convenient, but then you'll need a male-male BNC adapter for some occasions.

For my prototype unit, I built an enclosure out of double-sided printed circuit board material soldered together into a rectangular box, with one side temporarily left open for access.

Each end cap of the box was drilled and fitted with a BNC chassis jack, female on the RF In end and male on the RF Out end. The box was made exactly long enough for the WBA-6 board to fit precisely.

Table 3-2: WBA-6 parts list and sources

Circuit Symbol	Description	Radio Shack#
C-1,2	Capacitor, 0.01µF, chip	❷ PCC103B
C-3	Capacitor, 1.5µF, chip	❷ PCT5155
Cf	Capacitor, 470ρF, feedthru	*Optional*
L-1	Ferrite bead	❷ P9823
R-1	Resistor, 511Ω, metal film, chip	❷ P511FBK
U-1	Monolithic amplifier; DC-2 GHz	❸ MAR-6
Misc	Printed Circuit Board, 2-sided	❺ 276-1499
Input	BNC Chassis Jack, female (In)	❹ PE4014
Option	BNC Chassis Jack, male (Out), or↻	❹ PE4211
Option	BNC Male-Male Adapter (Out)	❹ PE9000
Kit	20dB Gain Preamp Kit, 2GHz	❶ WBA-6

WBA-6 Kit:

Electronic Rainbow, Inc.
6254 La Pas Trail
Indianapolis, IN 46268
(317) 291-7262; FAX: (317) 291-7269

Electronic Parts and Supplies

DigiKey Corporation
701 Brooks Avenue South
Thief River Falls, MN 56701-0677
(800) 344-4539; FAX: (218) 681-3380

Hosfelt Electronics (*Surplus Outlet*)
2700 Sunset Blvd
Steubenville, OH 43952-1158
(800) 524-6464; FAX: (614) 264-5414

MAR-6 Monolithic Amplifier

❸

Mini-Circuit Labs, Inc.
PO Box 350166
Brooklyn, NY 11235-0003
(800) 654-7949; FAX: (417) 335-5945

Coaxial Connectors and Accessories

❹

Pasternak Enterprises
PO Box 16759
Irvine, CA 92713
(714) 261-1920; FAX: (714) 261-7451

❺

Radio Shack Stores *(nearly all)*

between the center lugs of the BNC connectors so as to minimize the lengths of the <u>RF Input</u> and output leads.

The WBA-6 board was soldered along one of its long edges to the inside surface foil of the enclosure. The rig looks terrible because of the soldering it took to "weld" the seams of the "box" together, but the double shielding is total and the preamp works fine. After the unit was tested, a mating panel was soldered over the open side to RF-seal the enclosure. A small hole drilled through one end admits a wire for easy connection of DC power.

A tab was soldered to the outside ground foil of the box for the ground (–) power lug. For critical needs, it is advisable that DC power to the preamp box be shunted to ground by a capacitor to dump outside AC interference that might have penetrated into the line. Put that cap just inside the enclosure, between the DC and ground. Any value from 470 pF to 1000 pF will be satisfactory.

In fact, a cap from the power supply feed to ground is a good idea wherever that feed might have picked up noise, and those locations will vary from layout to layout. The objective is to amplify only the signal.

The RF-OUT end of the box feeds scanners, frequency counters, RF voltmeters, etc. The RF-IN side accepts a portable antenna or coaxial cable from a remote antenna. Be sure to label the RF-IN (antenna) side of the preamp so it can be distinguished from the output side which connects to the receiver, frequency counter, RF detector or other equipment.

POWER

All that's left to do is connect the (–) side of a 12V power source to the ground shell of the enclosure and the (+) side to the wire that goes into the box. Power requirements are about 16mA @ 12V. Regulated DC is preferred for stable and quiet operation, but a filtered 12V will be fine for most cases. Batteries are *very* quiet: a 9V battery is ample if you don't need maximum gain.

PERFORMANCE

So now, what can we expect from the WBA-6? A lot, actually. 20dB is a multiplier of 100, 10dB is a multiplier of 10, and each 3dB increment is a multiplier of 2. So 23dB gain multiplies signals by 200. 12dB multiplies by a factor of 16.

For math fans, the dB (decibel) is defined as ten times the logarithm of the ratio of one level of power to another. It's typically Power Out to Power In, or:

$$dB_{Gain} = 10\,Log_{10}\frac{P_{Out}}{P_{In}}$$

Voltage (E) and current (I) ratios are expressed as:

$$dB_{Gain} = 10\,Log_{10}\left(\frac{E_{Out}}{E_{In}}\right) or \left(\frac{I_{Out}}{I_{In}}\right)$$

GAIN CONTROL

Most hobbyists won't care about the actual gain in a given application, but there are times when reduced gain is better than running full bore so you should have some sort of control. For instance, 23dB of gain at 250 MHz is likely to cause overload and interference in a scanner, so we need a method of attenuation, or gain control. In fact, most receivers cannot benefit by more than about 10dB of gain.

Gain Control on the WBA-6 is possible by varying the supply voltage. A range of 5-13V offers a good range of control. This is done by grounding one end lug of a potentiometer with a max resistance something near 5kΩ, and feeding the +12V supply lead to the other end lug of the pot. Connect the WBA-6's power feed line to the center lug of the pot, and you're set.

Purists will use a variable regulated power supply instead of a potentiometer, and they're right. But the WBA-6 will prove satisfactory for some receivers, and is really useful for instrumentation. I observed good performance above 760 MHz on my PRO-2006, where it often made a difference between hearing and not hearing.

If you like the WBA-6, then contact Electronic Rainbow, Inc. for their catalog of other fine kits, some of which can be combined with the WBA-6 for "tandem" or cascaded operation.

Electronic Rainbow, Inc. supplies other simple and easy kits for amplification of stronger signals like television, and for CATV distribution systems, including satellite.

Figure 3-12: WBA-6 performance

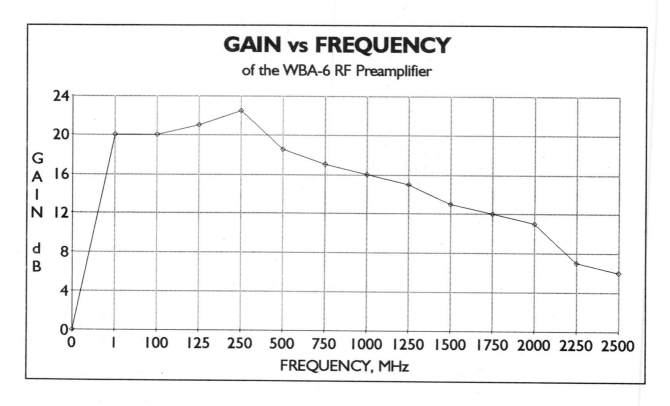

Figure 3-13: Wideband RF preamp schematic

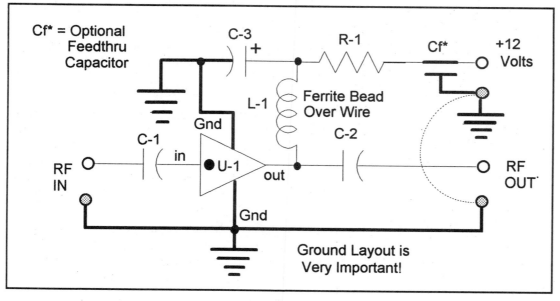

Figure 3-14: Wideband RF preamp, parts layout

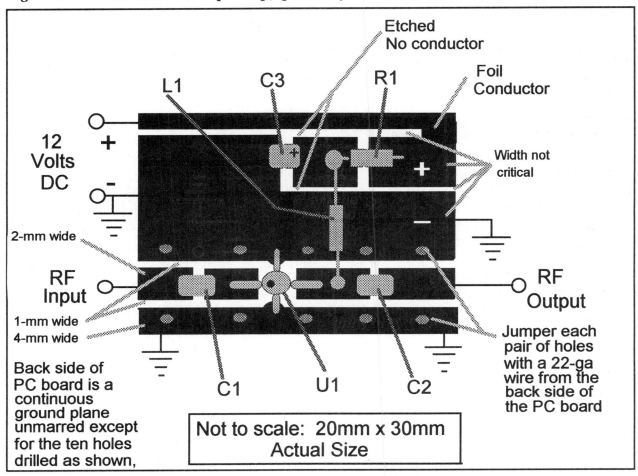

Etched
No conductor

Foil
Conductor

L1   C3   R1

12
Volts
DC

+

−

Width not
critical

+

−

2-mm wide

RF
Input

RF
Output

1-mm wide
4-mm wide

Jumper each
pair of holes
with a 22-ga
wire from the
back side of
the PC board

Back side of
PC board is a
continuous
ground plane
unmarred except
for the ten holes
drilled as shown,

C1   U1   C2

Not to scale: 20mm x 30mm
Actual Size

Figure 3-15: WBA-6 printed circuit board

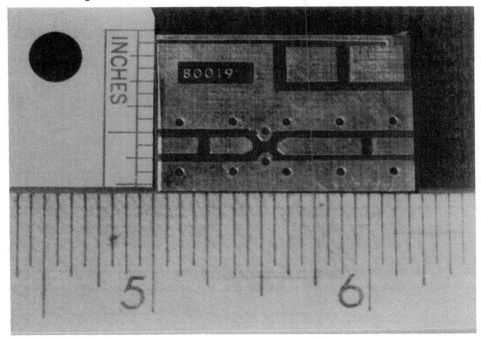

GENERAL PURPOSE RF PREAMPLIFIER — J-FET VERSION

Here's another preamplifier for general purposes though it doesn't have the performance of the WBA-6. This one is generic and not likely to be good for more than 40-50 MHz, but it's easy. See *Figure 3-16*.

If your construction techniques are good, you might be able to extract useful performance up to 100 MHz.

At the other end, this preamp will be useful close to the audio range, so it takes up where the WBA-6 leaves off at the lower end of the spectrum.

If VHF performance is important to you, then use chip-type components for all resistors and use 0.01 µF chip capacitors in place of the specified 1 µF caps. The 10 µF cap will do as shown (tantalum) but you should use a decoupling capacitor on the DC power lead where it enters the enclosure that houses this preamp.

As usual, you'll want to mount this circuit inside a shielded, metal enclosure as described in the previous section on the WBA-6 preamp.

Variable gain can be achieved by substituting a series combination of a 100Ω fixed resistor and a 1kΩ trimmer potentiometer in place of the 1kΩ resistor in the emitter of Q-2. Adjust the trimmer for desired gain/results. All leads should be kept short, and a printed circuit board is best for this project. Power the preamp with regulated +5 V. If you're interested in 30 MHz and below, perf-board construction will be fine.

As with most homebrew preamps, this one is best for instrumentation and less ideal for receivers, but it will work for both if you can accept modest performance.

It's especially suited for amplifying signals to be sent to test instrumentation such as oscilloscopes, RF voltmeters, frequency counters, etc. Little more need be said here; just build it... and good things will come.

Figure 3-16: General purpose preamp

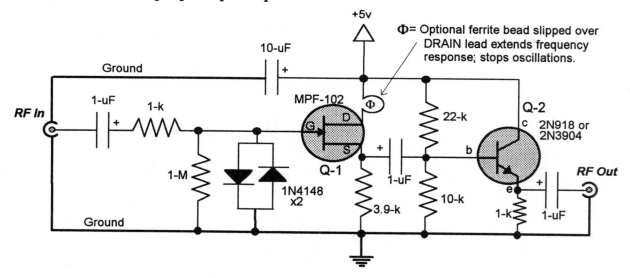

STATUS INDICATOR and LOGIC PROBE

Bob Scott, of Alexandria, Virginia, came up with a circuit that trips my trigger; makes my cup runneth over; and amazes me no end for its simplicity and usefulness around shop and shack.

It's easy to build and, since it costs only a buck or two, can be considered almost free. I really don't know what to call this circuit because it has so many uses, but I will focus on two, so depending on what you do with it, this circuit will either be a Logic Probe or an LED status indicator. One perfect application is for a Carrier-ON Indicator to indicate Squelch Breaks in your receiver! *See MOD-31 in my Vol-2 for an early version of this circuit.*

Anything from a pilot lamp to a warning light can be called a status indicator. The neat thing about this one (and they're all simple) is the dual color feature rather than just a light that goes on or off.

This one goes red or green, yellow or blue, whatever happens to be your preference to indicate some kind of an off/on; safe/danger; go/no-go; or yes/no status.

In that sense, my Status Indicator is not ideal for pure ON-OFF situations where you want no current to be drawn when something is off.

It would be great to indicate whether a door is open or closed; a liquid level is in the safe or dangerous zone; or perhaps the status of your receiver's squelch. Or the condition of almost anything properly wired to it. And, it's fun. In Chapter 9 you'll learn my definition of "fun." Honestly, this project is *really* fun!

KEY PARTS

Another neat thing about my Status Indicator is that it needs only one LED if you can find the two-lead, bi-color variety like Radio Shack's #276-012. That's right, a single LED of the right type can light at one or the other of two colors, usually red and green, depending on which way current flows through it.

If you can't locate a bi-color LED, just use two of any color you like, wired in parallel, but cathode to anode and anode to cathode. A 1 kΩ resistor in series with one side (doesn't matter which) completes the dual color status indicator section.

You'll need a CMOS Hex Inverter chip to drive the LED unit. It's almost as simple as wiring the LEDs together, as you'll see in *Figure 3-17*. Total parts count can be as few as five or as many as seven if you're forced to use two LEDs.

You can use most any sort of Hex Inverter, I suppose, but I prefer CMOS because such parts draw only about 5 mA for this circuit. You could almost breathe on it to make it work. There are at least two readily available CMOS Hex Buffers, the 74HC04 (my favorite) and the 4049.

The latter type is found almost anywhere, except Radio Shack, under the following part numbers: CD-4049; NTE-4049; ECG-4049; and MC14049.

SOURCES

Retail electronics supply houses usually stock the NTE or ECG lines, either of which will work fine. DigiKey and other national supply firms carry National Semiconductor's CD-4049 or Motorola's MC14049. I like the high-speed CMOS 74HC series over the 4000 series because of generally faster operation at lower currents, but for use as a Status Indicator, who cares? Just get whichever chip is handiest and lower in cost.

If and when you get into things digital, it makes sense to focus your activities on one or two logic families in order to avoid having to stock a parts warehouse to meet basic needs. The 74HC and 4000 series of CMOS logic will meet a variety of needs without sending you to the poorhouse.

ASSEMBLY

Wiring is not at all critical; just guard against foolish shorts, solder globs, and errors. Installation can be wherever and however best suits the needs of your application. The circuit can be installed in one location and the LED in another with a pair of wires between. Or, the circuit and LED can be remotely installed somewhere with but three wires feeding it from the main location. For that scenario, you'll need a ground wire, a +5V power lead, and one wire to carry the signal.

There are two important considerations for this circuit, one of which is the power supply that's specified to be a regulated +5V, routinely available in almost all things electronic nowadays. The 4049-series, however is capable of DC power and signal inputs as high as +18V while the 74HC04 is limited to +5.5V max, DC power and signal.

Pick your poison. Just be sure to use the specified 2.2 µF capacitor as shown in *Figure 3-17* to filter any spikes and transients before they get to the chip. The 100 pF capacitor on the input is optional, but might be useful if the signal source is to be any distance from the circuit.

Eliminate the 100 pF capacitor if your application is for a Logic Probe, as discussed below.

TRIGGERING THE CIRCUITRY

The second, but very important, consideration for this circuit is that the signal input MUST be approximately equal to the power supply voltage for "high" inputs and approximately equal to

Figure 3-17: Logic probe or status indicator

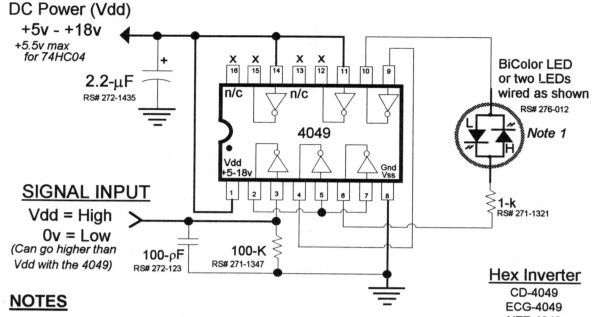

NOTES

1. You can use two different colored LEDs wired as shown or a single bi-color LED. "L" signifies the LED that will light when the INPUT is "Low" while "H" shows the LED that will light when the INPUT is "High". A bi-color LED has two leads; reverse the connections to alter the color sequence.

2. The 4049 Hex Inverter is more easily obtained than the 74HC04 and allows signal levels higher than the DC supply!

ground potential (0V) for "low" inputs. You cannot, for example, power the circuit with +12V and then use signal levels of 5V and 0V.

The circuit will be confused over the 5V and possibly not know how to act, or else it will ignore it and think it is a low.

Generally speaking, signal levels must be within about ± 10% of the power supply and ground levels. In the case of a +12V supply, the high signal input will have to be around 11V while the low input will have to be less than 1V.

Summarizing, the signal logic has to be the same level as your power supply and ground.

So if you're looking to display the status of 5V logic, use +5V power, etc.

Incidentally, this signal and DC power consideration is pretty much universal for all digital logic chips, especially in the CMOS families.

Select your chips accordingly: 4000-series for 5 to 15 volts and 74HC series for 5 volts only. Only a very few chips can mix logic levels and we'll point them out if we run across them. The 4049 chip can accept logic levels HIGHER than the power supply voltage, unlike the 74HC04, so it's probably the better choice for routine applications.

LOGIC PROBE?

This circuit can also be used as a Logic Probe... of the sort that costs $20-40 ready-made. A logic probe is an indicator of logic levels. Commercial models have overvoltage protection and some fancy stuff that's seldom needed by the hobbyist. A logic probe is great for quick and dirty checks to see if a test point is "high" or "low."

There's nothing much to my own unit, and yours can be just as fancy as you want it to be. Start with the housing for the circuit. Radio Shack's #61-2626 penlight flashlight makes a good probe housing.

The mechanical part I'll leave up to you. Just build this circuit using the 4049 Hex Inverter (not the 74HC04!) into whatever you want, with three conductors for the outside world.

Obviously, the signal input should be a needle or other pointed tip with which to touch the signal trace. The other two conductors should be alligator-clip leads about 8-10" long, one black for ground and one red for (+) volts.

As with the Status Indicator, it is mandatory that the Logic Probe be powered with the same supply voltage as the logic level you're about to measure. Most nowadays are +5V, but some CB radios and other rigs of the past used +8V and +15V logic.

Therefore, you must determine your expected logic levels in advance and be sure to connect the alligator clips to the proper points.

If you're measuring +8V logic, it will have a +8V power supply in it where you can attach the alligator clips. It's the same for +15V and +5V.

Those are the only logic levels I know about – short of negative logic, which is not too common nowadays. The Logic Probe will not handle negative logic; strictly signals 0V to +15V.

3.3V logic is coming into vogue these days and I think the Logic Probe will handle it, especially with a 74HC04 chip, but beware: the 74HC04 cannot take more than +5V power or signal!

The 4049 might gag on less than 5V, but you could safely try it on 3.3V if there is a need – and eventually, you will see one.

HOW IT WORKS – CIRCUIT WALKTHROUGH

Okay, for those who like a little theory with their breakfast, here's how the circuit works. Say we have it powered up with +5V DC, but no signal at the input.

The GREEN or left LED in the schematic will be lit. Here's why: With no signal on Pin 3, the 100k resistor pulls the input to a Low or 0-volts. A Low passes through the buffer as a Low but gets inverted to a High (+5V) at Pin 2. This High is split two ways, one to Pin 5 and the other to Pin 7.

Now we have to split our thinking. First, the High at Pin 5 gets inverted to a Low at Pin 4 and is fed to an Input at Pin 9 which is inverted to a High at Pin 10.

This Pin 10 High is fed to the top of the two LEDs, so we'll see +5V on the anode of the "L" LED and on the cathode of the "H" LED. Now let's go back to the split from Pin 2 and evaluate the other half of the action.

The High at Pin 2 also feeds an Input at Pin 7 to be inverted to a Low Output at Pin 6. This Low is fed to the bottom of the LEDs through the 1k resistor.

Thus there is a low (0V) on the cathode of the "L" LED and on the anode of the "H" LED. Simple enough. Now, do you see that +5V on the cathode of the "H" LED and the 0V on the anode of the "H" LED?

Sure enough, that is a reverse-bias condition and the "H" LED cannot conduct, therefore it will not be lit. But look at the "L" LED! +5V on the anode and 0V on the cathode is a forward bias condition and therefore the LED will light!

If you select a GREEN LED to indicate Low, then that's what you'll see: Green!

Now suppose +5V is on the Signal Input at Pin 3? That high becomes a Low at Pin 2 which feeds Lows to Pins 5 and 7. The outputs of those sections are inverted to Highs at Pins 4 and 6. The High at Pin 6 is fed through the 1k resistor to the cathode of the "L" and anode of the "H" LEDs.

Meanwhile, the High at Pin 4 feeds to Pin 9 to be inverted to a Low at Pin 10 and thereby feeds the anode of the "L" LED and the cathode of the "H" LED.

The "L" LED cannot light because it is reverse-biased, but the "H" LED certainly will light, thanks to its forward bias!

The sixth Inverter section at Pins 14 and 15 is not used, so we tie its input to +5V so that it will not oscillate and cause problems.

Unused inputs of all CMOS circuits must be tied either Low or High and not allowed to float! Unused outputs of CMOS circuits should be left floating, as shown.

The 1k resistor is a required current limiter for the LEDs. Most LEDs will burn out when current exceeds about 25-35 mA.

The brightness of an LED does not appreciably change as its current is varied, unlike incandescent lamps, so it makes sense to limit the current to a very safe value, not only for the LED, but also for the chip that has to produce that current.

The 2.2µF capacitor cleans up any noise on the DC power feed while the 100pF capacitor cleans noise from the signal line in cases where you have to use a long signal conductor.

Enjoy the circuit as both a practical application and a great training-aid!

SUMMARY and CONCLUSION

I could go on and on with the helpful little circuits, techniques, tips, hints and kinks, but pretty soon there would be no room left for modifications. I suppose we'd better be moving on.

If this sort of project (the backside of scanner hacking) interests you as much as it does me, then check out the *World Scanner Report,* which regularly covers even the black magic aspects of hacking.

Now you need to muster up a proper measure of Patience, Attitude, and Intestinal Fortitude. Gather the right tools and materials and *let's go!*

We're moving from the sandbox...

to the beach.

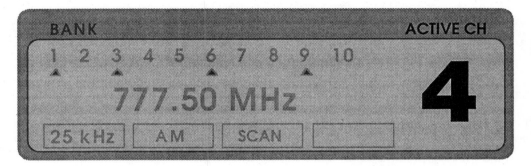

MEMORY MODS

MEMORY TYPES

Increasing a scanner's programmable and storable memory is one of the more popular modifications to come down Hacker Highway. Unfortunately, there is no hope of extending the memory of *most* scanners.

Three general types of programmable memory are used by modern scanners. The most common is *on-board* RAM integrated with the CPU function in a single chip. This kind cannot be modified, and it includes about 90% of all scanners. Next, and the most easily modified for extended memory, are those dozen or so scanners that have a separate outboard static RAM chip (SRAM) to hold the channel and frequency programming. Less common, but definitely modifiable, are a few scanners using EEPROM (Electronically-Erasable Programmable Read-Only Memory). Let's take a closer look at each of the three sorts of memory.

INTEGRATED WITH THE CPU

Modern scanners are controlled by a multifunction microcomputer chip called a Central Processor Unit (CPU), which is really a sort of computer. Its primary function, of course, is to operate the

scanner according to a "plan" or program. This program is better called "firmware" and can be burned into read-only-memory (ROM) that's integrated (combined) with the computing function. The communication path between the memory (that contains the program) and the CPU that executes it, is etched into the silicon iself, which is encapsulated in the package of the IC. In integrated units, such firmware is not alterable nor accessible from the "outside."

Such highly integrated chips (CPU plus memory functions, at least) are expensive to bring to production, but cheap to make. It can cost more than $400,000 to design and lay out such a chip, but only a few dollars each to produce.

Short of replacing the CPU with one containing your own program *(fat chance!)* there is no hope of altering any scanner function that is exclusively controlled by the instructions sent from integrated memory to the CPU. That's because the path between those two parts of the chip is internal, and cannot be accessed. Because it's less expensive to make and mount one chip rather than two, this type of CPU reduces cost, both to buy and in the assembly process. That's why they're in such common use.

Most CPU's also contain the LCD Display Driver function, which translate computer instructions into characters we read on the display. Some exceptions occur in the PRO-2004/5/6 series that uses a separate LCD driver.

This is of no consequence to hacking in the past, but it affects the Ultimate Scanners of the future because the *CE-232 Scanner/Computer Interface* captures and makes use of the data that flows from the CPU to the LCD Display Driver in the PRO-2004/5/6, to perform some very powerful functions not possible with scanners using highly integrated parts.

Again, that's because the path between the CPU (computer) and the LCD driver consists of sub-micron traces of CMOS circuitry. We just cannot get to it because it's buried within the chip.

Another common feature provided by many chips, including highly integrated ones, is *programmable* memory. Most CPUs hold a small amount of RAM (Random Access Memory), sufficient to store anywhere from ten to a hundred channels or so, but again there is no way to break the path between the functions (memory and processing) to add our own circuitry. This is true for most scanners, and on those there is no way to increase memory.

Fortunately, two other memory technologies, used by a few scanners, *do* offer possibilities for expansion.

EEPROM

EEPROM is the least common of the accessible memory technologies.

The PRO-43, BC-2500XLT, BC-200XLT, and BC-100XLT use EEPROM. It is possible to expand the capacity of EEPROM-based systems, though not by such huge proportions as the SRAM type. See the mod at the end of this section (on the PRO-43) for how to extend EEPROM memory.

SRAM

A handful of scanners use a separate SRAM (Static RAM) chip for storage of frequencies and custom channel settings. It is this type of memory that can be easily and economically expanded by factors of 2, 4, 8, 16, and even 64 times the original volume!

Scanners that employ accessible SRAM memory include (at least) those in the following list.

Radio Shack	Uniden
PRO-32	BC-590XLT
PRO-34	BC-600XLT
PRO-37	BC-760XLT
PRO-39	BC-950XLT
PRO-2004	
PRO-2005	Regency
PRO-2006	R-1600
PRO-2021	
PRO-2022	
PRO-2032	
PRO-2035	

There may well be other scanners that use SRAM – if you know of one, be sure to pass on the information to me and your fellow hobbyists. If you're curious about your scanner's potential for memory expansion, you can just about forget it for those with fewer than 100 channels.

The CPU's RAM easily handles 10 to 80 channels or so. If your scanner is not on the above list, but has 100 or more channels, then look over its schematic diagram and parts list, or scrutinize its Logic/CPU Board for any of the following markings on schematics, parts lists, or the physical chips themselves:

> uPD446G-15
> TC-5517CF-20
> LC-3517BM-15
> CXK5864BP
> MB-8416-20LPF

...or anything similar. You can usually disregard the last few digits and characters, which often refer to manufacturer (for custom chips) or lot numbers. Remember, some manufacturers make scanners for more than one label, but when we get into the guts the part number tells the story.

SRAM chips that appear in scanners are generally characterized by a rectangular shape, with 24 or more pins, and half the pins will appear on each of the longest sides (none at the ends).

SRAM chips in a schematic diagram can be tentatively identified by 18 or more of their pins going straight to the CPU chip.

Any chip with less than 24-pins is not likely to be an SRAM; neither is any chip in a square format.

SRAMs are generally *rectangular* with 24 to 32 pins. Pinout notation of SRAM chips will include mystic codes such as:

A0, A1...A9, etc.
R/W
CE
I01, I02...I08, etc.
OE

If your scanner uses SRAM, then it's a prime candidate for a magnificent expansion of its memory. The following procedures are the latest, best, and greatest for SRAM Extended Memories.

EXTENDED MEMORY THE EASY WAY

(16 Blocks)

6,400 channels for the PRO-2004/5/6

3,200 channels for the PRO-2021/2022/2032 and PRO-39/37/34/32

1,600 channels for the BC-760/950XLT, BC-590/600XLT, and R-1600

NOTE: this first section deals with the smaller 16-Block Extended Memory. Read it, but review the larger 64-Block Extended Memory before making up your mind which way to go.

HOW MUCH MEMORY?

Years ago, a scanner with ANY memory was a marvel, but now 50-400 channels is almost boring. Even 1,000 channels isn't all that great, with computer interfacing having come of age. And remember, the Ultimate Scanner is always umbilically attached to its computer...

My Vol 1 & 2 introduced potent paths to 6,400 channels in the PRO-2004/5/6; 3,200 channels in the PRO-39/37/34/32, PRO-2021/2022/2032 and 1,600 in the BC-760/950XLT, BC-590/600XLT, and R-1600. *Bunches!*

Since those books were published, I have refined these techniques for extended memories of 25,600, 12,800, and 6,400 channels, respectively. Obviously, one could stuff all the communications of a sizable municipality into such a unit.

Surprisingly, some people are comfortable with the smaller versions, so I will present the latest techniques for both and you can make up your own mind which way to go.

LABOR, SKILL...

Costs of my original MOD-16, 19, 37, and 51 Extended Memories were modest, so the major investment was labor. These versions of Extended Memory called for the large DIP style of SRAM chip which had to be built on a perf board and wired to the pads where the old SRAM was pulled. Lots of work with 24 wires, but still, following my instructions, thousands of hobbyists extended their scanner limited memory!

If you want the gory details of these older mods, refer to back issues of the *World Scanner Report*, and my books, for MODs 16, 19, 37, and 51.

My latest procedures and techniques will skimp on verbiage and offer mostly the hard core info. It should suffice for most hobbyists, but snag the above references if you want to go with this, but need highly detailed instructions.

There's now a way to reduce the labor (and real-estate volume) of Extended Memory mods by 50% or more. Now we can do away with the separate board and 24 gosh-awful wires that were required for the "huge" DIP static RAM chips.

Thanks to better availability of surface mount memory chips, we just remove the scanner's stock memory chip and replace it, almost pin-for-pin, with a new and larger one!

Make a couple of trace cuts on the scanner's printed circuit board; add a jumper or two; and route several wires out to external switches for 25,600, 12,800, 6,400, 3,200 or 1,600 programmable channels, and you'll be the first on your Block to have an Anti-Alzheimer's Scanner. And the new memory will be very efficiently organized!

First, we'll discuss the fundamentals for the basic 16-Block Memory Expansion. Details of the huge 64-Block Expansion will follow later.

OPPORTUNITY or TURNIP?

Most expandable scanners use a 16k (2k x 8) surface-mount SRAM chip. See *Table 4-1* to identify your scanner, hopefully as one that can benefit from Extended Memory.

These are the only ones to my knowledge that use this SRAM, and which qualify for this memory hack. When you learn of others, please pass on the information.

Table 4-1: Stock SRAM identification

Scanner	Circuit Symbol	Stock SRAM Part #
PRO-2004	IC-504	TC5517CF-20 or μPD446G-45
PRO-2005	IC-505	LC3517BM-15 or any of above
PRO-2006	IC-505	LC3517BM-15 or any of above
PRO-2032	Probably IC-2	Probably any of the above
PRO-2022	IC-6	Any of the above
PRO-2021	IC-12	Any of the above
PRO-39	IC-2	Any of the above
PRO-37	IC-2	Any of the above
PRO-34	IC-2	Any of the above
PRO-32	IC-2	Any of the above
BC-760/950XLT	IC-13	MB8416-20LPF
BC-590/600XLT	Probably IC-13	Probably MB8416-20LPF
R-1600	Probably IC-13	Probably MB8416-20LPF
PRO-2035	IC-502	CXK5864CM or LC3664BML

(This is an 8k x 8 SRAM)

Once you've identified your scanner's memory chip, you'll want to acquire the upgrade replacement, a 32k x 8 SRAM (256k) in surface mount technology (SMT) style.

A generic part number is: **62256LFP12**.

MOSEL makes MS62256L-10FC, Motorola's is MCM60L256AF10, and NEC's version is uPD43256AGU-12LL.

The last two digits in these part numbers, a code for the speed of the chip, are not too important. Anything resembling -10, -12, or -15 is fine with the larger numbers indicating slower speeds and, therefore, lower prices.

Hitachi, Samsung, NEC, Toshiba, and others produce these chips, so instead of using an exact part number, just tell your supplier that you want

"...a 256k static RAM, low power, flat-pack, surface-mount, organized as 32k x 8 bits, with 28 pins"

...and you might receive the correct part.

Offer the above part numbers if you need a cross reference. The next section provides details on larger *128k x 8* Extended Memory chips.

If you draw a blank trying to find these parts, drop me a line on my BBS and I'll try to help.

Besides this SRAM chip, you'll need four switches as simple as SPST toggle types, or maybe a 4-segment DIP switch, or even a BCD-encoded switch.

If you are green on switches, then stick with toggle or DIP switches to access the extended memory Blocks.

You can also use my KeyBoard Memory Block Controller (KMBC), MODs 28 or 28a, as featured in Vol-2 of my *SMH* and in back issues of the *World Scanner Report*. This article will show the DIP switch method since the KMBC hasn't changed.

Before you go off half-cocked, please understand that extending the memory of your scanner is *almost* as simple as removing the stock SRAM chip and installing the new one.

Almost.

The stock chip has 24 pins, but the new one has 28 pins. This adds only a slight complication, depending on your scanner. For instance, the

PRO-2005 and PRO-2006 already have 28-pin pads right where the stock 24-pin chip will be removed — four pads are unused! This makes the job a breeze. For most other scanners, including the PRO-2004, you'll have to bend up four pins, (1, 2, 27 and 28) of the new chip and solder the remaining 24 pins to the existing 24 pads.

Please note that most scanners will require minor trace cuts, a short jumper or two, several wires from the area of the new chip to run out to the four switches and four 100k resistors.

It's NOT a one-step task, and it's NOT a snap, so (as I cautioned you earlier) plan ahead.

Review the instructions before starting, and make sure you have everything you need. By the way, don't let the detail in *Figure 4-1* worry you – the worst part will be getting your scanner torn down and the old chip removed.

Lets get to work.

NOTE: The PRO-2035 Extended Memory is covered separately later.

Figure 4-1: Memory augmentation

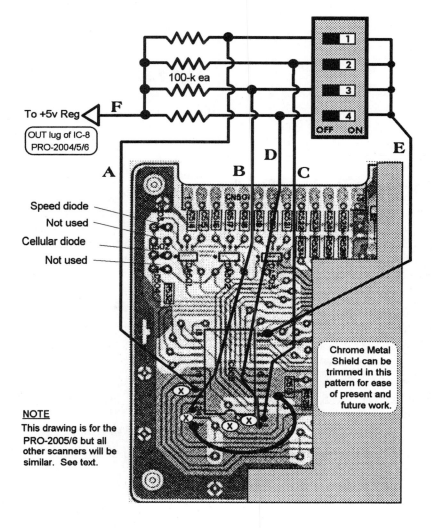

100-k ea

To +5v Reg F

OUT lug of IC-8
PRO-2004/5/6

A   B   D   C   E

Speed diode
Not used
Cellular diode
Not used

Chrome Metal
Shield can be
trimmed in this
pattern for ease
of present and
future work.

NOTE
This drawing is for the
PRO-2005/6 but all
other scanners will be
similar. See text.

PRO-2005 & PRO-2006 ONLY

Remove the front panel from the body of the radio. Remove the Logic/Display Board from inside the front panel. Specific instructions are covered in the *World Scanner Report* and in *SMH* Vol-2. Desolder and remove the chrome metal shield that covers the back side of this board. Locate and remove IC-505.

Otherwise, a good bet is to first snip each pin until the chip comes loose. Then carefully desolder the cut pin ends from the pads and clean all pads so they are bright and shiny.

Desoldering wick and a very thin-tipped *low-power* soldering pencil are mandatory! Be very careful – too hot an iron, or too much time applied to the board, may LIFT the solder pads from the circuit board, and that requires major surgery to repair.

ARE YOU STUBBORN ENOUGH TO WANT THE ORIGINAL PART?

If you're handy with desoldering techniques, and have some need for the old part, you can try to remove that chip without destroying it.

If you wish to remove the original SRAM intact, it can be done, but there is a risk of damaging traces and pin pads on the board. I have pulled hundreds of them, and still occasionally damage a pad or two. My method employs repeated applications of desoldering wick to first draw off all the excess solder from the pins and pads of the SRAM.

It takes repeated applications of the desoldering wick to remove all possible solder, and even then most pins will remain tightly stuck to the pads. When the pins and pads are as solder-free as possible, I slip a sewing needle under a row of pins while gently lifting up at one end.

I touch the soldering pencil's tip to the first pin-pad closest to the raised end of the needle, and if all is well, that pin will "pop" loose.

Then I slip the needle in a little further, and in the same motion, I move the soldering tip back to the next pin where it will "pop" free... on to the 3rd pin... 4th... etc., until one side is free.

The process is repeated for the other side. This procedure hardly ever goes smoothly, but it does work after a fashion. I am less fearful of it because I know how to repair damaged traces and pads. Do you?

CIRCUIT BOARD SURGERY

When the SRAM has been removed, clean the old pads with desoldering wick so that they are smooth and shiny. Repair any damage before proceeding.

Refer to *Figure 4-1*. Make four trace cuts as follows. CUT on EACH side of pad 24 so that it is completely isolated. Then CUT to isolate pad 21 completely. Finally, CUT the trace to the previously unused pad just above old pad 1. (This will become pad 2 for the new chip.)

Solder a jumper wire (+5V feed) from new pad 28 to an exposed solder point on the unbroken part of the trace that was cut to isolate old pad 24. A perfect spot is one of the component solder pads for the trace that connects C511, R525, and C513. Skip ahead to ALL SCANNERS.

PRO-2004 & SIMILAR SCANNERS

Locate and remove the stock SRAM chip. Specific instructions are minimal for these scanners because they are older and/or the mechanical information has been published in back issues of the *WSR* and/or in my books. Refer to the chip removal guidelines given above for the PRO-2005/6.

After the old chip has been removed, cut the appropriate circuit traces so that old pads 21 and 24 are completely isolated on the circuit board. Continue just below in ALL SCANNERS.

ALL SCANNERS

Lay the new chip on the old pads so its pins line up with the pads beneath them. If your scanner does not have previously unused pads for new pins 1, 2, 27, and 28 *(and most won't),* then carefully bend those pins on the chip **up** so they protrude straight out from the sides of the chip.

The PRO-2005/6 has 28 pads.

All the rest, including the PRO-2004, have 24 pads. Hence, pins 1, 2, 27, and 28 of the new chip won't have any mating pads and therefore must be bent up so that wires can later be soldered to these pins.

Pin #14 of the new chip goes to pad #12 of the old chip. Likewise, pad 13 for the old chip gets pin 15 of the new chip. Position the new chip so that perfect pin alignment is achieved.

These four pins must not touch anything! Solder one end-corner pin of the new chip (14 or 15) to its pad.

Ensure that alignment remains correct, adjust if necessary, and then solder a diagonally opposite pin to its pad – that will hold all remaining pins in position. Inspect the chip carefully, looking at every pin.

If all is well and alignment is perfect, solder the remaining pins to their respective pads.

WIRING and SWITCHES

Solder suitable length wires to each of the *new* pads/pins 1, 2, 14, 23, and 26, and route these 5 wires out to where the Block Selector switches will be located. Wire the switches and resistors as shown in *Figure 4-1*. Observe that one side of all switches are wired together, and then fed from a source of *regulated* +5V.

Avoid using the CPU +5V supply if you can. Instead, run the wire to a +5V source for the receiver. If not feasible, then go ahead and use the CPU's +5V source, but ensure that it remains very close to +5V despite the additional load. If it doesn't, find or make another source.

If you use DIP switches, install somewhere on the scanner a standard IC-DIP socket to match the pin requirements of the DIP switch, to allow your DIP switch to be quickly plugged in and out. Several spare DIP switches can be kept handy, preset to your preferred Memory Blocks! DIP switches allow a tidy and compact installation.

These switches are tiny, and can be installed in cramped spaces. Therefore, it may make sense to install a larger switch Block than required by your immediate needs.

For instance, our 16-Block Extended Memory requires 4 switches, but why not install an 8-switch DIP Block and use the spare 4 switches for other mods and hacks later?

Think about it...

NOTE FOR SCANNERS OTHER THAN THE PRO-2005 & 2006

Solder a jumper or hookup wire from the elevated *new* pin 28 to a solder joint on the trace that was cut away from old pin 24. Solder a jumper wire from the elevated *new* pin 27 to a solder joint on the trace that was cut away from old pin 21.

OPERATION

This variation of the Extended Memory Mod will yield 16 Blocks of ordinary channels, each Block programmable with the same number of channels the scanner had before the project began.

The PRO-2004/5/6 will have 16 Blocks of 400 channels each, for 6,400 channels; the BC760/950/590/600XLT will have 1,600 channels and the others will have 3,200 channels.

BANKS FOR THE MEMORIES

You may never use all this memory, but quantity is NOT the main idea here! Instead, it's to gain the sixteen Blocks of 400, 200, or 100 channels each, which essentially gives you 16 identical scanners all lined up in a row, individually programmable, and with one at a time available for use.

The Block concept is an elaboration of the Bank concept, but which allows up to 16 different complete programs for your scanner. You can dedicate one Block to railroads, another to aviation, others still for military, medical, emergency, and several for scratch and messing around, but save a couple for the real serious stuff. In other words, an Extended Memory allows greater flexibility in setting up a scanner to do the things you want it to do!

You're not obligated to use all 1,600-to-6,400 channels, but you will find immediate uses for the 16 Blocks!

And *Figure 4-2* shows how those Blocks are accessed:

Table 4-2: Programming 16-Block identifiers

SW#4	SW#3	SW#2	SW#1	BLOCK ID IN CH-1	MEM BLOCK#	BINARY EQUIV
OFF	OFF	OFF	OFF	100**0**.000	00	0000
OFF	OFF	OFF	ON	100**1**.000	01	0001
OFF	OFF	ON	OFF	100**2**.000	02	0010
OFF	OFF	ON	ON	100**3**.000	03	0011
OFF	ON	OFF	OFF	100**4**.000	04	0100
OFF	ON	OFF	ON	100**5**.000	05	0101
OFF	ON	ON	OFF	100**6**.000	06	0110
OFF	ON	ON	ON	100**7**.000	07	0111
ON	OFF	OFF	OFF	100**8**.000	08	1000
ON	OFF	OFF	ON	100**9**.000	09	1001
ON	OFF	ON	OFF	101**0**.000	10	1010
ON	OFF	ON	ON	101**1**.000	11	1011
ON	ON	OFF	OFF	101**2**.000	12	1100
ON	ON	OFF	ON	101**3**.000	13	1101
ON	ON	ON	OFF	101**4**.000	14	1110
ON	ON	ON	ON	101**5**.000	15	1111

COUNTING SCHEME

The 4 switches yield 16 combinations of settings, from all *OFF* to all *ON*. Each combination activates one Block of original programmable channels. When you change Blocks, one is switched out and another switched in.

The actual scheme is binary and might not be familiar to all scannists, but it is the easiest counting system of them all; simpler than the decimal system! It's especially easy if you've never learned to count by ten, or never looked down at your fingers.

If you are uncomfortable with the binary counting system, it will help to program a coded frequency into Channel 1 of each Block for a quick reference to which Block you're in at any time. If we refer to all switches OFF as the *"home Block,"* then a frequency in Ch-1 such as 100**0**.000 will clue you to Block 00 while a frequency of 101**5**.000 programmed into Ch-1 of the Block with all switches ON will clue you to Block 15.

Refer to *Table 4-2* for the pattern and program clues. If your scanner won't accept 1000MHz, then use something else, like 90**0**.000 to 91**5**.000, or 50**0**.000 to 51**5**.000.

CAVEAT: You should develop a habit of turning off *all* the Block switches when the scanner is not in use.

Those 100k resistors each draw a small current from the memory retention circuit when a desktop scanner is disconnected from power, or when batteries are removed from a portable.

WHAT'S STORED

Some scanners, such as the PRO-2004/5/6, will not only store all those frequencies in the SRAM, but also custom settings of MODE, DELAY, and LOCKOUT. Other scanners may store only frequencies in the SRAM chip and custom channel data in the CPU's RAM.

In that case, a LOCKOUT and/or DELAY set to one channel in a certain Block will LockOut or Delay that same channel in all Blocks. Sorry, that's a function of the scanner's CPU and firmware and can't be helped.

With exception of Priority Channel and selected Scan Banks, the PRO-2004/5/6 are exempt from this limitation because the SRAM stores all pertinent channel data.

GARBAGE = NOISE

After this mod is finished and you fire up the scanner for the first time, there is likely to be a bunch of strange frequencies seemingly programmed into the channels.

Don't believe what you see because this is "noise" that was present in the chip when it was first fired up. Be sure to do a Restart or Master Clear before doing any programming. For the PRO-2004/5/6, this involves pressing the RESTART button on the rear chassis.

Press the little button inside the battery compartment for the PRO-34 and PRO-37. On the PRO-2021 and 2022, the Uniden radios, and everything else, do a Master Clear or Restart before doing any programming.

WHAT IF 16 MEMORY BLOCKS AREN'T ENOUGH?

Some people would call you crazier than an outhouse mouse if you couldn't "make do" with 1,600 to 6,400 channels. Well, if you are using a computer, those channels can fill quickly – particularly if you've bought one of the really large FCC databases.

I ran out of breathing room within weeks after I did the basic memory mod on my old PRO-2004 and PRO-34.

It wasn't a shortage of channels as much as the 16 Blocks ran short when I allocated one for general operations, one for emergencies and disasters; several for federal government; four or five for business and industrial; a couple for military; one each for aviation, railroads, space, medical and state, a couple for local governments, and a couple for scratch. I just got started and hit a dead end! Kind of like running out of channels. ☹

But there's a fix for that...

I went back to the parts books and located a memory SRAM that's four times larger than the 16 Block 32k x 8 SRAM. *Ahah!* 64 Blocks was my ticket! Never mind the 25,600 channels it yielded; *hell, I'd never use THAT many.*

But then came the HB-232 and CE-232 Computer Interfaces to do all the finger punching for me. Now, there is NO REASON not to be a channel hog! I don't have to work to stuff a few thousand channels, so why not stuff'em? My computer can work harder than I can!

Whatever your situation, 6,400 channels and 16 Blocks might not be enough for your needs, so the next step up involves labor similar to that described for 1600-6400 channels above, and a new part. Several compatible 128k x 8 (1Mb) SRAMs are available, and the procedure for installing it in your scanner doesn't change.

The result will be an astounding 64-Blocks times the standard base number of channels in your scanner, or 25,600 for the PRO-2004/5/6; 6,400 channels for the BC-760/950XLT and BC590/600XLT; and 12,800 channels for the other scanners on the list! Again, it's the 64 Blocks that's the primary advantage here.

I'm sure there are a number of manufacturers of the 128k x 8 SRAM, but the one I use is the Samsung KM681000LG-8.

Again, the last digit or two are speed indicators and are not important for scanner memory applications. Any speed will do. I am told that one reliable supplier of these SRAM chips is Vantage Electronics at (201) 777-4100. Another is Time Electronics, (800) 772-8638. You can also try Active Electronics at (800) 343-0874. Other possible sources include DigiKey, JameCo, and Mouser Electronics.

If you strike out, contact me on my BBS.

ADAPTING THE CHIPS:

The 128k x 8 SRAM has 32 pins, and installs pretty much like the 28 pin 32k x 8 SRAM.

In the case of the PRO-2005/6, there will be no place to solder pins 1, 2, 31, and 32 because of overhang; and for all other scanners, eight pins 1, 2, 3, 4, 29, 30, 31, and 32 will have to overhang the normal installation area. Therefore most of these overhang pins must be elevated for individual connection to wires.

Can't be helped, but fortunately, these pins will go out to the switch block and require hookup wires anyway.

Pin #1 is NOT USED in the 128k chip, period.

You can cut it off, if it bothers you. Otherwise, there is almost no difference between the 128k x 8 and 32k x 8 SRAMs. The 128k x 8 SRAM is longer and slightly wider than the 32k x 8 and stock SRAMs. As it comes out of the package, the "footprint" of the chip is too wide to solder down on the stock SRAM pads, but not to worry! There will be a perfect mate with the PCB pads if the "feet" of the SRAM pins are bent straight down like the pins of a "normal" DIP chip. These pin feet can be properly bent out flat in a small vise, one side at a time, or with a pair of "duckbill" pliers with smooth and straight jaws. Lacking these tools, bend a few feet at a time down straight using a regular pair of pliers.

DO NOT bend just one pin foot at a time. *DO NOT* bend down pin feet 1, 2, 31, and 32 and if your scanner is not a PRO-2005/6, then don't bend pin feet 1-4 and 29-32, since these pins have to be out straight or slightly elevated above the body of the chip anyway.

Figure 4-2 shows the functional pinouts for four SRAM chips, including stock SRAMs that come with the scanners. A casual study of these chips reveals that almost all pin functions are in the same relative positions. If you superimposed the four chips, aligned at the bottoms, you will note near-perfect correlations.

Relative to the stock 2k x 8 SRAM, the 32k x 8 version has 4 more address lines, A11-A14. The 128k x 8 SRAM has six more address lines than the stock SRAM, A11-A16; plus one additional Chip Enable function (CE2 at pin 30) and one unused pin, #1.

The same PCB work (pad isolation and jumpers) must be done for this 64-Block version as the 16-Block one, regardless of scanner. *Figure 4-3* will guide you.

If there remains any doubt on what to do after reading this, refer to the *World Scanner Report* Vol 1 #8 and Vol 3 #4.

Figure 4-2: Static RAM pin and pad comparison

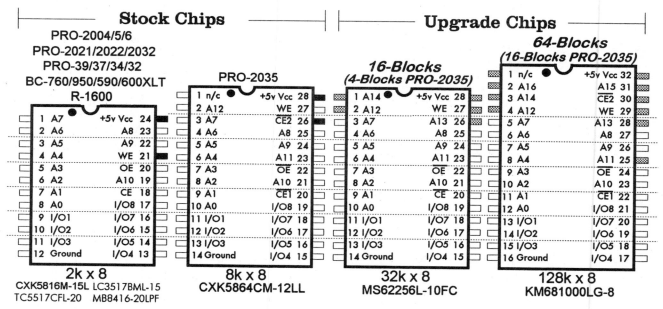

LEGEND

▬ = Pads for these pins on stock chips will have to be isolated to account for differences in replacement chips.
☐ = Pads and pins for these chips are compatible and will not require any modification or alteration.
▨ = These pins on replacement chips may require special treatment, depending on specific scanner. See text.

COMMENTS: The PRO-2035's 8kx8 SRAM can be used as a 4-Block Upgrade for other scanners, but why bother? The dotted lines make it easier for the eye to follow pin-for-pin comparisons of the four chips.

Figure 4-3: High capacity SRAM wiring diagram

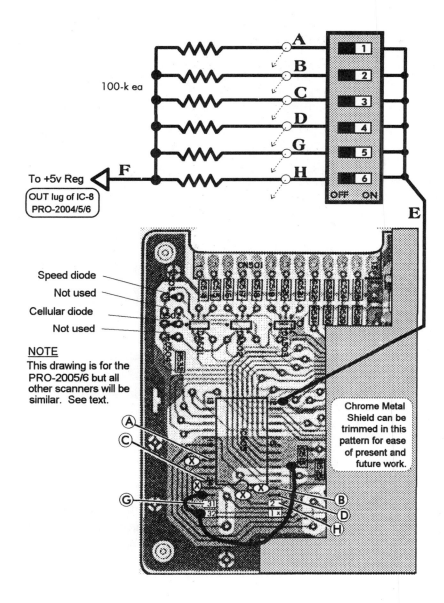

It is easily seen, then, why memory expansion techniques using surface mount SRAM chips require a LOT less labor than the larger DIP chips specified in earlier versions of this mod.

The labor savings with surface mount SRAMs for extending the memory of these scanners should motivate many couch potatoes.

There will be less chance of error, and reliability will be enhanced by this new technique. Use it!

Here's how to deploy the 128k x 8 SRAM in your scanner.

INSTALLATION DIFFERENCES

If your objective is 64 Blocks, the preceeding 16 Block discussion is a good general guideline. The methods and techniques are much the same with exception of the need for six Block Selector Switches instead of four, six 100k pull-down resistors instead of four, and the wiring plan shown in *Figure 4-3,* above.

As we continue, you'll learn the details of the point-to-point wiring plan; please follow them exactly and check off your progress.

In reading the layout data, the letter codes A–H refer to *Figure 4-3*. Also, note the following:

* Elevated pin; no pad – requires direct wire.

"Low" switch lugs go to ground.

SRAM layout – refer to *Figure 4-3*

PIN #		Destination
2*	H	Switch 6
3*	D	Switch 4
4	B	Switch 2
16	E	Common with all "low" Switch lugs (ground)
25	A	Switch 1
28	C	Switch 3
30	-	Common to pin 32 below
31*	G	Switch 5
32*		CPU +5V; also to common as pin 30 above.
-	F	To regular +5V regulated

PRO-2005/6 ONLY

Remove the old SRAM. Clean the old SRAM pads on the PCB with desoldering wick. Isolate old pads 21 and 24.

Isolate what will become a new pad 2 (just above old pad 1).

Bend (out and slightly up) pins 1, 2, 31, and 32 of the new chip so they won't touch the PCB when the chip is installed.

Install the new chip, ensuring good solder joints for each pin to the old pads. Pins 16 and 17 of the new chip go to old pads 12 and 13, respectively.

Solder a jumper between pins 32 and 30 of the new chip.

Solder a jumper from the existing, uncut trace (C513 and R-525) that used to go to old pad 24 to pin 32 of the new chip.

Solder suitable length wires to each of pins 2, 3, 4, 16, 25, 28, 31, and 32 and route these wires out to where your Block Switches will be located.

Wire the Block Switches in accordance with *Figure 4-3*.

PRO-2004 AND OTHER APPLICABLE SCANNERS

Remove the old SRAM.

Clean the old SRAM pads on the PCB with desoldering wick.

Isolate old pads 21 and 24. Bend (out and slightly up) pins 1, 2, 3, 4, 29, 30, 31 and 32 of the new chip so they can't touch the PCB when the chip is installed.

Install the new chip, ensuring good solder joints for each pin to the old pads.

Pins 16 and 17 of the new chip go to old pads 12 and 13, respectively.

Solder a jumper between pins 32 and 30 of the new chip.

Solder a jumper from the PCB trace that was cut from old pad 21 to the elevated pin 29 of the new chip.

Solder a jumper from the trace that used to go to old pad 24 to pin 32 of the new chip.

Solder suitable length wires to each of pins 2, 3, 4, 16, 25, 28, 31 and 32 and route these wires out to where your Block Switches will be located.

Wire the Block Switches in accordance with *Figure 4-3* and the wiring instructions in this section.

PROGRAMMING

Table 4-3 illustrates the same memory-aid technique that I recommend for 16-Block mods. Channel 1 simply carries a frequency of which the 3rd and 4th digits combine to identify that particular block. And who knows? You might get lucky and use an identifier that's actually a useful frequency!

The identifier is a little complicated, but it beats learning to think in binary. You'll get used to it.

And if you've simply gotta know what all those one's and zero's really mean... here's the shortest course in binary numbers you've ever seen.

Binary code sets a discrete value for each position, with values that ascend as one moves from right to left. The rightmost position is worth 1, the next position is worth 2, the next 4, etc. Each position is worth twice as much as the one to the right. If there's a zero in a position, its value is zero. If there's a "1" there, then its value is as stated.

Any integer can be expressed through some combinations of 1s and 0s, by simply adding the values of occupied (by a 1) positions. For instance, if the rightmost position is the only one with a "1" in it, the total value of the binary number is 1. If the next one is also filled (with a "1"), then the total value is 1+2. And so on...

Position value	32	16	8	4	2	1
Binary code	1	0	1	1	0	0

So in this case, reading right to left, it's:

0 + 0 + 4 + 8 + 0 + 32 = Channel 44!

Similarly, 010011 is 1+2+0+0+16+0 = 19.

I won't give you a test, but if you look at either of the block programming tables you'll now be able to understand the rightmost column.

Aintcha proud?!?

THE BEST OF THE BEST!

And this wraps up one of the best do-it-yourself mods of all time. It adds functionality, fun, practicality, and value. It's cheap, and doing it is an education that adds to your manual skill and technical understanding. What more do you want?

Technical support for all my modifications are always available through my computer bulletin board.

Limited mail support is also available if you don't have a computer and modem – but why don't you? Remember, to be ultimate, the scanner *must* have a host computer!

Follow my instructions, be patient, have the right tools and materials on hand – especially the service manual for your scanner, triple-check your work, and you're not likely to encounter trouble.

A true TurboWhopper!
This PRO-2006 has every kind of tuning and center channel indicator. It looks like a lot, but every LED has a purpose.

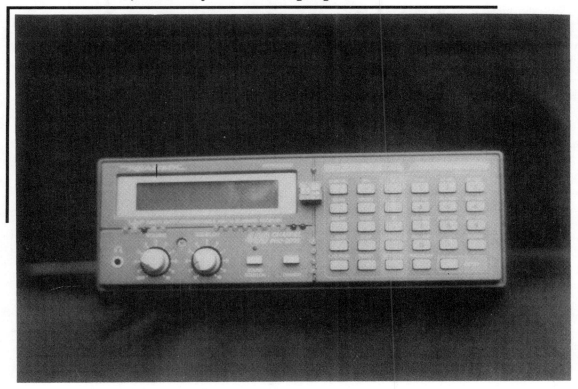

Table 4-3: Programming 64-block identifiers

SW#6	SW#5	SW#4	SW#3	SW#2	SW#1	BLOCK ID, CH1	MEM BLOCK#	BINARY EQUIV
OFF	OFF	OFF	OFF	OFF	OFF	1000.000	00	000000
OFF	OFF	OFF	OFF	OFF	ON	1001.000	01	000001
OFF	OFF	OFF	OFF	ON	OFF	1002.000	02	000010
OFF	OFF	OFF	OFF	ON	ON	1003.000	03	000011
OFF	OFF	OFF	ON	OFF	OFF	1004.000	04	000100
OFF	OFF	OFF	ON	OFF	ON	1005.000	05	000101
OFF	OFF	OFF	ON	ON	OFF	1006.000	06	000110
OFF	OFF	OFF	ON	ON	ON	1007.000	07	000111
OFF	OFF	ON	OFF	OFF	OFF	1008.000	08	001000
OFF	OFF	ON	OFF	OFF	ON	1009.000	09	001001
OFF	OFF	ON	OFF	ON	OFF	1010.000	10	001010
OFF	OFF	ON	OFF	ON	ON	1011.000	11	001011
OFF	OFF	ON	ON	OFF	OFF	1012.000	12	001100
OFF	OFF	ON	ON	OFF	ON	1013.000	13	001101
OFF	OFF	ON	ON	ON	OFF	1014.000	14	001110
OFF	OFF	ON	ON	ON	ON	1015.000	15	001111
OFF	ON	OFF	OFF	OFF	OFF	1016.000	16	010000
OFF	ON	OFF	OFF	OFF	ON	1017.000	17	010001
OFF	ON	OFF	OFF	ON	OFF	1018.000	18	010010
OFF	ON	OFF	OFF	ON	ON	1019.000	19	010011
OFF	ON	OFF	ON	OFF	OFF	1020.000	20	010100
OFF	ON	OFF	ON	OFF	ON	1021.000	21	010101
OFF	ON	OFF	ON	ON	OFF	1022.000	22	010110
OFF	ON	OFF	ON	ON	ON	1023.000	23	010111
OFF	ON	ON	OFF	OFF	OFF	1024.000	24	011000
OFF	ON	ON	OFF	OFF	ON	1025.000	25	011001
OFF	ON	ON	OFF	ON	OFF	1026.000	26	011010
OFF	ON	ON	OFF	ON	ON	1027.000	27	011011
OFF	ON	ON	ON	OFF	OFF	1028.000	28	011100
OFF	ON	ON	ON	OFF	ON	1029.000	29	011101
OFF	ON	ON	ON	ON	OFF	1030.000	30	011110
OFF	ON	ON	ON	ON	ON	1031.000	31	011111
ON	OFF	OFF	OFF	OFF	OFF	1032.000	32	100000
ON	OFF	OFF	OFF	OFF	ON	1033.000	33	100001
ON	OFF	OFF	OFF	ON	OFF	1034.000	34	100010
ON	OFF	OFF	OFF	ON	ON	1035.000	35	100011
ON	OFF	OFF	ON	OFF	OFF	1036.000	36	100100
ON	OFF	OFF	ON	OFF	ON	1037.000	37	100101
ON	OFF	OFF	ON	ON	OFF	1038.000	38	100110
ON	OFF	OFF	ON	ON	ON	1039.000	39	100111
ON	OFF	ON	OFF	OFF	OFF	1040.000	40	101000
ON	OFF	ON	OFF	OFF	ON	1041.000	41	101001
ON	OFF	ON	OFF	ON	OFF	1042.000	42	101010
ON	OFF	ON	OFF	ON	ON	1043.000	43	101011
ON	OFF	ON	ON	OFF	OFF	1044.000	44	101100
ON	OFF	ON	ON	OFF	ON	1045.000	45	101101
ON	OFF	ON	ON	ON	OFF	1046.000	46	101110
ON	OFF	ON	ON	ON	ON	1047.000	47	101111
ON	ON	OFF	OFF	OFF	OFF	1048.000	48	100000
ON	ON	OFF	OFF	OFF	ON	1049.000	49	100001
ON	ON	OFF	OFF	ON	OFF	1050.000	50	100010
ON	ON	OFF	OFF	ON	ON	1051.000	51	100011
ON	ON	OFF	ON	OFF	OFF	1052.000	52	100100
ON	ON	OFF	ON	OFF	ON	1053.000	53	100101
ON	ON	OFF	ON	ON	OFF	1054.000	54	100110
ON	ON	OFF	ON	ON	ON	1055.000	55	100111
ON	ON	ON	OFF	OFF	OFF	1056.000	56	101000
ON	ON	ON	OFF	OFF	ON	1057.000	57	101001
ON	ON	ON	OFF	ON	OFF	1058.000	58	101010
ON	ON	ON	OFF	ON	ON	1059.000	59	101011
ON	ON	ON	ON	OFF	OFF	1060.000	60	101100
ON	ON	ON	ON	OFF	ON	1061.000	61	101101
ON	ON	ON	ON	ON	OFF	1062.000	62	101110
ON	ON	ON	ON	ON	ON	1063.000	63	101111

HELP FOR MEMORY MODS

There are several ways to control my Extended Memory Mods, including DIP switches, Keyboard Memory Block Controllers, and the CE-232 Scanner/Computer Interface, but there are none slicker than Mark Persson's LINKALL EXTENDED MEMORY CONTROLLER.

Unfortunately, the LINKALL is not something you can conjure up all by yourself. I will give it a few words, and let you decide if this is for you. LINKALL is a well established, commercial product of good repute, and it's been upgraded and enhanced just in time for me to bring you the good news.

LINKALL EVOLUTION

The original LINKALL Extended Memory Controller that revolutionized the control of PRO 200x scanners with extended memory has now been upgraded with more features and can now control either the 6,400 or the 25,600 channel memory upgrade. LINKALL lets you scan all or selected portions of Extended Memory *as if it came stock with the scanner*!

The new LINKALL printed circuit board has shrunk to a tiny 2" x 4" thanks to a small microcontroller unit (MCU) that does virtually all the work. Stuffing the new LINKALL into a heavily modified scanner is much easier than the older generations.

Low power consumption and low noise are assured by the use of an MCU with a SLEEP mode. This allows the processor to only perform tasks when necessary and literally shut itself off while retaining its internal memory.

Among the many features of the new LINKALL are a self test mode, Display LED test, No-Blocks-Programmed Warning Mode, and the two-speed Keyboard Memory Block Controller feature that advances the Block address automatically at two Blocks per second then shifts gears to the higher speed 4 Blocks per second.

This is a great feature for the larger 64 Block Memories. The new LINKALL still has that great auto increment feature whereby only selected Blocks are scanned and all others are skipped.

For example, if only Blocks 1, 17, 39, 43, and 55 are selected, then when the scanner hits Channel 400 of Block 1, LINKALL automatically switches to Block Address 17. At Channel 400 of Block 17, LINKALL switches to Block 39, and so on, in a continuous loop until the autoscan process is stopped by you.

Block selections will be retained until you change them, even when power is off. No external computer control is needed. The module is totally contained in the scanner with only one toggle switch for mode selection.

All operating controls use the existing front panel keypad of your scanner without disrupting existing scanner functions.

Installation is EASY,with fully illustrated and concise directions. Friendly and helpful technical support is also available if needed. A six month warranty is standard. Expert installations are available for those who don't have the time or inclination to do it themselves.

LINKALL is very affordable. For current prices and availability on LINKALL, and other technical services/products, send a SASE to:

Mark Persson
1369 Lombardy Blvd.
Bay Shore, NY 11706.

16,000-ch EXTENDED MEMORY FOR THE PRO-2035

IC-502, the stock memory chip in the PRO-2035, is an uncommon but conventional static RAM, configured as 8k x 8 (64k). Consider then, if 8k x 8 yields 1,000 channels, a drop-in 32k x 8 replacement will yield 4,000 channels and with only slightly more work, a 128k x 8 SRAM will yield 16,000 channels! I see no reason to mess with the measly 4,000 channels when 16,000 are much better and, for many of us, will eliminate one more trip back inside when we run out of room a year or two later.

If you insist on the 4,000 channel mod, refer to back issues of *Monitoring Times* magazine and the *World Scanner Report* where the details were published. The material on memory mods for scanners on the previous pages will also be helpful.

This presentation goes for the gusto. In a way, it virtually eliminates running out of memory in the future. Of course, we've said that before... but there's never too much!

Now don't get me wrong, the PRO-2035's factory-stock 1,000 channels are ample for many needs. 4,000 channels are even *more ample*. The problem is the organization of 1,000 channels into ten banks of 100 channels each.

Banks are not subdivided, so we're limited to ten easily memorized configurations of related frequency groups. While some channel configurations that are arranged logically by subject matter will not exceed 100 channels, many will. This reduces the available logical Banks to nine or fewer, depending on how you like to organize. If you're an avid scannist, a typical organization of 1,000 channels in ten Banks may not be comfortable.

There's no way to program the PRO-2035 with a wide diversity of interests and still have a logical, effective organization of the programming. The Bank limitations of the scanner will stop you dead in your tracks before you start. You'll have to accept a serious compromise in the organization.

Serious scannists seek to eliminate compromises. We want it all! 16,000 channels may go beyond immediate needs, but the 160 Scan (and Search) Banks that are a byproduct of this Extended Memory are not at all exorbitant!

FURTHER CHANGES FOR THE PRO-2035

These instructions are expressly for the 16,000 channel, 160-Bank, and 16-Block Extended Memory using a 128k x 8 SRAM (because of incredible ease and low cost).

For those not familiar with Extended Memory mods, you should probably get up to speed by reviewing my *Scanner Modification Handbooks*. And don't grumble about having to "buy another book," either!

For one thing, I can't put everything into one book unless you're willing to pay a lot more money. Two, it's dumb to be repetitious. Three, check out the price difference between a 20 channel scanner and a 200 channel scanner.

The modest cost of a second book and the proper service manual will be offset by the thousands of extra channels you will gain from my prescription.

Meanwhile, the instructions here are adequate unless you like to solder with a welding torch, in which case discretion might be the better part of valor. You can always hire someone to do it.

PARTS AND ECONOMICS

Cost of this modification will include about $35 for the SRAM chip; $10 for the switches, and a quarter or so for the resistors. Call it $50 for the whole enchilada. That's a penny per three channels. Don't you wish a 20 channel scanner cost 7¢? On the other hand, who wants a 20 channel scanner?

Pick up a low-power 128k x 8 SRAM. Speed is not too important, 150-ns or faster will do. Low power (LP) rating is important. The replacement SRAM should be the surface mount (SMT) style.

The Samsung KM681000ALG-8 is ideal for this project but any pin-for-pin equivalent from most any manufacturer will do. The Samsung part number can be cross-referenced by your supplier if they don't stock that brand. Try Future-Active Electronics, (800) 757-9438, if you don't have a favored supplier. If your resources fail, contact me on my BBS and I may be able to direct you to a source.

You'll also need four SPST toggle switches (Radio Shack 275-624) and four small 100k resistors (Radio Shack 271-1347).

Okay... got *everything?* Let's get started.

PROCEDURE

Disassemble the Logic/CPU board so that you can fully access IC-502, the resident SRAM.

Access to the PRO-2035's Logic/CPU board is painless and fairly easy. (*Everything else in this radio is out in the wide open spaces; no disassembly required!*) Remove external AC or DC power before launching the invasion.

Remove the four screws that hold the front panel to the chassis; disconnect all cables that go from the front panel to various places around the receiver. Unscrew the black ground wire from the main chassis.

NOTE: Memory will be lost if and when CN-502 is disconnected from the main receiver board for more than a few seconds.

For this Extended Memory mod, that's acceptable – you've got a lot of re-programming to do anyway – but expect it.

For other kinds of work in this area, you might not want to lose memory. If so, you can leave CN-502 plugged in with the understanding that the Memory Battery will be providing "keep alive" power to the Logic/CPU board and therefore there's risk of serious damage if you aren't sure of what you're doing. One ZAP and the party's over!

Disconnect CN-502 if you have any doubt. *Disconnect it anyway for this MEMORY modification.*

Remove the four screws that hold the metal shield over the Logic/CPU board and carefully lift up and remove the shield. Remove the two remaining screws that hold the Logic/CPU board to the front panel.

Now comes the only tricky part: the Logic/CPU board remains held tight to the front panel by virtue of that white 15-pin connector, CN-503, much in the same fashion that secures the PRO-2005/6 Logic boards in their front panels. You will have to "jiggle" and work the board up and off the 15 male pins of the keyboard PCB underneath.

You can slip a flat-blade screwdriver under the Logic Board to apply gentle, leveraged prying. Be careful and patient as you work the board up and off the pins below.

This process is harder to explain than to show, but you're there and I'm here, so bear with me and use your imagination. It might help to have the unit open in front of you as you read this.

PIN-LINE AGAIN

When the Logic/CPU board is free, you can commence with any of the various retrofits. Adjacent to CN-503 are 15 unused, plated-thru holes that scream for a purpose!

I suggest you insert and solder a 15-pin strip of pin-line sockets to facilitate EASY connection of things to CN-503 later down the line. The metal shield has to be "nibbled" or notched out about 0.5" to leave room for this strip.

Any number of devices and mods may later connect to CN-503, from computer interfaces to Search and Store modules, or even a remote control! There is no sense in soldering anything directly to CN-503, nor mechanically inserting pins into it when there is the convenience of those holes adjacent to the connector.

A strip of pin-line sockets will make future work in this area a piece of cake! Even though not required for this Extended Memory mod, as long as you have access now, do it!

REMOVING THE OLD SRAM

Locate and remove IC-502. If you're good at desoldering, you can try to remove this chip without destroying it.

Otherwise, the best bet is to first snip each pin close to the body of the chip and remove it before ever heating the pads.

Then carefully desolder the cut pins from the pads. Clean the pads so they are smooth and shiny, using your soldering pencil and desoldering wick.

The hardest part of this job is removing the stock SRAM chip and that wouldn't be so troublesome except it's vital to preserve the integrity of the solder pads. This is not difficult; just slow down and take your time. Liberal use of desoldering wick before exerting force on the pads will help.

Clip the pins away from the body of the chip before applying heat to the pads to reduce chances of damage to the pads.

This destroys the stock SRAM chip, but so what? You have no use for it anyway. See the previous extended memory procedures for details on how to remove the stock SRAM intact.

The job's a piece of cake hereafter.

PREPARING THE NEW SRAM

Identify pins 1-3, 28, and 31-32 of the new SRAM chip and carefully bend or work them up so they protrude straight out the side of the chip and so they will be well above the contact points of the remaining pins.

These pins will not be soldered to the Logic/CPU board, and must not touch the corresponding pads beneath them. Let these six pins "float" even with or slightly above the body of the chip, but no higher. Don't break them!

Figure 4-5: Straightening and configuring the SRAM IC's "feet:"

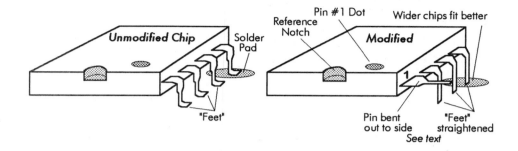

Using flat, "duck-bill" pliers or something comparable, straighten the "feet" of the remaining 26 pins of the new SRAM chip so that they point straight down. This is necessary because the new chip is wider than the stock chip by enough that the "feet" of the new chip will not seat well on the stock pads. The fit will be perfect if these "feet" are straightened first. Examine *Figure 4-5*.

INSTALLING THE NEW CHIP

Position the new chip on the existing solder pads in exactly the same orientation as the old chip. Refer to *Figures 4-6, 4-7,* and *4-8*. Pins 16 and 17 of the new chip should be seated on pads 14 and 15 for the old chip. When the match is perfect, lightly tack pin 16 to pad #14.

No board traces go to new pins 1-2 and 31-32, but these pins should "float" above the board anyway! Ensure that the chip's pin 28 floats!

Adjust the chip, if necessary, so that the remaining 25 pins are matched square on their pads and lightly tack-solder pin 17 to its pad. Now the chip should be immovable on the board. If the remaining 24 pins are still perfectly matched to their pads, then solder them to their respective pads, one at a time, making sure each is clean and perfect before doing the next one.

When you're finished, pins 1, 2, 3, 28, 31, and 32 should be well above their pads, touching nothing.

ADDING PARTS

Carefully solder 100kΩ resistors (1/8 watt, with thin and flexible leads) to free-floating pins 2, 3, 28, and 31. Solder the free ends of these four resistors to any PCB ground, or to pin 16 of the

new chip if you're not sure. See *Figure 4-6* for the schematic, but pick the physical arrangement yourself. When you bend the resistor wires, minimize the stress on the chip's pins.

Position the bodies of the resistors against the flat surface of the PCB and secure them with dots of superglue or hot glue. This is to ensure that they are immovable and do not subsequently break off the pins of the SRAM.

WIRING

Solder flexible, insulated hookup wires, about 12" long, one each to the leads of the resistors that go to the pins of the SRAM.

Position these wires flat against the PC board and secure with a dab of hot glue. Let the loose ends of these wires float free for the time being.

RE-ASSEMBLY

Reassemble the Logic/CPU board into the front panel in reverse order of removal. Reinstall the front panel onto the scanner.

Route the hookup wires installed in Step 10 to wherever you plan to mount the four Block Switches (you did plan ahead, right?): most likely you decided on the rear panel if you're using conventional switches, or inside the front panel if you have planned a way to install micro-mini toggles there.

I like to use DIP switches for memory mods and other things. There is a bit of room on the front panel of the PRO-2035, if you'd like to use this approach. Be careful, and continue to plan ahead.

Figure 4-6: 16,000 channel extended memory for PRO-2035

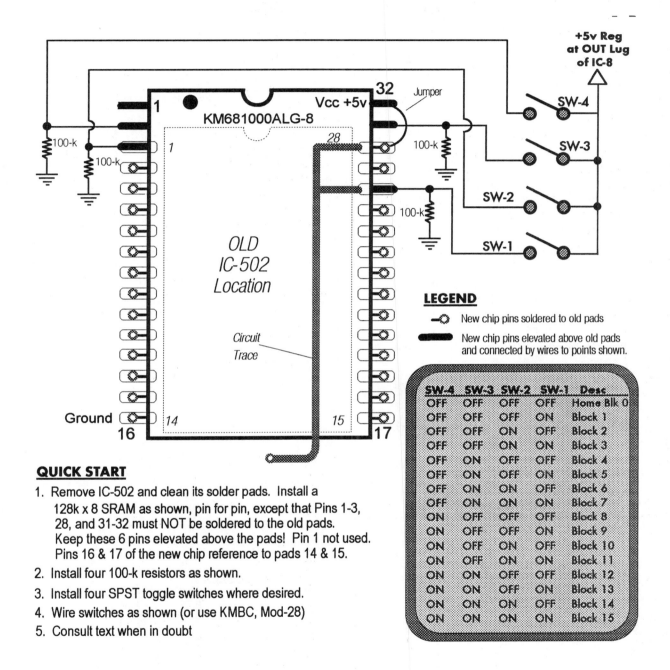

LEGEND

—◌ New chip pins soldered to old pads

▬▬ New chip pins elevated above old pads
     and connected by wires to points shown.

SW-4	SW-3	SW-2	SW-1	Desc
OFF	OFF	OFF	OFF	Home Blk 0
OFF	OFF	OFF	ON	Block 1
OFF	OFF	ON	OFF	Block 2
OFF	OFF	ON	ON	Block 3
OFF	ON	OFF	OFF	Block 4
OFF	ON	OFF	ON	Block 5
OFF	ON	ON	OFF	Block 6
OFF	ON	ON	ON	Block 7
ON	OFF	OFF	OFF	Block 8
ON	OFF	OFF	ON	Block 9
ON	OFF	ON	OFF	Block 10
ON	OFF	ON	ON	Block 11
ON	ON	OFF	OFF	Block 12
ON	ON	OFF	ON	Block 13
ON	ON	ON	OFF	Block 14
ON	ON	ON	ON	Block 15

QUICK START

1. Remove IC-502 and clean its solder pads. Install a
   128k x 8 SRAM as shown, pin for pin, except that Pins 1-3,
   28, and 31-32 must NOT be soldered to the old pads.
   Keep these 6 pins elevated above the pads! Pin 1 not used.
   Pins 16 & 17 of the new chip reference to pads 14 & 15.

2. Install four 100-k resistors as shown.

3. Install four SPST toggle switches where desired.

4. Wire switches as shown (or use KMBC, Mod-28)

5. Consult text when in doubt

CONTINUING ASSEMBLY

Install the four switches at your choice of location. Solder a jumper wire from end to matching end of the four switches. Leave the other matching ends free.

Solder a hookup wire from the jumpered ends of the four switches to the OUT lug of IC-8, located in the front-left corner of the main receiver board. (*regulated +5V*).

Solder the wire from the SRAM, pin 28 to the free lug on one of the switches that you designate as SW-1. Solder the wire from pin 3 to the free lug on the switch that you designate SW-2. Solder the wire from the SRAM, pin 31, to the free lug on one of the switches that you designate as SW-3. Lastly, solder the wire from the SRAM, pin 2, to the free lug on the switch that you designate as SW-4.

This completes the work! Clean up any mess to where you can safely test the scanner. Check all your work under a magnifying glass and strong light. Watch for solder-blobs and cold solder joints (they look grainy and dull). CAREFULLY inspect your work.

NOTE: In lieu of toggle or DIP switches, you can use the Keyboard Memory Block Controller (KMBC), MOD-28, featured in Vol-2 of my *Scanner Modification Handbook.* The KMBC provides a method by which you press two keys of the scanner's keyboard to auto-switch among the memory Blocks. Slick!

The CE-232 Scanner/Computer Interface's User Switches or OutByte bits can also be used to control Extended Memory Blocks!

TESTING & OPERATION

Put the Block Switches in the OFF position. That is the Home Block (Block 0) or the first 1,000 channels. Test the scanner for all functions and programmability. Program 1000.000 into Ch-1. Troubleshoot, diagnose, and fix any discrepancies before moving on. Problems (if any) will typically be solder blobs or bad solder joints on the pins of the SRAM.

When all is well, turn on Block Switch #1; turn the scanner OFF and then back ON. Whatever random data (noise) *was* in Ch-1 should disappear and be replaced by 0's. Program 1001.000 into Ch-1. Turn OFF Block Switch #1 and Block

Switch #2 ON. Turn the scanner OFF and then back ON.

Whatever was in Ch-1 should disappear and be replaced by 0's. Program 1002.000 into Ch-1. Turn both Block Switches 1 and 2 ON. Turn the scanner OFF and then back ON. Whatever was in Ch-1 should disappear and be replaced by 0's. Program 1003.000 into Ch-1. Repeat this procedure for the remaining Blocks 4-15.

Now turn all Block Switches OFF; press **MANUAL 1 MANUAL**, in that sequence, and 1000.000 should return to the display. You can now test each of the switch positions, one at a time, to ensure that whatever was programmed into Ch-1 is retained. If so, all is well. You can now prepare a much better organization for your Monitoring Plan.

Operation is simple: the four Block switches offer 16 combinations (count 'em), of 1,000 channels and 10 banks each, which is like having 16 PRO-2035's, except that only one at a time can be in use. Still, that gives you 16,000 channels and 160-banks for under $50. Beat that!

Well, I suppose the 25,600 channel Extended Memory for the PRO-2004/5/6 series beats it. You're done.

Or *are* you...?

DOUBLE-BUBBLE, TOIL AND TROUBLE

Figure 4-7: Stacking memory chips

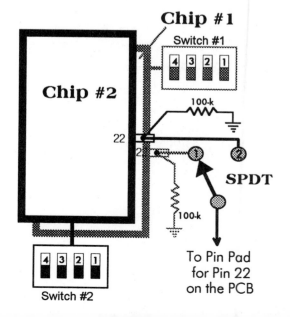

OPTIONS

If you want to go completely hog-wild, you can stack a pair of 128k x 8 SRAM circuits (double everything), pin for pin, except that pins 22 of each chip which must be raised and isolated from everything else, and wired per *Figure 4-7*.

This little hack provides 32,000 channels in 32 Blocks of 1,000 each. You'll also get 320 Scan Banks and 320 Search Banks for the modest extra cost and effort.

Incidentally, this procedure can be employed to double any stock or extended SRAM memory. You need only double up on the chips, pin for pin, except isolate the chip-enable (CE) pins of each chip and wire them to an SPDT switch as shown.

Extended address pins/switches must be kept separate, of course.

What's the limit? I dunno. If you hit a brick wall somewhere let everyone know on my BBS.

Figure 4-8: PRO-2035 logic board connections

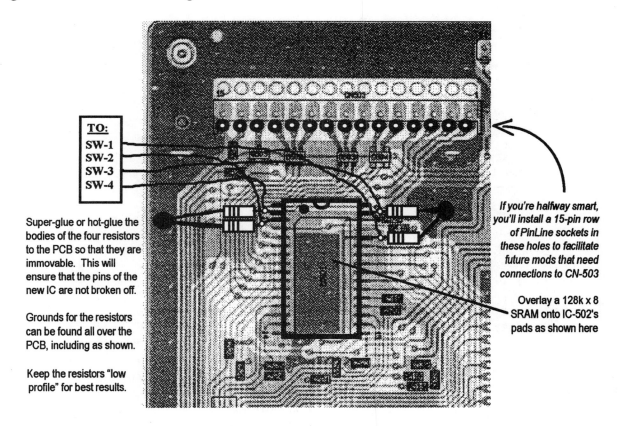

TO:
SW-1
SW-2
SW-3
SW-4

Super-glue or hot-glue the bodies of the four resistors to the PCB so that they are immovable. This will ensure that the pins of the new IC are not broken off.

Grounds for the resistors can be found all over the PCB, including as shown.

Keep the resistors "low profile" for best results.

If you're halfway smart, you'll install a 15-pin row of PinLine sockets in these holes to facilitate future mods that need connections to CN-503

Overlay a 128k x 8 SRAM onto IC-502's pads as shown here

EXTENDED MEMORY FOR THE PRO-43 (and certain other scanners)

The PRO-43 is a class act, and one that uses a different sort of memory storage than most other scanners: EEPROM. Electrically-Eraseable Programmable Read Only Memory, sometimes called E²PROM, just hasn't found its way into hobby radio to any appreciable extent, and is used for main memory in the PRO-43, PRO-2036, BC-

8500XLT, BC-2500XLT, BC-200XLT, and BC-100XLT. The BC-9000XLT probably uses E²PROM, but that's a guess because I haven't ripped one open yet. Reader comments on that?

No matter, memory extension procedure for E²PROM scanners is pretty standard, so the discussion here for the PRO-43 will serve as a guide for the rest. If you're not certain about the type of memory chip used by your scanner, then check the preceeding discussions of CPU and SRAM memory, and then continue to read for tips on identifying E²PROM chips.

IDENTIFYING EEPROMs

As you can see, several different formats are used by the industry.

> *CAUTION:* When handling any E²PROM devices, exercise extreme care to maintain the same electrical potential as the chip. At all costs, avoid static. ESD can kill one of these chips, and you won't know it till you try to get it to remember. For precautions, read the static warnings at the front of the book.

The PRO-43's E²PROMs (two of 'em) look like this sketch. They are tiny 8-pin surface-mount chip about the size of a housefly.

Figure 4-9: PRO-43 E²PROM layout

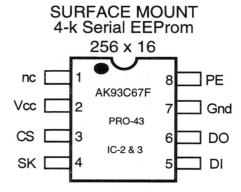

The E²PROMs in the BC-100/200XLT look like those in the PRO-43, but differ in pinout, storage capacity, and organization.

Figure 4-10: BC-100/200 E²PROM

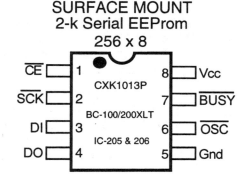

The E²PROM below is used in the BC-8500XLT *and* the PRO-2036. Yes, the two are twins of each other, and we'll know soon enough if it's also found in the 9000. Circuit symbols may differ, but they're the same rig, and from the same manufacturer.

Incidentally, the Uniden Service Manual, on page 13, makes an error regarding the pinout for this chip. The function of pin 14 is incorrectly depicted as "I/O 3" – it should be "Ground", and the row of pins 15-28 was inverted somehow. The figure is correct as seen from the top.

Figure 4-11: BC-8500 (& PRO-2036)

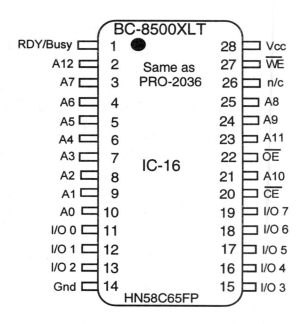

This is another style of EEPROM, in this case from the BC-2500XLT. I wish I could tell you more about this chip, but Uniden's Service Manual for the BC-2500XLT was never intended to let the reader decipher some of the details.

Figure 4-12: BC-2500 layout

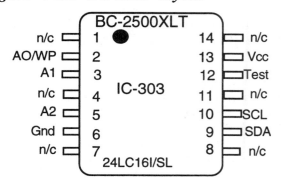

A GENERAL APPROACH TO E²PROM EXTENDED MEMORIES

Before we dig into the PRO-43, let me tell you how to do the rest of the pack and then you can follow the diagram and approach for the PRO-43. The procedures will not vary from one scanner to the next, other than the mechanics of disassembly and physical installation of things.

The first thing to do is get a second E²PROM (or a pair, depending on whether your scanner uses one or two), identical to the one in your scanner. In many cases, the only way you'll be able to get one is direct from the manufacturer of your scanner as a replacement part. That is one good reason why you need the service manual! It lists part numbers, so you can't go wrong.

E²PROM differs radically from SRAM because you don't just hop out and buy a bigger chip. For one thing, there probably aren't any bigger chips of the same general type as your original; and even if there were, it would be a nightmare to do the upgrade. EEPROM just doesn't work like SRAM and requires a different method of handling and hacking.

On the other hand, Extended Memories using EEPROM are going to be quite easy for the most part, because the hard part has already been done... me telling you how to do it. It's generally harder to talk about than to do.

You see, all you do is "piggy back" the EEPROM(s) that reside in your scanner with another, pin for pin, except for one. Some scanners, like the PRO-43 and the BC-200XLT, use two EEPROMs while others use just one.

MULTIPLYING EEPROMS

The approach is to "piggy back" another E²PROM atop the original(s), and solder down each pin to the one below it... except for the CE or CS pin. (Chip-Enable or Chip-Select). This pin on each EEPROM must be kept separate from its brother.

In fact, you have to go so far as to lift or isolate the original CE or CS pin from the circuit trace and let it hang free... just like the one on the upgrade chip(s). The conclusion to this process is to switch the CE or CS pins, with one or the other active at a time. This results in double the memory that you had before.

There is no real limit to the number of EEPROM chips that can be stacked or piggy-backed, so long as only one is set active at a time. Basically, this means that if the CE or CS pin is low (0V), the chip will be inactive, and when that pin is high (+5V), the chip is active. Obviously, then, only one EEPROM chip (or pair) should be active at a time, and therefore all CE/CS pins should be "low" with exception of the chip(s) required to be active for the desired functionality.

The procedure I'm presenting for this section shows just one extra EEPROM chip per stock chip, but you can triple, quadruple, ad nauseam, the number of stacked chips so long as only one CE/CS pin at a time is active-high. The CE/CS pins in those scanners that use two EEPROMs, as the PRO-43 and BC-200XLT do, will put a pair of chips at a time active-high.

"CHIP ENABLE" or "SELECT" PINS

There are two ways to isolate the CE/CS pins of EEPROMS. Perhaps the easiest is to just slice the circuit trace that goes to the CE/CS pin. A second way calls for the pin to be desoldered from the pad and raised up so that it doesn't touch anything. This is the most certain isolation, but is more difficult and risky. The first technique is easiest, but you'll have to determine if the circuit trace dead-ends at the chip's CE/CS pin or continues on somewhere else underneath the chip where you can't see. Again, the service manual will be of great assistance.

The next step calls for a 100kΩ resistor to be installed from ground to the floating CE/CS pin of each EEPROM to be used, stock and new. These resistors can and should be as small as possible with $1/8$ or $1/10$ watt quite suitable. The purpose of these resistors is to "pull down" the CE/CS pin to a low (inactive) state whenever +5V is not applied to the pin. Hence, these resistors are often called "pulldown resistors." Study *Figures 4-13* and *14* and you'll catch the idea righteously quick.

The last step is to install a switch to apply +5V to the CE/CS pin(s) that you want to go active, arranged in such a way that only one chip or matched pair of chips can be active at a time. Unpredictable and possibly embarrassing things may happen if both the stock and extra chips are active at the same time.

Figure 4-13: PRO-43 extended memory schematic

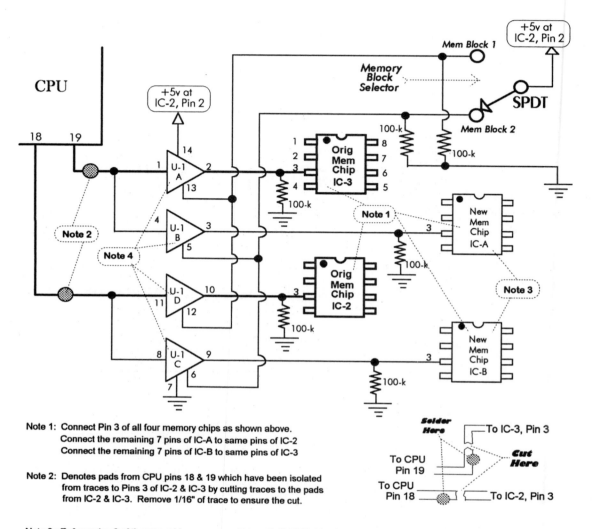

Note 1: Connect Pin 3 of all four memory chips as shown above.
Connect the remaining 7 pins of IC-A to same pins of IC-2
Connect the remaining 7 pins of IC-B to same pins of IC-3

Note 2: Denotes pads from CPU pins 18 & 19 which have been isolated
from traces to Pins 3 of IC-2 & IC-3 by cutting traces to the pads
from IC-2 & IC-3. Remove 1/16" of trace to ensure the cut.

Note 3: Reform pins 3 of the new add-on memory chips and all 4066 chip pins as shown below. Carefully straighten
the pins, first out to the side. Use "duckbill" pliers or flat grippers of some sort. Then bend upwards a
little to facilitate soldering of individual wires

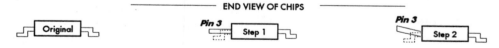

NOTE 4: CONNECTIONS TO CD-4066 OR 74HC4066 CHIP - TOP VIEW

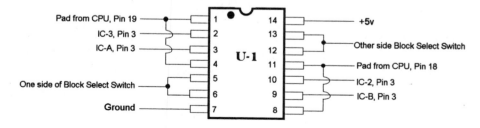

FINDING ROOM

The PRO-43 and similar compact handheld units lack "real estate" on which to install a big ol' DPDT switch. In those scanners that use just one E²PROM chip, the switch need only be an SPDT type, but those with a pair of E²PROMs will have to be controlled with a DPDT switch.

For these cases, I've specified a solid-state 4066 quad CMOS bilateral switch to do the difficult switching for you, with control by a simple SPDT switch that has a better chance of finding a nice home in that confined space.

The 4066 chip is not exactly mandatory, but believe me, it will make for a cleaner installation allowing you to place a micro-mini SPDT switch almost anywhere that will fit. A DPDT switch won't fit just anywhere.

Some people may be tempted to use the original KEYLOCK switch for this purpose and that's fine, except that my hacking philosophy hates giving up *any* functions to gain others.

That KEYLOCK switch is valuable at times and there is no sense in doing without. Don't use it unless your mind is made up – and if that's the case, you're on your own.

That will work, but something *else* is now missing.

Well, let's get on with it.

Figure 4-14: The PRO-43 layout

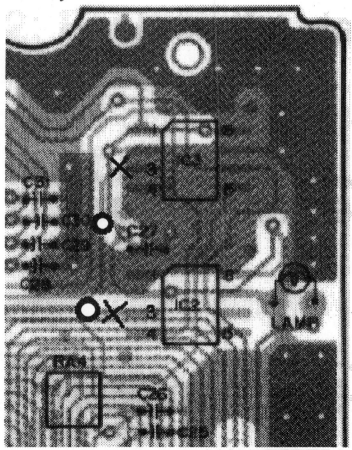

Cut circuit traces to each of pins 3 at IC-2 and IC-3 as shown at the "Xs".

Create solder pads as shown at ●

THE CHALLENGE

You want the truth, right? Okay...

Extending the memory of the PRO-43 is do-able, but it is definitely a job for the most competent and patient hacker, with the right tools and the right attitude. X-ray vision will help, also.

Space is cramped, and there are 677 ways to blow the brains outa that scanner.

I've done it. So have others. But this jewel of a scanner doesn't deserve to be hacked to death. So if you're taking on this job, be certain that you're willing to put in the time and effort it needs to have a reasonable chance of success. No, I'm not dooming you to failure – just ensuring that if you screw it up you won't come yelling at me.

On the other hand, everyone's watching and wanting to learn more about this mod. So if you'll share your experience with your fellow scannists, we'll all benefit.

PROCEDURE

If you have no other mods down there apart from the cellular and 54-88MHz restoration, then you might have few problems. Just get the exact replacement chips so that pin compatibility is assured. Then, you can piggy-back the two new EEPROMs atop the old ones to minimize extra wiring, and you'll conserve valuable real estate.

Get two AK93C67F from Tandy 800-442-2425: IC-2 and IC-3 in the PRO-43. If you can find a plain 93C67F, it's usually less expensive than a Tandy part. I haven't located a good source, so keep Tandy in mind – and about $30 in hand...

GOING FOR IT

First you must tear down the PRO-43 to the Logic/CPU board. It does not have to be removed from inside the front panel, but it is definitely a job to get to the top side of the Logic/CPU board. Here's how:

Remove the battery, antenna, and rear plastic cover (four screws). Remove six screws that hold the top circuit board in place. Using a vacuum-type solder sucker, remove the solder from the antenna wire that protrudes through the board. And here's a little advance warning: more than one hacker has forgotten to resolder that antenna lead when re-assembling. Sorta reduces sensitivity...

Look between the boards to see the bare wire that goes from the antenna BNC connector up through the top board.

Do not unsolder that wire from the BNC connector! Just remove the solder around it from the top board so that it is loose in the hole.

Unsolder and bend the antenna ground tab fully up from the board.

Carefully lift the top board, unplugging the black connector at the base, and lay the board aside on its bundle of colored wires.

Remove the two screws from the next board and lift it, unplugging the white connector at the bottom.

Lift it up and lay it aside on its brown wire (unplugged if necessary). Desolder one corner at a time and remove the metal shield from the Logic/CPU board, to expose the working area.

PRO-43 SURGERY

Identify the two circuit traces that go from pin 3 of each of IC-2 and IC-3 to the CPU.

Cut and isolate each pin 3 by slitting and removing the circuit trace that goes up to the pins. Pin 3 of each chip must not touch anything other than the pad to which it is soldered.

Prepare a solder pad for each trace that goes to the CPU. There are unused solder pads on each trace from IC-3 and IC-2 to the CPU which can be used.

Presolder each feed-thru pad so that solder adheres well to it. Locate a place in which to install the SPDT switch.

I am still working to smooth this procedure, and prototype versions of a mod are a lot different from the final result. Find any reasonable place to install a micro-mini SPDT toggle switch. There are many possibilities, from a magnetic switch to a pair of mini DIP switches to a regular toggle switch. There isn't room for a conventional switch of any kind on the top control panel.

INSTALLING THE NEW MEMORY

Review *Figure 4-13* and *Figure 4-14* carefully, and lay out the parts to comply with them. Position the two replacement EEPROMs atop the stock chips, pin for pin, and lightly solder each new pin to the old one below, except for pin #3 of each chip that must float free and touch nothing.

Solder a wire from the CENTER (common) lug of the switch to either pin 2 of IC-2 or IC-3, or to one of the trace pads on the path between the two pins.

This is a source of +5V needed to switch the CE pins of the old and new pairs of EEPROMs. Look at the area just right of the CPU and to the right of IC2 and 3, viewed from the radio backside.

There is an open space where the 4066 chip can be laid out, dead-bug style. Turn the 4066 upside down; and flatten its pins to the side.

Temporarily replace the metal shield and upper circuit board so you can see where things can comfortably lay flat without bothering anything.

At what appears to be a great spot of real estate, the HEADPHONE jack will stop you dead in your tracks. Look it over, and then forget it!

Now's the time to trim the shield to allow for the piggy-backed EEPROMs, as needed. Check for perfect fit of everything before continuing.

FINAL ASSEMBLY

Take your time and inspect everything very carefully. Recheck the instructions, because you really do not want to go through this again.

When everything looks like it will go together, continue the final assembly. Triple check the orientation of the 4066 chip, and attach it with a drop of super-glue to the PCB.

Add the six resistors, and wire everything according to the diagram. The six resistors should probably be soldered to the 4066 pins.

And what do you get for all this effort? The PRO-43 is already one of the best scanners ever made. This just makes it better.

Is it the Ultimate Scanner?

Well, if it's wired to your computer it would be. But since it's not, it's no more than excellent.

But one of these days...

H. Marshall McLuhan

"Our electrically-configured world has forced us to move from the habit of data classification to the mode of pattern recognition."

The end!
**This is the butt-end of a TurboWhopper PRO-2006. Do you think that's
really a power cord sneaking out of the left (your left) side?**

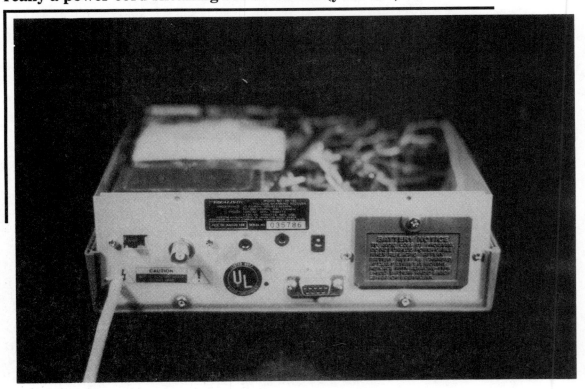

BANK   ACTIVE CH

1 2 3 4 5 6 7 8 9 10

98.1 MHz   **5**

SCA ON   WFM   DELAY

SUBSIDIARY CARRIER AUTHORIZATION (SCA)

WHAT IS A SUBCARRIER?

The high fidelity industry, and FM listeners in general, use a subcarrier technique to support broadcasts available in almost all areas of North America. We call it FM stereo.

FM subcarrier broadcasting was first demonstrated in 1953 by its incredibly prolific inventor, the late Major Edwin H. Armstrong. Multiplexing of more than one program on a carrier was authorized by the FCC in 1955.

You're receiving a subcarrier whenever you listen to commercial FM stereo, because the difference between right and left channels is carried in that subcarrier signal.

Your tuner simply applies that difference to the primary FM signal, generating separate left and right signals that go to amplifiers and then speakers.

Virtually ignored by the consumer press, and by the usual listener, is another sort of subcarrier broadcast... SCA.

...AND WHAT ABOUT SCA?

There is a muddy distinction between FM-SCA and FM stereo, both of which are transmitted *simultaneously* on the same frequency, from the same FM station. FM-Stereo and FM-SCA are both "multiplexed" transmissions, which means there's a primary signal plus one or more secondary signals that carry specialized data.

Any FM broadcast receiver can detect SCA with a simple detector, modification, or adapter. Many FM stations supplement regular programming with SCA because of the profitable things that can be done with this interesting medium.

SCA can be received as clearly and reliably in the local service area as the regular FM signal, and with excellent audio fidelity.

The two most common subcarrier frequencies are 67kHz (the original one), and 92kHz (a more recently authorized subcarrier). One FM station can simultaneously transmit four signals: the regular stereo program, two music or voice programs on subcarriers, such as a radio reading service for the blind at 67kHz, and foreground music at 92kHz. There is a relatively new subcarrier at 57kHz, exclusively for digital data such as highway condition alerts and paging.

By the way, the term "SCA" is synonymous with "SCS," Subcarrier Communications Service. Canada has a similar service called SCMO.

SCA is a monaural signal with bandwidth up to 7kHz, or a bit better than the best AM stations. Tuning an SCA transmission is simple. FM-SCA, however, is not intended for public reception, and conventional FM detection methods will not work.

This is why the "pay as you listen" concept of SCA works. The intent is to provide a paid subscription service similar to cable TV, but broadcast over the air! FM-SCA stations typically rent or lease a special receiver that is internally tuned and locked *only* to their frequency.

LEGALITIES

When the ECPA of 1986 was concocted, the FM Broadcast Industry jumped on the bandwagon to have SCA brought under protection of the Act. Sometimes it's very good to have a powerful lobby working for you, even if it may be against the interest of the majority.

The lobby of the Broadcast Industry was apparently more effective than other lobbies. It's legal to use a back yard satellite dish antenna to receive non-scrambled network transmissions. It's also legal to copy API and UPI and other copyrighted transmissions from the HF bands. It's legal to listen to police broadcasts, and to military aviation.

But it is *illegal* to intercept SCA broadcasts! The power of money never ceases to amaze me, as it

produces laws against the monitoring of certain radio waves that pass across your property, into and through your home and body. Yet, radio waves generated by less politically powerful industries may be legally monitored.

Apparently it is not illegal to *own* radio equipment that can intercept SCA transmissions incidental to the main purpose of the receiver.

There might be legal jeopardy if your radio were designed solely for reception of subcarriers, but that's for the lawyers. The bottom line is that without an adapter or the special SCS receiver that the industry rents out, you cannot legally detect any but the normal programming.

PERMISSION

Monitoring of specific SCA transmissions can be made legal if you have obtained from your local broadcaster(s) authorization to do so for non-commercial hobby purposes. Whether you can actually get such permission is not certain, but it has happened.

If the interesting world of SCA appeals to you, there is a simple and low technology way to modify PRO-2004/5/6 scanners and regular FM Broadcast receivers to detect subcarrier signals.

To make listening legal, draft a letter to the FM Broadcast station owner/manager. Explain that you are a radio hobbyist, interested in modifying your scanner to detect their subcarrier(s). Explain that you will neither record nor disseminate the program material and that the intercept will be solely for your hobby use. Enclose a return letter prepared for signature, and a stamped envelope: make the response easy.

When permission is granted, you can proceed, and with good reason!

SCA programming has broadened since 1977, when the majority of SCA was used for background music in elevators, stores, and dentist's offices.

Now, radio reading services to the blind are found in most metropolitan areas, usually on the subcarriers of public broadcast stations (PBS). Ethnic programming has entered major markets on either the 67 or 92kHz subcarrier.

Foreground and light rock music predominates on 92kHz, while many stations have an easy-listening SCA signal at 67kHz. With the demise of easy-listening on many commercial FM-stereo stations, SCA may be the only way to hear that format in some areas. In some regions of the country, sports news, religious programs, medical data, and special events can be received on SCA.

A cost effective way to listen to SCA is with an FM-SCS adapter fitted to your FM receiver. Installation of an SCA adapter into a scanner with FM broadcast-band capability is not a complicated procedure and does not require technical expertise.

The rest of this section focuses on how to build and install SCA in your PRO-2004/5/6 scanner.

SCA KITS AND SERVICES

After receiving permission to detect SCA signals from the appropriate station, you can roll your own from the information given in this chapter or, if you don't have the time and energy, you can buy what you need.

The following company offers SCA adapter kits and installation services for your scanner or other FM receiver:

FM ATLAS Publishing & Electronics

PO Box 336

Esko, MN 55733-0336

This company offers two inexpensive, easy to assemble and install SCA adapter kits, the ELF-1A and the ELF-II. The best tonal quality is available from the ELF-1A, but unfortunately, each unit supports detection of only one of the three possible subcarriers, and you must make the choice when you place your order.

The ELF-II has a tuning control that allows subcarrier selection, so for the scanning hobbyist, this is the best way to go. The slightly degraded tonal quality of the ELF-II is probably not audible from a scanner's speaker, anyway.

The ELF-II SCA adapter kit consists of an etched and drilled printed circuit board about an inch or so square, a 14-pin IC, and about a dozen resistors and capacitors.

The kit does not include a socket for the IC so I suggest you add one rather than solder the chip in place. Radio Shack sells them.

The ELF-II is easily assembled within a half hour or so, and special techniques are not necessary. The kit includes a trimmer potentiometer to be installed on the circuit board, but I suggest that

you leave it out and install a comparable pot on the exterior of your scanner. That will allow you to easily tune the subcarriers.

There's no significant power dissipated, so any 25-100k pot will do, whether linear or audio taper.

SCA FOR THE PRO-2004, PRO-2005, AND PRO-2006

The ELF-II board is best installed inside the scanner away from the power transformer and the speaker where it could pick up interference. Otherwise, location and positioning are not critical.

The ELF-II board has four wires or external connections: +8V, ground, SCA-IN, and SCA-OUT.

A DPDT switch (toggle or slide) or a DPDT relay and an SPST are required to complete the project, so that you can switch between regular FM programming and SCA as desired.

The switch and the three-wire tuning control are the only necessary external controls, and they can be installed wherever convenient.

The ELF Kit instructions are adequate, but it is suggested that even if you buy the kit you follow my guidelines for home-brew construction. See *Figures 5-1* and *5-2*.

ROLL YOUR OWN SCA ADAPTER!

(*Thanks to* FM Atlas *and Bruce Elving for the circuit.*)

If you are competent with electronic parts and soldering, you can whip up your own SCA detector board (just like the ELF-II) at low cost.

A printed circuit board is preferred, but you can use "perfboard" with point-to-point wiring for similar results.

Refer to *Figures 5-1* and *5-2* for schematic diagram and installation hints for the PRO-2004/5/6 scanners. Differences between the scanners are noted in the figures.

There's not much that's special about this simple circuit, but a few of the parts are critical to proper operation, such as the FSK Demodulator/Tone Decoder chip that's the heart of the SCA adapter: the XR-2211CP.

It's made by:

EXAR Corporation
2222 Qume Drive/PO Box 49007
San Jose, CA 95161-9007
(408) 434-6400, FAX (408) 943-8245

I have used 2211 chips from other manufacturers, as well, but Exar's is domestic and therefore, preferred.

The XR-2211CP is available from national electronic distributors and is not difficult to find, but contact me on my BBS if you can't locate a supplier.

You'll need a method to switch the SCA decoder in and out of circuit. A simple DPDT switch will work just fine, but a DPDT relay might even be better for some applications.

I like to install a DIP switch block on the front of a scanner, with each switch segment dedicated to the control of something specific. There is no room on the front panel of the PRO-2005/6 for any serious switches and I absolutely loathe reaching in behind my scanners to fumble for a switch.

DIP switches are easy to install on the front panels of most base scanners, by means of a mating DIP socket. DIP switches, however, are the SPST variety and worthless for the DPDT needs of the SCA adapter. Yet, a single DIP switch segment can feed power to the coil of a DPDT relay to accomplish the intended effect. A small relay will fit somewhere in the scanner that's out of the way.

PARTS DISCUSSION

C-5 is one of the more critical parts in the SCA adapter and should be the mylar type for best results. Radio Shack doesn't ordinarily stock mylar capacitors of this size (.001 µF) but their "Hi-Q" ceramic disk capacitor might work. C-6 isn't critical as to type, but the value should be within the range of 220-270 pF.

The total series resistance of R-2 and R-3 sets the tuning factor for the desired subcarrier. Minimum resistance is probably more critical than maximum, so R-2 should be not less than 4.7kΩ nor more than 8.2kΩ. R-3, the tuning potentiometer, may be any value from 25kΩ to 100kΩ (50kΩ works for me).

If you are in the mood for experimenting, you can substitute R-2 with a 10kΩ precision trimmer

potentiometer, initially set to about 7kΩ. R-2 sets the upper tuning range limits of the SCA detector, but too low a value might blow the chip, so be careful.

C-4 should be 0.1µF, but C-3 can be considerably higher since it's just for decoupling. LED-1 is optional and not necessary, but is useful as a visible tuning indicator for center-frequency. LED-1 can be left out, with pin 5 not connected, if you like.

R-4, R-1, R-5, C-1, C-2, and C-7 are not critical, but don't go hog-wild with substitutions.

INSTALLING THE SCA ADAPTER

See the above discussion of the ELF-II kit from FM Atlas and the figures for connection hints to the PRO-2004 and PRO-2005/2006.

PRO-2004. My procedure deviates from the ELF-II kit instructions for the PRO-2004. I recommend that you mount the ELF-II Board anywhere that's out of the way. Remember: you'll be making lots of modifications, and you don't want to use up valuable "real estate" without a plan. You'll want to install a DPDT switch or relay and a 25-100k potentiometer somewhere on the case of the scanner. A mini trim pot fits just inside the faceplates of the PRO-2004/5/6 with a screwdriver access hole.

The SCA-IN tap in the PRO-2004 is at IC-4, pin 2. Just solder the wire from SCA-IN directly to pin 2 of IC-4. Cut the RED wire at CN-4 and wire the two cut ends to the SCA Switch as shown in *Figure 5-3*.

Wire the SCA-OUT to the switch or relay as shown. Power for the SCA Board should be tapped from the emitter of Q-32 in the scanner and routed to the other section of the switch or relay before going on to the SCA board.

The ground lead on the SCA board can go to any scanner ground. Solder three hookup wires to the three points for the SCA tuning control and connect those three wires to the potentiometer you installed, pin for pin.

HINT: if you study the foils around those three holes for the trimmer you'll discover that only two wires are really necessary. If that confuses you, use three wires; it's no big deal.

PRO-2005 and PRO-2006. You guys have it a little easier. Mount the SCA board anywhere out of the way. Install a DPDT switch or relay and a 25-100k potentiometer somewhere, probably on the rear case of the scanner.

The critical SCA-IN tap in the PRO-2005/2006 is at a small circuit trace that comes from IC-6, pin 10. Just follow that trace (viewed from the top side of the board) for about an inch, to where it terminates at an "unused solder pad." Solder hookup wire from this pad to the SCA-IN terminal on the SCA board.

Power for the SCA board is taken from the emitter of Q-32 and routed through one section of the switch before going on to the SCA Board.

The ground lead on the SCA board can go to any scanner ground point. Now locate CN-5 on the left-rear Main Board. There is a cable bundle that goes from CN-5 to the VOLUME control on the front of the scanner.

Locate the RED wire at pin #3 of CN-5 and cut it at a point halfway between the connector and where the red wire disappears into the cable bundle sheath. Strip and tin the two cut ends and then splice a hookup wire to each.

Be sure to insulate the splices, preferably with heat shrink tubing. Route these two hookup wires to the vicinity of where the switch or relay will be installed.

Solder three hookup wires to the three spots on the SCA board for the SCA Tuning control and connect those wires to the three lugs of the new potentiometer, pin for pin, on the rear case of the scanner.

Again, two wires will get the job done if you study the foils around those three holes for the trimmer.

Now, let's take a look at the ELF-II schematic, in *Figure 5-1.*

Figure 5-1: Schematic, SCA adapter

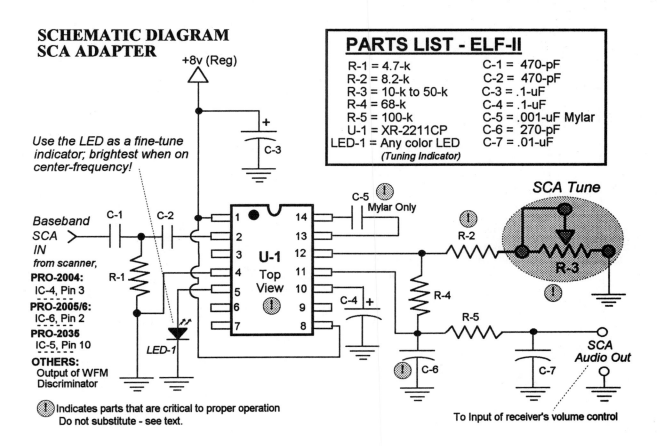

SCHEMATIC DIAGRAM SCA ADAPTER

Use the LED as a fine-tune indicator; brightest when on center-frequency!

+8v (Reg)

Baseband SCA IN
from scanner,
PRO-2004: IC-4, Pin 3
PRO-2005/6: IC-6, Pin 2
PRO-2035 IC-5, Pin 10
OTHERS: Output of WFM Discriminator

Indicates parts that are critical to proper operation. Do not substitute - see text.

SCA Tune

SCA Audio Out

To Input of receiver's volume control

PARTS LIST - ELF-II

R-1 = 4.7-k	C-1 = 470-pF
R-2 = 8.2-k	C-2 = 470-pF
R-3 = 10-k to 50-k	C-3 = .1-uF
R-4 = 68-k	C-4 = .1-uF
R-5 = 100-k	C-5 = .001-uF Mylar
U-1 = XR-2211CP	C-6 = 270-pF
LED-1 = Any color LED	C-7 = .01-uF
(Tuning Indicator)	

Figure 5-2 SCA installation hints

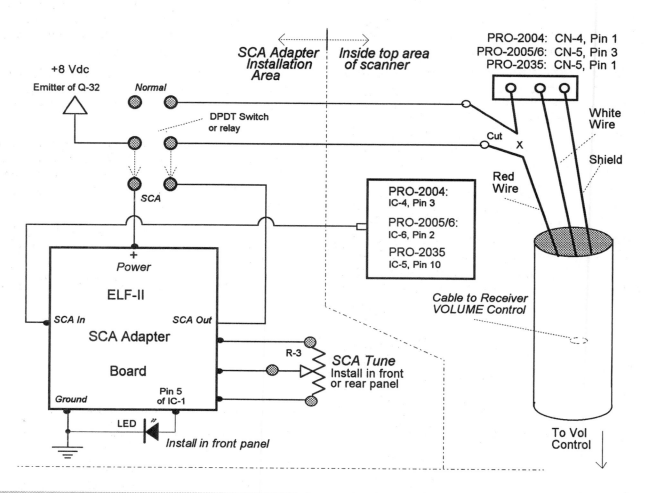

OTHER SCANNERS

The SCA adapter is a simple board (see *Figures 5-3* and *5-4*) that can be successfully installed in almost any scanner or radio that covers the FM broadcast band, such as the Regency Z-60 and the Realistic PRO-2003. There may be others.

You can contact suppliers of SCA adapter kits, and mention the type of scanner or receiver you have and ask whether they offer guidance or explicit installation instructions for your unit.

If your scanner doesn't cover 88-108MHz, forget it, or install the SCA Adapter in a consumer FM receiver per the kit supplier's directions.

YET ANOTHER WARNING

Remember – it is illegal to monitor an SCA transmission without the permission of the broadcaster. Whether or not you have that

permisssion, so far you have done nothing wrong. You've built the SCA unit, but haven't turned it on. Now, if you have that permission...

OPERATION IS SIMPLE

Program your scanner for an FM broadcast signal known to have SCA programming. Keep the SCA switch OFF until you've tuned in the station.

Flip the ATT switch on the rear of the scanner (PRO-2004/5/6) back and forth between the 0 and −10dB positions and select the position that produces the best reception of the regular FM signal.

Then flip the SCA switch ON and adjust the SCA Tuning Control until a signal pops in. When in the SCA mode, you'll hear all kinds of weird noises, and maybe even some very distorted signals as you adjust the SCA Tuning Control. When you hit a subcarrier, though, there will be no doubt that you've done something right. That's SCA! You may have to turn the VOLUME up a little higher than normal. Fine tune for the clearest reception to enjoy commercial-free programming.

If you like, flip the SCA switch ON and OFF to ensure that you're receiving two different programs.

Now and again, especially with Muzak™ programming, there will be occasional silent pauses for up to 90 seconds, but a typical pause is about 10 seconds.

You see, technical people tend to talk more openly, at least in my experience, so that's where you will probably strike oil.

Of course, you can just mail a stack of permission requests to every station in range, and as you receive replies, you'll learn which ones offer it.

There is another resource to draw upon: the *FM ATLAS AND STATION DIRECTORY,* available from sources that provide ELF SCA Adapter Kits. It will be a great addition to your radio library if you are an FM-DX nut or an SCA freak.

Figure 5-3: Both sides of SCA board

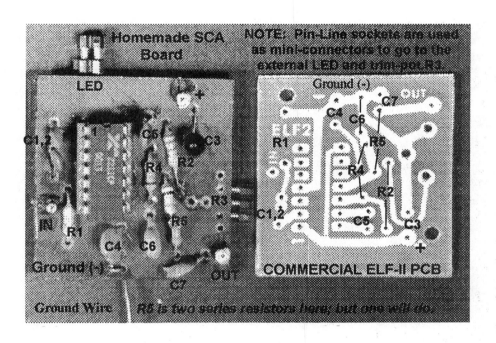

WHO DOES IT?

How can you learn which FM stations offer SCA programming? There won't be a program list in your local "Entertainment Guide," that's for sure.

You could call the stations. It's possible that only the station engineering and managerial teams know anything about SCA, so if a station receptionist gives you a bland reply, ask for an engineer or manager. Your best answer will generally come from an engineer, and not just because he knows more about the technology.

SUCCESS!

So, you finally have SCA bragging rights, and can actually pump Muzak™ into your bathroom just like a department store! You might also find some audio novels for the blind, sports and weather information, and a few other things that are even more interesting than elevator music.

And remember... it's not that SCA is so fascinating. A scannist like you simply wants anything penetrating his personal ether to be available for monitoring.

Just in case you're skeptical about the value of the pin-line concept, take a look at these extreme examples. There simply is no better, cheaper, or more effective way to get such things done!

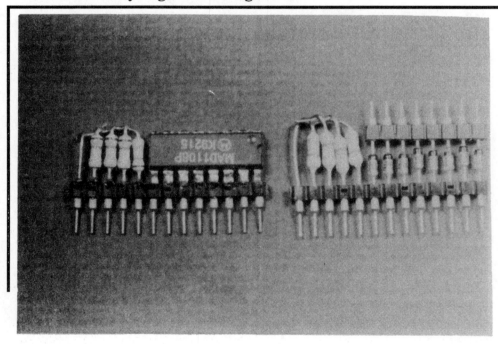

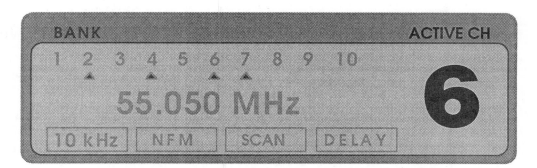

BANK   ACTIVE CH

1 2 3 4 5 6 7 8 9 10

55.050 MHz   6

10 kHz   NFM   SCAN   DELAY

DATA TONE SQUELCH

INTELLIGENCE FOR PRO-2004/5/6 and PRO-2035

Here's a great (and easy) mod that lets the PRO-2004/5/6 and PRO-2035 recognize worthless computer data and other single or multiple tone signals. After pausing on unwanted signals for a second or so, it resumes SCAN or SEARCH. *Intelligent!*

This modification may resemble a Tone Decoder/Rejecter, but they're different circuits with different functions.

The Data/Tone Squelch can serve in a limited capacity as a Tone Decoder/Rejecter (TDR) but it's designed for the broader need to discriminate against many forms of *non-voice signals* and not just one specific tone.

Another difference is that the TDR will work in most any scanner whereas the DATA/TONE SQUELCH is only for the PRO-2004, PRO-2005, PRO-2006, and PRO-2035.

I am seeking ways to apply it to other scanners, but for now, it is for only those scanners that were manufactured with a SOUND SQUELCH function. The Data/Tone Squelch will hereafter be referred to as "DSQ," while Sound Squelch will be called "SSQ."

FEWER LOCKOUTS!

One impact of the DSQ is that you no longer must lock out those Trunked Data Channels when you're monitoring 800 MHz SMR! Those data channels usually change every day, which makes manual LockOut programming a real chore.

A scanner equipped with my DSQ circuit won't lock onto those obnoxious signals, including cellular data, continuous tones, DES/DVP, Improved Mobile Telephone Service (IMTS) tones, digital pagers, and most other non-voice signals.

My DSQ will even discriminate against static. In other words, it discriminates against all but two kinds of signals: voice and silent (dead) carriers!

The latter is okay, because the resident SSQ function takes care of silent signals. In fact, my DSQ works *with* the SSQ but is independent in every way except that the Sound Squelch button on the front panel activates/deactivates both functions. Two SPST switches can provide separate control of SSQ and DSQ if that's important to you. Construction and installation of the DSQ are within the ability of most hobbyists who have learned which end of the soldering iron to grab.

ADVICE: You should have the Service Manual for your scanner before doing any modification. Order directly from Tandy National Parts Center, at (800) 442-2425.

CONSTRUCTION

Build the DSQ circuit on perf board that's about 1" x 1.5" – though smaller is fine if you're good at micro circuits.

Refer to Figures 6-1 through 6-6. Use an IC socket (XU-1) for U-1, but don't plug in U-1 in until the board has been finished and checked for errors.

Don't install C-1 yet, but keep it handy – you'll see why as we go on. Note that pins 1, 6, 7, 8, 9, 10, 11, 13, and 14 of U-1 are unused. Snip those pins from XU-1 before inserting the socket into the board.

Figure 6-1: Mounting an accessory board

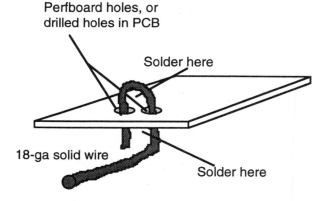

Attach a stiff bare copper wire (#18 ga) to the ground trace of the board, as in *Figure 6-1*.

Loop it through the holes in the perf board, pinch it down for rigidity and then solder it to the main ground trace of the DSQ. Leave about 1 inch of this bare wire free. It will simplify installation of the DSQ board inside the scanner.

WIRING & CONSTRUCTION

Solder a RED hookup wire to pin 3 of XU-1.

Solder a YELLOW hookup wire to the junction of D-1 and D-2.

Solder a WHITE hookup wire to the anode of D-4.

Solder an ORANGE wire to the cathode of D-4.

Solder a BLUE wire to the cathode of D-3.

These wires should be 8-10" long, and will be routed and trimmed later.

Construction and layout are not critical and can vary from my suggestions, which are about as simple as possible and involve no loops, jumpers, or other weird wiring techniques. Make your board as small as practical, though, so that it won't take up too much space inside the scanner.

You may be doing many modifications in the future, so space might become valuable. Install the DSQ board in an out of the way place, though VR-1 should be accessible for initial adjustments.

The bare ground wire on the DSQ board can be soldered to the chassis or to a printed circuit board ground trace, thereby making the mount much easier. This bare wire can be bolted to the chassis if you don't have a heavy duty soldering gun. Once soldered or bolted, this stiff wire should make the DSQ board relatively immobile.

PRO-2004 ONLY: Solder the (+) leg of C-1 directly to IC-5, pin 14.

PRO-2005/6 ONLY: Solder the (+) leg of C-1 directly to IC-5, pin 7.

PRO-2035 ONLY: Solder the (+) leg of C-1 directly to IC-6, pin 14.

PRO-2004/5/6/2035 ALL:

Solder the free end of the YELLOW hookup wire to the (–) leg of C-1.

Solder the BARE ground wire to the chassis or a circuit ground in the scanner.

Solder the free end of the RED wire at pin 3 of XU-1 to the OUTPUT leg of IC-8, the +5V regulator on the main chassis of the scanner.

IC-8 is the same in all four scanners, PRO-2004/5/6 and PRO-2035.

PRO-2004 ONLY: Locate CN-504 on the Logic/CPU board, PC-3, and follow its wire bundle back to the top of the main receiver board.

Locate the sky blue wire that connects to the main board at the right end of the row of wires, and desolder that wire from the board.

For identification, that wire comes from pin 15 of CN-504. Let it hang loose until needed.

PRO-2005/6 ONLY:

Locate CN-3 on the main receiver board and follow its wire bundle up to the Logic/CPU board.

Locate the sky blue wire that connects to pin 4 of CN-3. Clip that blue wire halfway between CN-3 and the Logic/CPU board. Let the two cut ends hang loose for a moment.

PRO-2035 ONLY:

Locate CN-3 on the main receiver board and follow its wire bundle up to the Logic/CPU board.

Locate the light blue wire that connects to pin 5 of CN-3. Clip that blue wire halfway between CN-3 and the Logic/CPU board. Let the two cut ends hang loose for a moment.

PRO-2004/5/6/2035 ALL:

Install two SPST switches of your choosing in a place of your choosing on the scanner's front or rear panels. For rear panel installations, Radio Shack's micro-mini toggle switches, #275-624, will be just fine.

These switches can also be put into the front panel, and this isn't difficult to do on the PRO-2004 where there is plenty of room. It is more difficult on the PRO-2005/6/2035 where the Logic/CPU board must first be removed.

One neat choice of switch for any of the PRO-2004/5/6/2035 is a 4, 6, or 8 position DIP switch. Extra switch positions will be useful on other mods – they won't be wasted!

PRO-2004/5/6/2035 ALL:

Solder the ORANGE wire of the DSQ board to the bottom lug of one switch. This switch will control the stock SOUND SQUELCH (SSQ) function, ON or OFF.

Solder the BLUE wire of the DSQ board to the bottom lug of the other switch.

This switch will control the new DATA/TONE SQUELCH (DSQ) function, ON or OFF.

Solder a bare jumper wire from the free lug of one switch to the free lug of the other switch.

PRO-2004 ONLY:
Solder the sky blue wire that was removed from the main board to the bare jumper wire between the lugs of the two switches.

Solder the WHITE wire of the DSQ board to the empty spot on the main scanner board where the sky blue wire was removed. This completes installation: Proceed to "Adjustment of VR-1."

PRO-2005/6/2035 ONLY:
Splice the WHITE wire of the DSQ board to the cut sky blue wire that goes to CN-3 of the main scanner board.

Splice one end of a hookup wire to the other cut end of the blue wire that goes to the Logic /CPU board in the front panel.

Insulate the splices! Solder the other end of this new hookup wire to the common bare jumper wire between the top lugs of the two switches.

ALL: This completes your installation: proceed to "Adjustment of VR-1," next.

ADJUSTMENT OF VR-1

PRO-2004/5/6/2035 ALL:

Push the front panel SOUND SQUELCH button ON. Turn the SSQ OFF and the DSQ ON. Attach a voltmeter's (–) to ground and its (+) to pin 5 of U-1. Tune the scanner to a strong and noisy data channel or to a loud, single tone carrier. Cellular or trunked data channels are ideal!

Measure the DC voltage at pin 5 of U-1 (4.1 to 4.5V typical). Calculate 80% of that voltage; then put the voltmeter at pin 4 of U-1 and adjust VR-1 for that 80% level of the above measurement. It's typically between 3.6 and 3.8V.

The exact adjustment isn't critical, but if set too low, voice signals will resume SCAN or SEARCH. If it's too high, data and tone signals won't trigger SCAN/SEARCH RESUME.

Another way to find the optimum setting is to put a voltmeter (+) on pin 2 of U-1 and (–) to ground and tune the scanner to a cellular or trunked data channel.

Adjust VR-1, first one way and then the other, and then to a point so that the voltage on pin 2 of U-1 just achieves a steady +5V. It takes a stable +5V for about one second to trigger the SCAN/SEARCH RESUME function, but don't adjust VR-1 any further than necessary to stabilize the DATA/TONE voltage at pin 2.

OPERATION & TECHNICAL NOTES

Remember that the SOUND SQUELCH button on the front panel must be ON before either SSQ or DSQ can work. The SOUND SQUELCH button is kind of like a master on/off switch and the two SPST switches control one, the other, or both.

Voice signals will cause the scanner to stay locked as normal until the signal goes away. Minor adjustment of VR-1 may be necessary for optimum results, but the final setting will produce a voltage on pin 4 of U-1 of about 80% of the peak voltage on pin 5 of U-1.

The DC input signal at pin 5 of U-1 will be nearly zero on silent or quiet signals and about 4-4.5V with data and continuous tone signals. Pin 5 will show a very erratic and rapidly changing voltage from nearly 0-4V or so for voice signals.

The DC output voltage at pin 2 of U-1 will be nearly 0 on silent or quiet signals, and will be a steady +5V with data and continuous tone signals. Voice signals will cause a rapid fluctuation of the signal between 0-5V at pin 2 of U-1.

When the SOUND SQUELCH button is off, neither SOUND nor DATA SQUELCH will operate and scanner operation will be "stock."

IN CASE OF DIFFICULTY

The most critical parts of this mod are the rectifier circuit consisting of D-1, D-2, R-1, R-2, C-1, and C-2, and proper pin wiring of the LM-339 chip. Make sure the diode polarities are correct – the banded end is the cathode. Make sure polarities of capacitors are correct.

Tune to a strong, obnoxious cellular (879-881 MHz) or trunked data channel (851-866 MHz), and measure the DC voltage at pin 5 of U-1. There should be between 4 and 4.5 volts. You won't measure "too much," but not enough is possible. If so, check the wiring and components mentioned above.

Next most critical is the polarity and wiring of the two isolation diodes, D-3 and D-4. Last but not least is the wiring of U-1.

The circuit is so simple and affirmative in its action that you're not likely to encounter trouble if you follow these instructions.

Some PRO-2005 (not PRO-2004 or 2006 or 2035) may have a chirping or warbling, morse code type of sound on quiet channels after this mod has been done. If yours exhibits this weird

sound, change C-1 from 1.0 µF to 0.1 µF, Radio Shack #272-1432.

If the "tweet" is still there, then solder a 1000 µF capacitor (RS #272-1032) directly to pins 4 and 11 of IC-5 in the scanner.

Pin 4 should get the (+) lug of the capacitor while pin 11 gets the (–) lug. This is a peculiar problem in some PRO-2005's, but it's easy to correct if you encounter it.

INTRO TO THEORIES

To understand the simple operation of my DATA/TONE SQUELCH, it is first necessary to understand the PRO-2004/5/6's SOUND SQUELCH (SSQ) circuit on which we will "piggy back" the new DSQ circuit.

The circuits are identical among the PRO-2004/5/6 scanners but circuit symbols differ. I use a simple scheme for this discussion. **P4** means PRO-2004, **P5/6** means PRO-2005 and PRO-2006, **P35** means PRO-2035, and **P*** means ALL.

THEORY OF OPERATION OF THE SOUND SQUELCH

A weak portion of the receiver's audio is sampled at the detector and amplified through IC-5 (**P***).

The highly amplified audio is fed from IC5 (**P4**, pin 14; **P5/6**, pin 7; **P35**, IC6, pin 14) to a rectifier network (**P4**, D-41 and D-42; **P5/6**, D-43 and D-44; **P35**; dual diode D-41).

This rectifier network converts audio signals to a DC level proportional to the level of the audio signal, and is used as a bias to a switching transistor (**P4**, Q-21; **P5/6**, Q-19; **P35**, Q21). Most audio signals are strong enough to turn the transistor on while very weak or silent signals keep it off.

When the transistor is off, 5V is on its collector, but when the transistor is ON, the collector drops to nearly 0 volts. 5V and 0V forms the logic differential required by the CPU for making decisions.

The collector of the transistor is fed directly to the CPU (**P4**, IC-503, pin 24; **P5/6**, IC-501, pin 18; **P35**, IC-501, pin 34). When the SOUND SQUELCH button on the front panel is set to the ON position and when CPU's SSQ pin is at 0V, the scanner SCANs or SEARCHes as normal, locking on any signals that break the squelch. Similarly, when the SOUND SQUELCH button is off, the CPU's SSQ pin goes to ground, which keeps it at zero volts, no matter what.

When the SOUND SQUELCH button is on, and when the scanner encounters a silent or unmodulated carrier, then the transistor discussed above gets turned off and a 5V level on its collector is fed to the CPU's SSQ pin. 5V on the CPU's SSQ pin makes the scanner resume scanning within a second or so after stopping.

As long as there are voices or other audio signals present, the CPU's SSQ pin will be "0V low" and operation is normal. When that pin goes "+5V high," the CPU is programmed to resume scanning or searching.

THEORY OF OPERATION OF THE DATA/TONE SQUELCH

Since the CPU's SSQ pin responds only to low and high logic and really doesn't know the difference between voice and data, we can generate a separate but opposite logic circuit to make it discriminate against tones and data in the same way the SSQ discriminates against silent carriers.

All we need is a circuit that sends a "high" to the CPU's SSQ pin in the presence of strong, sustained audio signals such as data or continuous tones. My DSQ does this nicely, thank you, since voice signals are erratic, varying, and not at all like data or continuous tones. C-1 of our circuit samples the same audio as the SSQ but passes it to a new rectifier circuit, D-1 and D-2, which with R-1, R-2, and C-2, creates a DC signal proportional to the level of the audio signal.

This DC signal is fed to pin 5 of U-1, a Voltage Comparator IC. The reference voltage is adjusted by VR-1, and fed to pin 4 of U-1.

As long as the DC signal at pin 5 is less than the reference signal at pin 4, the output of U-1 at pin 2 will be zero volts "low." When the DC signal at pin 5 exceeds the reference voltage at pin 4, the output of U-1, pin 2, will go "high" to +5V.

The output of U-1, pin 2, is coupled to the CPU via isolation diode D-3. A "high" tells the CPU to make the scanner resume SCANning or SEARCHing while a "low" does nothing out of the ordinary.

When VR-1 is correctly adjusted, the output of U-1, pin 2, will never go "high" long enough to trigger the CPU unless data or continuous tones are present. Strong voice signals may make U-1's output go high momentarily, but the interval will not be long enough to trigger the CPU unless the talker does an extended "Ahhhhh" into the mike, because about 0.5 to 1 second is required before the CPU will trigger.

Most voice signals of interest will not send a lengthy "high" to the CPU, but continuous tones and data will! Therefore, my DATA/TONE SQUELCH works like, though *opposite* to, SOUND SQUELCH.

Isolation diodes D-3 and D-4, allow the SOUND SQUELCH and the DATA/TONE SQUELCH to work simultaneously or either at a time, and not interfere with each other.

Depending on the setting of the individual DSQ and SSQ switches, the scanner will resume SCANning or SEARCHing when it encounters data/tone signals, and silent carriers will not be affected by voice signals!

Table 6-1: Parts list for DSQ circuit

CKT SYM	DESCRIPTION	RADIO SHACK #
C-1	1µF/35V tantalum	#272-1434
C-2	2.2µF/35V tantalum	#272-1435
D1-4	1N4148 or 1N914 switching diodes	#276-1122
R-1	390-ohm	#271-018
R-2	12k; *use 10k and 2.2k in series if need be*	*
R-3	3.3k ohms	#271-1328
U-1	LM-339 comparator	#276-1712
VR-1	10k ohm trim pot	#271-282
XU-1	IC socket, 14-pin DIP, for U-1 above	#276-1999
Misc	Perf board	#276-1395
Misc	Hookup wire; #278-776 or #278-775 best	*
S1,2	Switch, SPST toggle switch	#275-624

Not available at Radio Shack

Figure 6-3: DSQ perfboard, component side

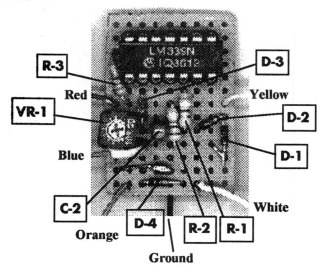

Figure 6-4: DSQ perfboard, solder side

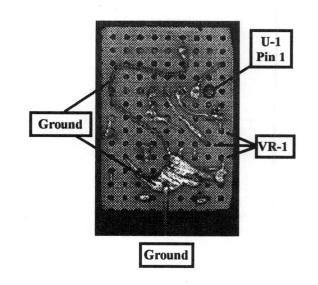

Figure 6-5: DSQ schematic

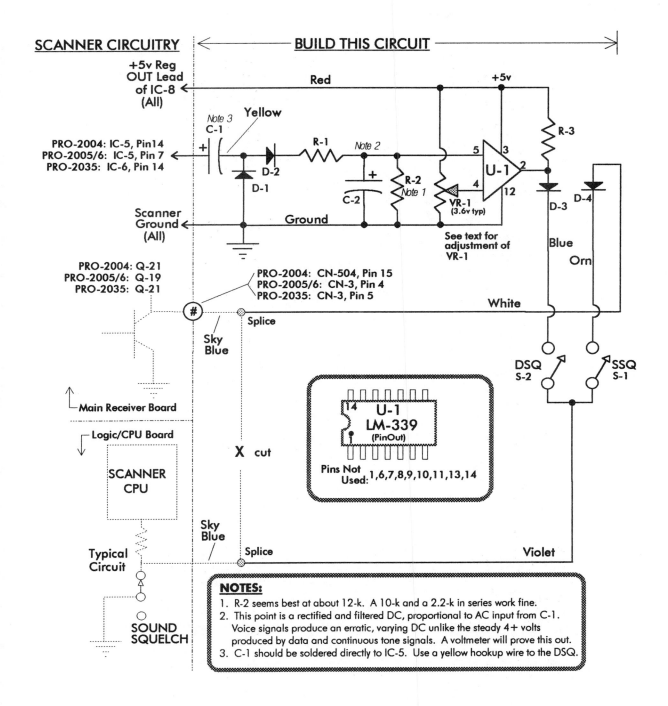

SCANNER CIRCUITRY

BUILD THIS CIRCUIT

+5v Reg
OUT Lead
of IC-8
(All)

Red

+5v

Yellow
Note 3
C-1

PRO-2004: IC-5, Pin14
PRO-2005/6: IC-5, Pin 7
PRO-2035: IC-6, Pin 14

D-2

R-1   Note 2

D-1

R-3

5   3
U-1
2

R-2
Note 1

4   12

VR-1
(3.6v typ)

D-3

D-4

Scanner
Ground
(All)

Ground

C-2

See text for
adjustment of
VR-1

Blue

Orn

PRO-2004: Q-21
PRO-2005/6: Q-19
PRO-2035: Q-21

PRO-2004: CN-504, Pin 15
PRO-2005/6: CN-3, Pin 4
PRO-2035: CN-3, Pin 5

#

Sky
Blue

Splice

White

DSQ
S-2

SSQ
S-1

Main Receiver Board

Logic/CPU Board

X cut

14   U-1
LM-339
(PinOut)

SCANNER
CPU

Pins Not
Used: 1,6,7,8,9,10,11,13,14

Typical
Circuit

Sky
Blue

Splice

Violet

SOUND
SQUELCH

NOTES:
1. R-2 seems best at about 12-k. A 10-k and a 2.2-k in series work fine.
2. This point is a rectified and filtered DC, proportional to AC input from C-1.
   Voice signals produce an erratic, varying DC unlike the steady 4+ volts
   produced by data and continuous tone signals. A voltmeter will prove this out.
3. C-1 should be soldered directly to IC-5. Use a yellow hookup wire to the DSQ.

Figure 6-6:   PCB details

DSQ installation – A

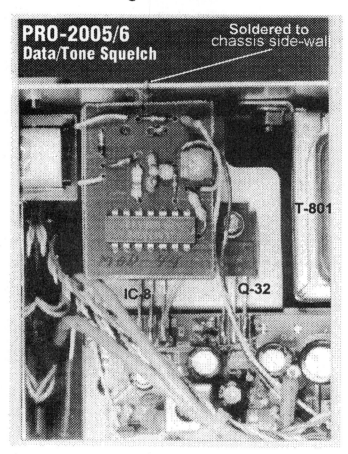

DSQ installation – B

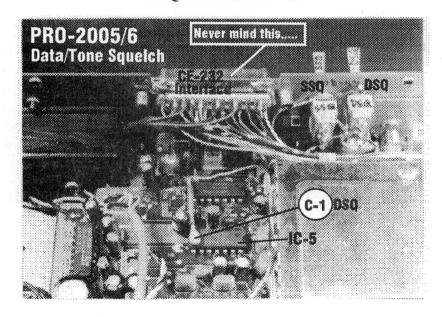

Figure 6-7: DSQ part location/layout

MORE INSTALLATION NOTES

Figures 6-6 and *6-7* show a DSQ installation in a PRO-2006. The DSQ board is mounted above IC-8, Q-32, and just forward of T-801.

The stiff ground wire of the DSQ board is bent straight up from the board, looped over the top of the chassis side wall, and then soldered to the side for a solid mount and a good ground.

The bottom of the DSQ board can be covered with a layer of hot glue or even a few pointy dots of silicone rubber sealant to protect it from shorting against anything below in case it gets shoved downward.

It will ordinarily remain in position just fine if #18 gauge ground wire is used for the mount. +5V power can be taken from the OUT lug of IC-8, just below the DSQ board.

The blue, orange, and white wires can be bundled and routed along a convenient path to their respective destinations. Wire length is not critical.

The DSQ and SSQ switches are installed on the rear panel of the scanner. Any SPST type of switch will do. Just install them where convenient and out of the way. C-1 should be installed at IC-5 and a yellow hookup wire looped around and routed back to the DSQ board.

REALLY SMART!

Once installed, this accessory adds intelligence, allowing the unit to do its own signal selection. That makes scanning more interesting because a higher percentage of audio will be meaningful.

Oh, yes...

There's another little point under the category of "intelligence": *operator* brainpower. Before screaming at me that this "easy" mod doesn't work, even after you've checked everything eleven times, take another look at the SOUND SQUELCH button on the front panel. If it's not ON, neither SSQ nor DSQ can work.

BANK   ACTIVE CH

1 2 3 4 5 6 7 8 9 10

Samuel Moor (Sam) Shoemaker

| 10 kHz | AM | SCAN | DELAY |

"Freedom of the press and freedom of the radio are the common means by which the common man gets his common information on which must depend his common sense."

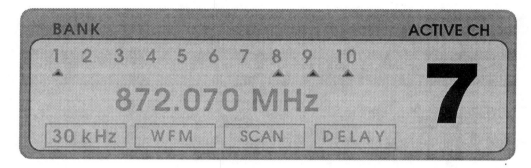

CELLULAR MODS
& OTHER WIZARDRY

THE MOST POPULAR MOD OF ALL...

Restoring or adding cellular band coverage is the scanner hack almost everyone wants. People who do it are the target of government, manufacturers, cellular telephone users, the cellular telephone industry, and other agencies and people who really should know better.

Despite them, I believe it's legal to modify your scanner to receive cellular, so long as you never resell it. I said "legal to modify your scanner," but I did *not* say that it's legal to use it for that purpose. This is another situation where it's legal to own something as long as it's never used.

THE LAW

There are laws pertaining to the reception of cellular signals and to the sale of cellular-capable receivers. Do NOT take my word for what's legal and what's not. Everything I say about this topic came from others just as unqualified as I am. If you're willing to risk your freedom based on

"high rumor" information, go ahead. But don't blame the result on me.

It's your responsibility to investigate these laws, or consult with an attorney, and you should be warned that some such legislation is Federal, and some varies from state to state. As of this writing, you probably can legally restore any blocked cellular coverage in your scanner. If you listen to cellular calls, however, you are violating the Electronic Communications Privacy Act of 1986 (Federal), plus any applicable state or local law.

The Telephone Disclosure and Dispute Resolution Act of 1994, Public Law 102-556, forbids the importation and manufacture of cellular-capable receivers, and became effective April 1, 1994. That Act did not forbid the sale of existing supplies of such scanners, nor did it address the cellular modifiable scanners already sold. It does not seem to address the action of modifying scanners, but it clearly stipulates that to be certified (hence salable), receivers may not be easily modified to support cellular reception.

MANUFACTURERS' RESPONSE

The manufacturers played it safe, and virtually all interpreted "easily modified" as "impossible." If cellular is important to you, forget any receivers legally brought into the USA, or made here, after April 24, 1994.

Just one more reason why April is the month of fools...

AMATEUR RECEIVERS

In this discussion, I've avoided the "sorta-partly capable" receiver sections of a variety of handheld transceivers.

One example will do for all: the original Alinco DJ-580T, of about 1993. It's absolutely *not* a scanner, but it scans. The design permits the owner to easily find and clip a single blue wire, which restores coverage of the cellular band.

Many similar products, aimed at the amateur radio market, were as easily "modified."

CELLULAR-CAPABLE RECEIVERS

A number of scanners were originally built with 800MHz coverage, and require no modification to receive cellular. Some such receivers, available only on the used market, are listed below:

J.I.L. SX-400	**AOR-950**
Regency MX-4000	**AOR-1000**
Regency MX-5000	**AOR-1500**
Uniden BC-800XLT	**AOR-2500**
ICOM R-7100	**AOR-3000**
ICOM R-7000	**Yaesu FRG-9600**
ICOM R-1	**ICOM R-9000**
ICOM R-100	**Kenwood RZ-1**
Yupiteru MVT-series	

THE PRO-2004 STORY

The PRO-2004 is absent from the above list, because just as it was introduced in late 1986, most units were recalled from the distribution system, presumably to regional service centers for addition of the cellular blocking diode. Clearly, this was a last minute retrofit effort, because the first wave of PRO-2004's to hit the stores had the anti-cellular diode hand-soldered to the bottom side of the Logic/CPU board. Later productions

had this diode machine-soldered into its proper spots on the top side of the board.

Several PRO-2004's, however, hit the streets in August and September of 1986, fully cellular-capable. Most were caught and "fixed" before sale, though.

Here's a bet you can win. If anyone ever claims that Radio Shack never sold a scanner that could receive cellular telephone calls, just focus their attention on page 89 of their 1987 Catalog (No. 406), whereon the 2004 specs clearly state:

> *"Continuous tuning from 25-520MHz and 760-1300MHz."*

The PRO-2004 was *designed and built* to be cellular-capable, and a few hit the street as such. Most, however, were retrofitted prior to sale and a green addendum sheet to the instructions was included. Yes, I have a copy of that, also.

CELLULAR-MODIFIABLE SCANNERS

The following is a list of scanners believed to be cellular modifiable because 800MHz circuitry was blocked at the factory, during production, and that blockage can be reversed.

PRO-2004	**BC-855XLT** [3]
PRO-2005	**BC-200XLT**
PRO-2006	**BC-205XLT**
PRO-2022	**BC-760XLT** [4]
PRO-2026	**BC-700XLTA** [4]
PRO-2027	**BC-890XLT** [4]
PRO-2030	**BC-950XLT**
PRO-2032	**BC-2500XLT** [3]
PRO-34	**Regency 4030**
PRO-37	**Regency 1600**
PRO-39	**PRO-43** [1]
PRO-46 [2]	**PRO-51** [2]
PRO-23 [2]	

Note 1: Date of mfg code 1A4, 2A4, xA3, xA2 (label in battery compartment), or no letter "A" in the serial number.

Note 2: Date of mfg code 1A4, 2A4, -A3, -A2 (label on back).

Note 3: Date of mfg code must not end in the letter D, except for OAID.

Note 4: Date of mfg code must not end in the letter D.

Please check the footnotes, because some of these model numbers were imported or manufactured after the cutoff date, and therefore were built as "impossible" to modify. Thus, some PRO-43's are modifiable and some are not, and that's true of several of these products.

For instance, PRO-43's imported before March, 1994, are modifiable, while some brought in during March, and all thereafter, are impossible to modify. Date codes of any -A2 or -A3 and only 1A4 and 2A4 are assured of being modifiable. 3A4 and up probably aren't.

THE BIRTH OF THE CELLULAR CRAZE

Ironically, it was Radio Shack's knee-jerk, paranoid reaction to the growing anti-cellular sentiment that ignited the tidal wave of scanner hacking! See, if these scanners could be so quickly and easily blocked against cellular, then somehow, an undo must be possible. And it was!

The service manual offered clues and the handsoldered diode on the bottom of the board stood out like a sore thumb. Scanner hacking was born and toddling by New Year's, 1987.

Other manufacturers followed Radio Shack's lead and deliberately blocked cellular coverage in their scanners. In most cases, the "undo" is as easy as pie, thereby proving that the manufacturers' intent was to be able to say they did not offer cellular-capable scanners. It worked for seven years.

The cellular industry went on deceiving their customers, promising privacy and security of communications. Government wasn't interested after it had washed its hands with the ECPA of 1986. And, manufacturers were delighted that they could burn both ends of the candle. *(Peddling "private" cellular telephones and scanners capable of breaking that privacy!)* Everybody was happy until the scanner market boomed and became something of a Page Two headline.

THE CTIA

Then the secret was out: cellular telephones really were not private after all. An outcry from the cellular user community coupled with a powerful lobby by the cellular industry managed to push through today's law that eliminates cellular-capable receivers, period.

The Cellular Telephone Industry Association (CTIA) and its members told prospective cellular telephone users not to worry: "those scanners are being made illegal." They were right...

Congress meekly followed its instructions, and the result was the end of cellular-capable scanner production/importation, plus penalties for those who *listen*.

RATIONALIZATION OR NATURAL LAW?

Radio waves do not conform to man's law.

They pass across your property, into your home, through your private bedroom, and even into and through your body. Yet, you are forbidden from detecting some of those waves, and now it's illegal to import, make, or sell equipment that does that detecting, at least in this country. Radio waves used to be public domain where reception was concerned. In the past, only Iron Curtain countries and other despotic governments restricted citizens' right to probe the airwaves.

Congress had only three options. They could do nothing. They could tell the CTIA and its membership that to claim privacy for cellular users they had to develop a technology that makes it (close to) impossible, or at least very expensive to intercept those transmissions. Or, it could cave in to the pressure from the big-money people, once again, and put the burden on the consumer.

A closing point, before we move on.....this business of secrecy and privacy seems weird to me. There are no laws to interfere with someone listening to your conversations over a table at a restaurant, or on a bus, train, plane, or anywhere out in public. And there's no Federal restriction against listening to cordless phones and baby monitors, which is really a whole new class of eavesdropping. Why cellular?

It's a lot like guns... when they're outlawed, only criminals and despots will have them. Someday, only those with sinister intent will be able to monitor your cellular conversations, and they will do it easily. If that doesn't seem possible to you, think of the now-infamous "Clipper Chip."

Restricted access to the airwaves is not the answer to security and privacy, but when laws are passed that pretend to do this – *look out, Bunky!* You better watch over your shoulder when someone wants to protect you... or your privacy.

ON WITH CELLULAR SCANNERS

Just ahead is a quick and dirty guide to the liberation of cellular capability in the scanners on the "list." Since this information has already been published to one extent or another elsewhere, I have skipped some of the gory details.

You really should have the service manual for your scanner anyway (I insist on it), so cut that diode, or add that resistor, and be done with it.

Just don't LISTEN to cellular signals, okay?

CELLULAR COMMUNICATION

Since my first two books were written, the cellular frequency allocations have grown a little. The initial base allocations were 870-890MHz, but now are as follows:

System A (Common Carrier – non Telco)

Base Control	879.390 - 879.990
Base Voice 1	*869.040 - 879.990*
Base Voice 2	*890.010 - 891.480*

System B (Wireline – Telco)

Base Control	880.020 - 880.620
Base Voice 1	*880.020 - 889.980*
Base Voice 2	*891.510 - 893.970*

Note: Cellular mobiles are exactly 45MHz below the base frequencies.

Coming up in *Figure 7-2* are the new cell site frequency plans for your reference (and use, if current anti-monitoring laws are ever repealed). Thanks to Bob Gehri of the *US Scanner News* for sharing this new plan with all of us. Those who are computer spreadsheet aficionados can easily create your own reference document.

Otherwise, I have no objections if you want to copy those two pages by whatever means, and paste up the bottom charts alongside the top ones, to make one reference sheet for each cellular service provider.

While you're at it, you may as well make up some blank sheets for notes to authenticate the charts I'm giving you.

ANALOG VS. DIGITAL

Let me make it clear that we're talking about analog (FM) cellular. Experts agree that digital (CDMA and TDMA) will be of use only in those markets where congestion is a problem, because those technologies increase efficiency of the band, permitting more users perMHz than analog FM.

And even where it's tough to get a channel (New York City, Chicago, Los Angeles, etc.), there must be analog cellular as well. What use is a phone that works ONLY within a few miles of a downtown office area? That's why GE, Nokia, etc. call their newest products "dual-mode."

Technically, CDMA (Qualcomm) and TDMA (almost everyone else) are "encrypted." Current legislation makes it illegal to crack such signals, so if you were to intercept a digital cellular call, and decode it, you'd get two demerits instead of one.

CHANNEL ALLOCATIONS

It now appears that 20 or 21 frequencies are assigned to each of 21 cell sites. They're really circular (with overlap), but it helps to understand if you consider each cell a hexagon *(Figure 7-1)*.

This creates a scheme with a minimum of two cell radii between any two cells share a frequency.

Figure 7-1: Cell configuration

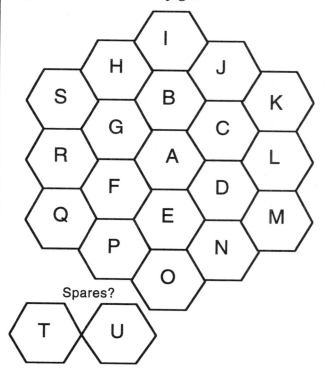

Spares?

Call it two buffer zones, if you like. In my first book, I suggested a seven-cell arrangement, like A-G, which offered a 1-cell buffer between any two identical cells. In retrospect, a 1-cell buffer is probably not enough under many conditions where radio signals are free to travel without hitting obstacles.

Thus, a 2-cell buffer is more logical and practical. If this is the case, then 19 equally arranged cells can be laid out to assure the minimum 2-cell buffering. This leaves what I would call two "spare" cells that can be brought into play for emergencies or for difficult situations where 2-cell buffers are not quite good enough.

Now please understand that for two reasons this is conjecture on my part: one, cellular companies do not casually release this kind of information, and two, I don't listen to cellular. As a radio engineer, I can suggest this is pretty close to the money, but that each metro region will surely have a different cellular implementation.

Also bear in mind that cells can be reduced in physical size when transmitter power is reduced. Cell sites can control transmit (Tx) power from the mobiles, so just about any concept is possible, and I'm sure there are hundreds of different implementations in use around the world. The plan shown here is so flexible that it can serve highly congested metropolitan regions as well as remote rural areas. If you are interested in mapping the cellular implementation for your region, then this information may help get you off on the right foot.

There are several books on the subject, if it fascinates you.

MAPPING YOUR AREA

If you are interested in this sort of activity, then you'll need a good S-meter with which to measure and assess relative signal strengths. You'll not be able to tell one cell site from another without one. Even with an S-meter, your work is cut out for you. There will be boatloads of data to gather, organize and process. It can be fun, though. Just remember that intercepting cellular signals is probably against the law, so proceed only at your own risk. I cannot accept responsibility for your choices.

Next comes the charts for typical cellular implementations, as *Figures 7-2* and *7-3*. Remember, by law, each community is served by two cellular providers, one definitely NOT a telephone company. After the charts, we get into the hard core of hacking those scanners to liberate the deliberately blocked cellular coverage.

Figure 7-2: Typical frequency plan for cell sites – Systems "A" and "B"

NON-WIRELINE COMPANY CELLULAR BASE BAND PLAN (Shaded line indicates control frequencies)

(Mobiles are exactly 45.0 MHz Lower)

#	A	B	C	D	E	F	G	H	I	J	K	L	M	N	O	P	Q	R	S	T	U
1	869.400	869.430	869.460	869.490	869.520	869.550	869.580	869.610	869.640	869.670	869.700	869.730	869.760	869.790	869.820	869.850	869.880	869.910	869.940	869.970	870.000
2	870.030	870.060	870.090	870.120	870.150	870.180	870.210	870.240	870.270	870.300	870.330	870.360	870.390	870.420	870.450	870.480	870.510	870.540	870.570	870.600	870.630
3	870.660	870.690	870.720	870.750	870.780	870.810	870.840	870.870	870.900	870.930	870.960	870.990	871.020	871.050	871.080	871.110	871.140	871.170	871.200	871.230	871.260
4	871.290	871.320	871.350	871.380	871.410	871.440	871.470	871.500	871.530	871.560	871.590	871.620	871.650	871.680	871.710	871.740	871.770	871.800	871.830	871.860	871.890
5	871.920	871.950	871.980	872.010	872.040	872.070	872.100	872.130	872.160	872.190	872.220	872.250	872.280	872.310	872.340	872.370	872.400	872.430	872.460	872.490	872.520
6	872.550	872.580	872.610	872.640	872.670	872.700	872.730	872.760	872.790	872.820	872.850	872.880	872.910	872.940	872.970	873.000	873.030	873.060	873.090	873.120	873.150
7	873.180	873.210	873.240	873.270	873.300	873.330	873.360	873.390	873.420	873.450	873.480	873.510	873.540	873.570	873.600	873.630	873.660	873.690	873.720	873.750	873.780
8	873.810	873.840	873.870	873.900	873.930	873.960	873.990	874.020	874.050	874.080	874.110	874.140	874.170	874.200	874.230	874.260	874.290	874.320	874.350	874.380	874.410
9	874.440	874.470	874.500	874.530	874.560	874.590	874.620	874.650	874.680	874.710	874.740	874.770	874.800	874.830	874.860	874.890	874.920	874.950	874.980	875.010	875.040
10	875.070	875.100	875.130	875.160	875.190	875.220	875.250	875.280	875.310	875.340	875.370	875.400	875.430	875.460	875.490	875.520	875.550	875.580	875.610	875.640	875.670
11	875.700	875.730	875.760	875.790	875.820	875.850	875.880	875.910	875.940	875.970	876.000	876.030	876.060	876.090	876.120	876.150	876.180	876.210	876.240	876.270	876.300
12	876.330	876.360	876.390	876.420	876.450	876.480	876.510	876.540	876.570	876.600	876.630	876.660	876.690	876.720	876.750	876.780	876.810	876.840	876.870	876.900	876.930
13	876.960	876.990	877.020	877.050	877.080	877.110	877.140	877.170	877.200	877.230	877.260	877.290	877.320	877.350	877.380	877.410	877.440	877.470	877.500	877.530	877.560
14	877.590	877.620	877.650	877.680	877.710	877.740	877.770	877.800	877.830	877.860	877.890	877.920	877.950	877.980	878.010	878.040	878.070	878.100	878.130	878.160	878.190
15	878.220	878.250	878.280	878.310	878.340	878.370	878.400	878.430	878.460	878.490	878.520	878.550	878.580	878.610	878.640	878.670	878.700	878.730	878.760	878.790	878.820
16	878.850	878.880	878.910	878.940	878.970	879.000	879.030	879.060	879.090	879.120	879.150	879.180	879.210	879.240	879.270	879.300	879.330	879.360			
17	879.390	879.420	879.450	879.480	879.510	879.540	879.570	879.600	879.630	879.660	879.690	879.720	879.750	879.780	879.810	879.840	879.870	879.900	879.930	879.960	879.990
19	890.610	890.640	890.670	890.700	890.730	890.760	890.790	890.820	890.850	890.880	890.910	890.940	890.970	891.000	891.030	891.060	891.090	891.120	891.150	891.180	891.210
20	891.240	891.270	891.300	891.330	891.360	891.390	891.420	891.450	891.480												

TELEPHONE COMPANY CELLULAR BASE BAND PLAN (Shaded line indicates control frequencies)

(Mobiles are exactly 45.0 MHz Lower)

#	A	B	C	D	E	F	G	H	I	J	K	L	M	N	O	P	Q	R	S	T	U
1	880.020	880.050	880.080	880.110	880.140	880.170	880.200	880.230	880.260	880.290	880.320	880.350	880.380	880.410	880.440	880.470	880.500	880.530	880.560	880.590	880.620
2	880.650	880.680	880.710	880.740	880.770	880.800	880.830	880.860	880.890	880.920	880.950	880.980	881.010	881.040	881.070	881.100	881.130	881.160	881.190	881.220	881.250
3	881.280	881.310	881.340	881.370	881.400	881.430	881.460	881.490	881.520	881.550	881.580	881.610	881.640	881.670	881.700	881.730	881.760	881.790	881.820	881.850	881.880
4	881.910	881.940	881.970	882.000	882.030	882.060	882.090	882.120	882.150	882.180	882.210	882.240	882.270	882.300	882.330	882.360	882.390	882.420	882.450	882.480	882.510
5	882.540	882.570	882.600	882.630	882.660	882.690	882.720	882.750	882.780	882.810	882.840	882.870	882.900	882.930	882.960	882.990	883.020	883.050	883.080	883.110	883.140
6	883.170	883.200	883.230	883.260	883.290	883.320	883.350	883.380	883.410	883.440	883.470	883.500	883.530	883.560	883.590	883.620	883.650	883.680	883.710	883.740	883.770
7	883.800	883.830	883.860	883.890	883.920	883.950	883.980	884.010	884.040	884.070	884.100	884.130	884.160	884.190	884.220	884.250	884.280	884.310	884.340	884.370	884.400
8	884.430	884.460	884.490	884.520	884.550	884.580	884.610	884.640	884.670	884.700	884.730	884.760	884.790	884.820	884.850	884.880	884.910	884.940	884.970	885.000	885.030
9	885.060	885.090	885.120	885.150	885.180	885.210	885.240	885.270	885.300	885.330	885.360	885.390	885.420	885.450	885.480	885.510	885.540	885.570	885.600	885.630	885.660
10	885.690	885.720	885.750	885.780	885.810	885.840	885.870	885.900	885.930	885.960	885.990	886.020	886.050	886.080	886.110	886.140	886.170	886.200	886.230	886.260	886.290
11	886.320	886.350	886.380	886.410	886.440	886.470	886.500	886.530	886.560	886.590	886.620	886.650	886.680	886.710	886.740	886.770	886.800	886.830	886.860	886.890	886.920
12	886.950	886.980	887.010	887.040	887.070	887.100	887.130	887.160	887.190	887.220	887.250	887.280	887.310	887.340	887.370	887.400	887.430	887.460	887.490	887.520	887.550
13	887.580	887.610	887.640	887.670	887.700	887.730	887.760	887.790	887.820	887.850	887.880	887.910	887.940	887.970	888.000	888.030	888.060	888.090	888.120	888.150	888.180
14	888.210	888.240	888.270	888.300	888.330	888.360	888.390	888.420	888.450	888.480	888.510	888.540	888.570	888.600	888.630	888.660	888.690	888.720	888.750	888.780	888.810
15	888.840	888.870	888.900	888.930	888.960	888.990	889.020	889.050	889.080	889.110	889.140	889.170	889.200	889.230	889.260	889.290	889.320	889.350	889.380	889.410	889.440
16	889.470	889.500	889.530	889.560	889.590	889.620	889.650	889.680	889.710	889.740	889.770	889.800	889.830	889.860	889.890	889.920	889.950	889.980			
17	891.990	892.020	892.050	892.080	892.110	892.140	892.170	892.200	892.230	892.260	892.290	892.320	892.350	892.380	892.410	892.440	892.470	892.500	892.530	892.560	892.590
18	892.620	892.650	892.680	892.710	892.740	892.770	892.800	892.830	892.860	892.890	892.920	892.950	892.980	893.010	893.040	893.070	893.100	893.130	893.160	893.190	893.220
19	893.250	893.280	893.310	893.340	893.370	893.400	893.430	893.460	893.490	893.520	893.550	893.580	893.610	893.640	893.670	893.700	893.730	893.760	893.790	893.820	893.850
20	893.880	893.910	893.940	893.970																	

Tutorial photographs...

1. Mis-hack. Note the damage to the pins and traces.

> **Don't make work for yourself** *(or for me!):* **be careful, take your time, use the right soldering iron, and remember how fragile some of these parts and boards can be.**

2. Re-hack. Note the repaired pins and traces. **Now it's a 25,600 channel memory block that works!**

ENHANCING FUNCTIONALITY...

Well, here we go.

I'm about to show you the tools and give you the know-how to stretch the capability of your scanner. If it's a candidate for The Ultimate Scanner, and you've already done the previous enhancements, this chapter will help you get lots closer to that goal, though your result will probably smell better than mine.

We're now moving into the trunked and cellular regions of the spectrum. PLEASE do not use your scanner for illegal purposes. For instance, DO NOT use it for cellular monitoring in the United States. On the other hand, owning a scanner with blocked cellular is like driving a Corvette with a 55 MPH governor.

Remember my warnings? Be patient. Get the service manual. Read the instructions. Read them again. Have a plan, so you don't add hardware in a space you'll need for something else. Double-check your work. Check it one more time.

PRO-2004 — Possibly the best scanner of all time (1986-1989)

Cellular: Clip or remove D-513. It's usually located on the top of the Logic/CPU board in the metal compartment, but early units have D-513 all by itself on the bottom (solder-side) of the board.

Note: The following add-a-diode modifications will require you to be a little intuitive with respect to where the new diodes are to be installed. The empty spots are not marked, but you can easily figure them out by first identifying those spots that *are* marked.

It's as simple as a 2nd grade number puzzle:

__ __ 3 4 __ 6 7

Question: what numbers go in the blank spots?

Easy Speedup: Add a 1N4148 diode to the empty spots for D-514. Gives a no-compromise 25% speedup of the SCAN mode. Polarity complies with that of other diodes in this row.

Extra 100 Channels: The PRO-2004 came with 300 channels, and another 100 are free for the taking by adding a 1N4148 diode to the empty spot for D-510. The result is 10 Scan Banks with 40 channels per bank, just like the PRO-2005/6. There are no side-effects to this mod.

CPU Upgrade: Not easy, but "do-able." Early production runs of the PRO-2004 came with a CPU with a part number of GRE-0327. Later production runs use a GRE-0327A. The only difference between them is the default cellular search increment of 30kHz (later).

In early units, the 30kHz step covers the old cellular allocation, 870-890MHz and 825-845MHz, outside of which the default step is 12.5kHz! Later units step at 30kHz over 868.970-894.000MHz and 823.970-849.000MHz, the new cellular allocations that were implemented in the middle of the 2004's production run. If you have an older 2004, you can remove the GRE-0327 CPU and replace it with a new GRE-0327A.

The chip is the large 64-pin DIP style and can be removed fairly easily. Before installing the new one, I suggest installing either a 64-pin DIP socket or two 32-pin strips of pin-line sockets.

Warning: Clipping D-511 or adding something anywhere else will either accomplish nothing at all, or will degrade the performance of your scanner. Don't believe everything you hear...

PRO-2005 — Good candidate for the Ultimate Scanner (1990)

A marginally-evolved PRO-2004 with an inferior case and keyboard, but easily modified:

Cellular: Remove top cover. Immediately behind the #3 key on the keyboard are two diodes standing on end. Clip the exposed leg of D-502 and spread the cut ends slightly. Do NOT clip D-503!

Easy Speedup: Add a 1N4148 diode to the empty spots for D-501. Gives a no-compromise 25% speedup of the SCAN mode. Comply with polarity of other diodes in this row.

CPU Upgrade? You *can* replace the existing CPU and clock resonator, CX-501, with PRO-2006 parts, and clip BOTH diodes behind the #3 key. Be forewarned, however, this is one "hairy" job and not for the inexperienced or the faint-of-heart. I have done it several times, but won't do it again for either love or money.

This, and a couple of other changes can turn a PRO-2005 into a PRO-2006, though. Study the schematics of both service manuals if you're interested in tackling the job.

PRO-2006 — Outstanding starting point for the Ultimate Scanner (1991-1994)

A substantially evolved PRO-2004 with an inferior case and keyboard, but easily modified. For years, this was the most popular and most hacked high-performance scanner in the hobby.

The PRO-2006 does have some electronic advantages over the PRO-2004 and PRO-2005, but the designs remain functionally the same.

Cellular: Remove the top cover. Immediately behind the #3 key on the keyboard are two diodes standing on end. Clip the exposed leg of D-502 and spread the cut ends slightly.

Easy speedup: Clip the exposed leg of the remaining diode, D-503, and spread the cut ends slightly. Gives a no-compromise 25% speedup of the SCAN mode.

Warning: Adding D-501 or D-504 diodes will either accomplish nothing at all, or will degrade the performance of the scanner. Don't believe everything you hear...

PRO-34 — An old workhorse handheld scanner, antiquated now, but still useful

Cellular: Spot welds, as cautioned in my last book, are really not a problem. All circuit boards and subassemblies are held in place by screws. Work your way to the bottom layer (Logic/CPU board) and clip an exposed lead of D-11.

Speedup: Not "easy" but this is the time to do it, if you must. Replace CX-1 with a 3.57MHz TV Colorburst quartz crystal. The case of the crystal should be wired to the middle hole of CX-1 (ground).

Warning: Clipping or adding any other diodes will accomplish either nothing at all, or will degrade the performance of your scanner. Don't believe everything you hear...

PRO-37— An evolved PRO-34, quickly replaced by the PRO-43

It's much the same design as the PRO-34; with some improvements and circuit symbol changes.

Cellular: Same instructions as for the PRO-34 above, except clip an exposed leg of D-13.

PRO-39 — A scaled down PRO-43 (Yawn.....)

Cellular: Once you get down to the Logic/CPU board, desolder the four legs of the rectangular metal shield on the Logic/CPU board to access the cellular diode.

Desolder and remove diode D-6.

PRO-43 — Best handheld scanner for the money (and that might be three too many words)

The cellular and 54-88MHz procedures work only with Date Codes of 2A4, 1A4, xA3, and xA2. It probably will not work with 3A4 and definitely not with 4A4 and up, nor if there is an "A" in the serial number.

Cellular: Once you get down to the Logic/CPU board, desolder the four legs of the rectangular metal shield on the Logic/CPU board to access the cellular diode. Carefully desolder diode D-4 and lay it aside for the next step.

54-88MHz Restoration: The original D-4 diode (you removed to liberate cellular) is soldered into the empty spots for D-3, retaining the same polarity orientation. This restores 54-88 Hz which ordinarily would not be worthwhile, except for the interesting Utility Band at 72-76MHz.

The rest of this spectrum is for VHF-Lo TV channels 2-6 and generally worthless. That Ute band can be hotter than a $2 pistol at times, though. A worthwhile mod, no side effects, when you're doing the cellular anyway.

Audio Improvement: The standard speaker of the PRO-43 produces terrible audio. It can be improved.

First, you can replace the speaker with a better one from Tandy National Parts (800) 442-2425. Ask for the *new* 500 mW replacement speaker. They probably won't have the old one, but make sure.

Next, there is another reasonable approach to improved audio in the PRO-43, considering the mushy sounds that come out of the stock unit. First, understand that power in the audio spectrum is largely contained in the bass end of the band while intelligibility is contained in the treble end.

More treble means less power required to convey understandable audio. With this in mind, remove C341, a tiny 0.015µF surface mount capacitor located on the bottom (solder side) of the AF (middle) board – See *Figure 7-4*. Flip the AF board so that you view it with the controls pointed up. Examine the PCB below the BNC connector: find a white, 2-pin female connector, CN-303.

To the right of CN-303 are six tiny components, three left to right and below them, three, top to bottom. The first two components of this top-to-bottom row are brown, unmarked chip capacitors while the third component is a black chip resistor marked "333". The middle component, the one just above the "333" resistor is C-341.

Figure 7-4: Audio modification – PRO-43

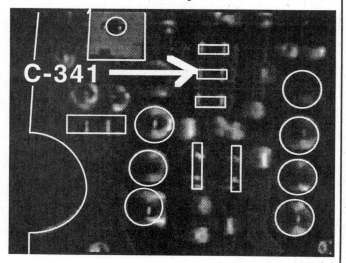

Make sure you've got it identified: C-341 is exactly 10 mm to the right of the left edge of the AF board, and exactly 13 mm down from the top edge of the AF board. Another positive proof is that C-341 is positioned directly between pins 4 and 5 of the LM-386N-1 chip which can be seen from the top side of the board. C-341 is slightly above a straight line drawn between pins 4 and 5 of the LM-386 while the "333" resistor is further below that line and closer to being between pins 3 and 6 of the LM-386.

Now you've got it! Use solder wick to absorb the solder from each end of C-341 and then pop it off by heating one end while exerting a mild pressure against C-341 with the tip of a tiny screwdriver.

S-Meter: Here's an easy S-meter for the PRO-43! The right circuit doesn't exist in most scanners to support an effective S-meter; but the PRO-43 has it – but there's also a lack of "real estate."

That's also okay: we can work around it!

The key S-meter point in the circuit is the cathode of D-302 located on the bottom (solder side) of the AF board (middle board). D-302 is a tiny gray chip diode located near the forward, outboard corner of T-302. D-302's cathode connects to one lug of T-302, and that's the spot you need to find.

Figure 7-5 will guide you.

Figure 7-5: Audio improvement and S-meter wiring – PRO-43

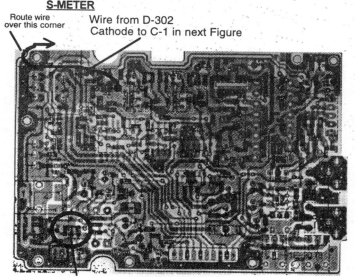

Solder hookup wire to the cathode of D-302 and route it to the topside of the AF board to feed the S-meter circuit in *Figure 7-6*. This wire ought not to be more than a couple of inches.

Route it forward and around the notch in the nearest corner of the circuit board next to the Volume Control, so that the wire protrudes into the "more spacious" component side of the board. Connect this wire to a lead of C-1, a 0.01μF ceramic disk capacitor. Solder the anode of D-1 to

a handy nearby ground (*I selected pin 7 of IC-302 for my ground*). Solder the free lead of C-1 to the cathode of our D-1.

Solder the anode of our D-2 to the junction of our C-1 and D-1. Finally, solder our R-1 and C-2 between the cathode of our D-2 and ground as shown.

Connect a wire to the junction of our D-2, R1, and C-2 for output to an S-meter of your choice.

Figure 7-6: S-meter circuit

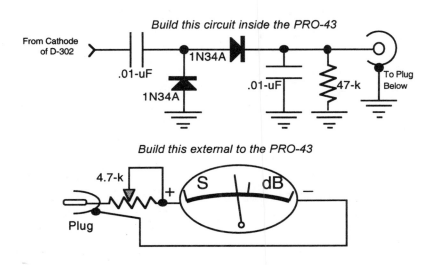

There won't be nearly enough room to actually install an S-Meter inside the PRO-43, so this wire and a ground wire must somehow exit the scanner to connect to an external meter. Exactly how you do that I will leave up to you, but I installed a miniature 3/32" phone jack in the right side of the metal frame wall just above and between IC-301 and D-301.

I used a precision scale to mark off precise points of location so that a 5/16" hole neatly drilled through the right side of the rear plastic case matches perfectly over the 3/32" phone jack. A standard 3/32" phone plug inserts into this jack for quick and easy connection of an external S-Meter.

LED S-METER

You can also build the 10-segment LED S-Meter as shown in Vol-2. After your chosen S-Meter is connected and halfway working, operate the PRO-43 near a known strong transmitter, perhaps a ham transmitter, a police cruiser, your favorite security guard's handheld, or right next to a cordless telephone, or anything else known to transmit a strong signal.

Tune the scanner to that frequency, and adjust the 4.7k trim pot so the meter reads exactly full scale. Other signals will read proportionally lower to yield "relative signal strength" measurements!

PRO-23, 46, and 51 — Not exciting, but not turnips, either!

These scanners cannot be hardware modified to receive cellular signals, but there is a keyboard programming technique that will permit such reception in a round-about way.

This technique works ONLY on those scanners sold before April of 1994, because Radio Shack got onto the workaround like flies on cow-pies and re-engineered the units to make any cellular reception impossible. Credit to Brian Peterson, Covina, CA, and *Monitoring Times* for the substance of this information.

1. With the radio turned off, press and hold the 2, 9, and LOCKOUT keys; turn the radio on and release the keys.

Russian Roulette: This may "toast" your stored frequencies. If your luck is bad, you'll have to reprogram them later.

2. Step to channel 23 on the PRO-51 or channel 15 on the PRO-23 to display 888.960MHz, a factory test frequency.

3. Press either the UP or DOWN search arrow to scan the cellular band in proper 30kHz steps. You can temporarily store up to ten active cellular frequencies by pressing MONITOR.

Permanently store these frequencies for scanning and searching:

1. STEP to the desired MONITOR channel and press PROGRAM, followed by the desired memory channel number (including those with factory-preprogrammed test frequencies).

2. Press in sequence PROGRAM, MONITOR, ENTER. Repeat steps 1 and 2 for each channel to go into memory.

There are limitations. If you are doing an Up/Down scan, and the scanning process takes you outside of the locked-out 800MHz frequency range, you can NOT get back into it by reversing the scan direction.

In other words, if you are scanning down and go past 869MHz, pressing UP (to reverse the scan) will simply cause the scanner to jump from 869MHz to 896MHz. All that you have to do in order to get back into the locked out range, is go back to the manual mode, select channel 23, and

start your Up/Down scan again from there. This is the biggest frustration in the trick.

However, let's say that you don't want that 888.9600 frequency on channel 23, and instead you want it at channel 100. Easy ...

1. Press MANUAL, 23, MANUAL.

2. Turn squelch ALL the way off, so you hear white noise.

3. Press either UP or DOWN search key (doesn't matter).

4. Press MONITOR, then MANUAL.

5. Press MANUAL, <ch#>, MANUAL.

In this case, <ch#> is the channel number on which you want to store the 888.9600 frequency. For example, if you wanted to store it on channel 100, you'd press MAN, 100, MAN.

6. Press PROGRAM, <mon>, ENTER.

Where you see <mon>, you should at this point press the MONITOR key as many times as it takes to find the monitor entry to where the 888.9600 frequency was transferred (1-10).

So if the frequency was transferred to monitor channel #3, you'd keep pressing monitor until you got TO mon-channel #3 and THEN you'd press ENTER.

The 888.9600 frequency has now been copied to the new channel that you selected. All of this rigamarole is needed since obviously, without the hardware mod you can't manually program cell frequencies.

These instructions works just fine for getting access to the 66-88MHz range too! After pressing 2, 9, LockOut, and turning your scanner on, channels 14, 15, and 16 will have frequencies stored in them that are between 66-88MHz range. These can be manipulated in the same manner as the 800MHz frequencies.

PRO-2032 — A passable unit: no turnip, but no cigar!

Cellular Restoration: Turn the PRO-2032 upside down and face its rear. Desolder and remove the microprocessor shield at the upper left, close to the volume and squelch controls.

Figure 7-7: PRO-2032 cellular restoration

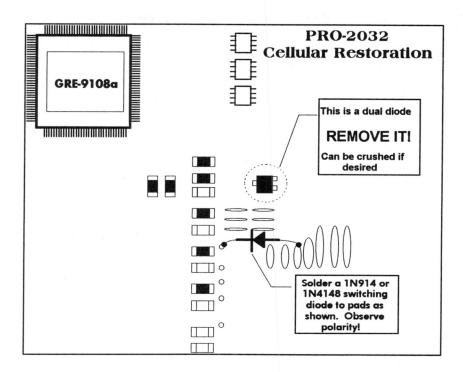

Refer to *Figure 7-7* and locate the dual, 3-pin diode near the lower right of the microprocessor chip. Desolder and remove this diode. Solder a 1N914 or 1N4148 switching diode across the solder pads as shown. Think ahead, and make sure the microprocessor shield won't short against the diode when it is replaced.

Insulate the diode if you like. Power up and enter 870.000MHz into a channel. If that frequency is accepted by the CPU, then disconnect power, and resolder the shield. Search will be in the proper 30kHz steps.

Increased Scan/Search speed: Replace the blue 8MHz ceramic resonator near pins 3-4-5 on the solder side of the microprocessor chip with a quartz microprocessor crystal of about 10MHz to 12MHz. Don't go any higher than 12MHz to minimize the risk of blowing the CPU. It might be a good idea to solder a wire to the metal case of the crystal and the other end to ground.

Squelch improvement: Replace the Squelch Hysteresis Resistor (surface mount chip resistor) between pins 12 and 14 of the MC-3361 NFM Discriminator chip with a 200k trimmer pot.

Adjust the pot to suit your taste for a tighter squelch. The trim pot will afford you a range of

adjustment to suit your preference. Too tight of a squelch is terrible when weak signals are being detected....sounds like a machine gun as the squelch kicks in and out.

See the *World Scanner Report*, V1N4 and V1N9, for helpful info and specs on various NFM Discriminator chips.

Also see V1N2, V1N4, and V4N3 for an even better Squelch mod for the PRO-2032 and most other rigs. This one will get you by, though, if you don't have any higher ambitions. ☺

BC-890XLT – Not a great scanner, but it works. (New models are not modifiable)

Access: Remove the 10 cabinet screws. Separate the halves. Unplug the speaker.

Remove 4 front panel screws and the bracket screw near the center of the main PCB to loosen the front panel. Squeeze the outside edges of the metal faceplate shield. Swing the front panel down toward you, to expose the Logic/CPU PCB.

Disconnect J4 and J5 (white and blue wires), and ribbon connectors J501, J502, and J503 – work them apart from a point close to the sockets. Remove the front panel and logic board.

Cellular: Position the PCB as shown in *Figure 7-8*. Locate the CPU (UC-1514), and three chip resistors near the CPU's lower right corner. Desolder the indicated resistor marked "104"

(100kΩ) and resolder it to the two empty pads nearest the memory retention battery, as shown in the drawing.

Reverse assemble the front panel and connectors. Test the radio by entering 880.980MHz. Cellular is now restored, with the desired 30kHz tuning steps.

Figure 7-8: BC-890 cellular modification

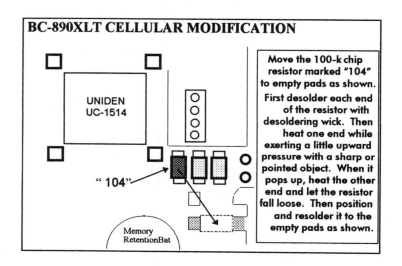

BC-2500XLT — A highly-touted scanner for no defensible reason. (New models are not cellular-modifiable)

Access: Remove the antenna and battery pack from the BC-2500XLT. Position it face down with the bottom facing you.

Remove the two black upper and two lower silver screws from the rear.

Remove the rear case. Lift the now-accessible circuit board away from the frame just enough to detach it from the white (11 pin) connector.

Don't strain the ribbon connector between the two.

Carefully, lay the PC board next to the main scanner body.

Locate the CPU chip, IC-301, "UNIDEN UC-1513A," and the group of five 100kΩ chip resistors marked "104" below it.

Desolder chip resistor R-317 (see *Figure 7-9*) with desoldering wick.

Heat one end while exerting a gentle upward pressure with a sharp or pointed object until it pops free.

Heat the other end until the resistor falls free. Position it on the empty solder pads one place to the left, and resolder it in place. *(In effect, this moves one end of R-317 from ground to +5V.)* One end of R-341 always goes to pin 33 of the CPU chip.

Reassemble by reversing steps 1 and 2.

Test by entering 880.980MHz. Cellular Search steps will be the proper 30kHz!

Figure 7-9: BC-1500 cellular restoration

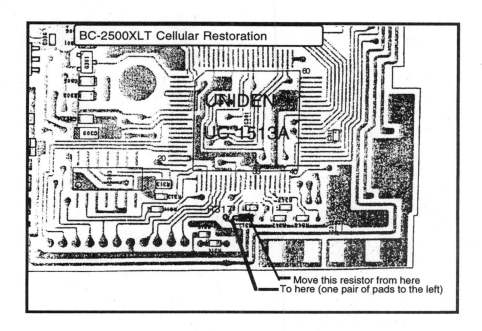

BC-200XLT, BC-205XLT, Regency 4030 — Decent handhelds, and the same radio!

This product, in its several guises, is everywhere. It's offered on television shopping channels, buried in general-merchandise catalogs, in swap meets, and nearly anywhere that electronics are sold.

It is definitely among the most successful of Uniden's products, if you judge by $ALES the way they do. It's been around so long, and wearing so many labels, that there's confusion resulting from production changes. I'll try to help

Cellular: The mechanics and specifics of this mod were published in Vols 1 & 2, and they differ somewhat due to at least one production change between books. Depending on the age of your unit, you may need one, the other, or THIS one that follows. Yep, Uniden made more subtle changes, enough to confuse many who followed the instructions in Vol-2.

Here's the hack you need to restore cellular in these radios built after my Vol-2.

Locate the 10k resistor, R-215, that goes from the CPU, pin 41, to ground. It may be a black chip

resistor, marked "103", or it could be color coded, brown-black-orange. Doesn't matter.

It's the resistor just above the "**den**" portion of the "Uni**den**" logo on the UC-1147 CPU chip.

Remove R-215 safely, if you can; otherwise crush it and then unsolder it. Clean up the pads.

Solder a small 10k resistor from the non-grounded pad of R-215 (CPU-pin 41) to IC-206, pin 8, which happens to be a handy source of +5V.

That's it, wrap it up. In effect, this mod removes a ground (low) via R-215 to CPU pin-41 and applies a high (+5V) via a new 10k resistor to pin 41.

In reality, it's just a logic change.

Speedup: These radios can be modestly sped up by removing a two-leaded black object called Y-201 in the left center of the board. It may be marked "400K".

Y-201 is a 400kHz ceramic resonator that connects to the CPU, pins 45 and 46. Replace it with an 800kHz ceramic resonator for a X2 speedup, if you don't mind a halved delay time.

Get DigiKey part no: P9947-ND, or I can supply in limited quantities.

BC-700XLTA — Let's help each other on this mystery!

Sorry, I have little information on this allegedly cellular restorable scanner.

If you know of anything or can cite a reference, please let me know. As always, such information will find itself onto the BBS and be available to everyone.

PRO-2022 — A PRO-34 clone, nice in its time, but now?

Comments: The PRO-2022 is a carbon copy of the PRO-34's design! I know, the 34 is a handheld and this one is a base and they do not look alike. Compare the schematics, though.

They're twins! Circuit symbols will differ widely, of course. Otherwise, what can be done to one can be done to the other.

Cellular: Clip or remove diode D-44.

Speedup: Replace CX-1 with a 3.57MHz TV Colorburst crystal for a modest speedup. If that's not handy, pick anything close in frequency.

PRO-2026 — A pseudo-clone of the BC-760XLT (new models are not modifiable)

Radio Shack isn't particular about who makes their scanners anymore. I guess the marketers decide that we want a certain performance at a certain price, and then they get bids from the manufacturers and take the low one.

Uniden makes this one, a semi-clone of the long-lived Uniden BC-760XLT, except that it's more hollow inside than its near-twin brother.

CTCSS is not feasible. It's easier to hack for cellular, though.

Cellular: Remove the four side screws from the bottom cover. Pull the cover loose and set it aside.

Facing the front of the 2026 and with the bottom side exposed, locate the small circuit board in the lower right-hand corner and find jumper L201.

Cut L201. If you're compulsively neat, desolder and remove the wire.

Reassemble the radio and find continuous 806-956MHz coverage and 30kHz search increments in the cellular band.

It's odd, but its near-twin BC-760XLT steps only in 12.5kHz increments!

BC-760XLT, BC-950XLT, Regency R-1600 — All the same radio, and new models are not modifiable

Cellular: Older units use a Motorola antenna connector while newer units have a BNC connector.

The procedure for older units is in Vol-1 of my *Scanner Modification Handbook,* and later units are covered in Vol-2. If either method fails, then the next mod should work for the last models just prior to those made after March, 1994:

All work is done on the solder side of the board.

For reference, locate a 24-pin surface mount chip, IC-13, a Sanyo LC3517BM-15, on the solder side of the board. Position the radio so the "Sanyo" logo on this chip is upside down. The work will then be done to the right and slightly above this Sanyo chip along the row of pins 1-32 of the CPU chip.

Incidentally, this Sanyo chip is the 2k x 8 SRAM that figures into the Extended Memory mods that your scanner deserves.

1. Completely isolate pin 26 of the CPU chip, IC-14, a UC-1246.

This involves a trace cut on each side of pin 26 to totally isolate it from everything.

Note: IC-14 is the large 64-pin chip found on the component side of the board, but we'll be working on its pins from the backside of the board. Identify pins 1-32 before you begin.

2. Make three jumpers as follows:

One jumper between pins 19 and 20 of the CPU chip.

A second jumper between newly isolated pin 26 and pin 27 of the CPU chip.

A third jumper between the two pins on the same side of Q-5, just above pin 27 of the CPU.

3. Finally, remove R-13, a 4.7k chip resistor, marked "472" that goes to pin 20 of the CPU.

Run a short connector wire from the jumpered pins 19 and 20 (above) to a nearby circuit board ground spot.

That's it – you're finished!

BC-855XLT — Not a great scanner, but some people say it works...

Access: Disconnect the power cord and with the bottom edge of the scanner facing you, turn it over on a soft surface to avoid scratching.

Remove the five Phillips-head cabinet screws and carefully separate the cabinet.

Grasp the speaker plug (not the wires), and carefully pull the plug from its socket.

Lay the two cabinet halves side-by-side.

Cellular: Find the fifth jumper in a row at the top of the right-hand circuit board.

Cut JV-209 at its midpoint and curl the cut ends apart so they can not touch anything, including each other.

Solder one end of a 10k resistor to the cathode of diode D201.

Solder the other end of this resistor to the cut end of JV-209 that's closest to the center area of the board; do not use excessive heat.

Check the jumper beneath the board; if it came loose, resolder, and hold it in place as the solder cools.

Plug in the A/C power cord; turn the scanner ON and press MANUAL : 880. : ENTER in that order. If 880.000 appears in the Display, the effort was a success; otherwise ERROR will be displayed as usual.

Don't panic when you hear nothing – you just checked the logic, not the audio. The speaker is disconnected. Snip off and remove excess wire from the resistor leads, plug in the speaker connector, and reassemble.

How it works: In the simplest analysis, a ground is connected to the CPU (IC-201 pin 10) via jumper JV-209, which places a 0V (low) at pin 10 to block the cellular coverage.

You've clipped JV-209 to remove that ground. You then applied +5V (high) to pin 10 via that 10k isolation resistor to program the CPU to cover the cellular bands. The cathode of D-201 was just a handy source of +5V.

Simple, huh?

Memory Upgrade: Examination of the schematic diagram suggests that 50 channels in the BC-855XLT may have been deliberately blocked.

A pinout of the CPU shows a 100 channel memory if pin 9 is raised from ground to +5V.

Referring to the above cellular restoration procedure, find the jumper wire immediately to the LEFT of JV-209, the one that was clipped. This will be JV-208 which also must be clipped.

Solder one end of a 10k resistor to the cathode of diode D201.

Solder the other end of this resistor to the cut end of JV-208 that's closest to the center area of the board; do not use excessive heat.

Test the scanner for memory channels 51-100. Some reports have it that the unit will be locked up when first turned on after the memory mod.

If so, disconnect the unit from all power for a short time to leak away internal power, and try again. No harm will come from this procedure, and if it fails, you can always remove the resistor and resolder the clipped jumper, JV-208.

Please tell me (and everyone else on the BBS) about your results.

PRO-2030 — A second generation PRO-2026

Credit: *Courtesy of (and thanks to) Neil Filby, WA6HDO, Chula Vista, CA.*

The cellular restoration for the PRO-2030 is essentially the same as for the PRO-2026, except that the location of the jumper differs slightly.

Access: Remove power cable, and flip the unit upside down.

Remove five (5) recessed screws from bottom panel. Carefully remove bottom panel. With display panel facing you, examine the portion of the printed circuit board that's attached to the display module.

Look for something similar to an RF coil, about 2" in from the front and 2" in from the right side.

Cellular: Cut the jumper marked L201.

Reinstall the bottom cover and reconnect power.

The scanner is now ready for use. Cellular frequencies are fully restored, and with the desired 30kHz spacing between channels.

What a coincidence!

PRO-46 — (Groan)

The Manual: Don't search for great secrets in this Uniden-built scanner, folks. But it will go cellular if you have the patience to dig in and sweat it out a little.

You really need the service manual for this unit, so get it as a reference, follow these instructions and *Figure 7-10* very carefully, or forget cellular capability.

Access: Disconnect the antenna and remove the battery pack. Extract the four screws from the rear case.

Push up from the bottom of the case so that it swings up and can be removed.

Examine the now visible main circuit board, and carefully pry it up from the area of the mating plug in the lower right corner so that it separates from the board beneath it.

Desolder the fragile copper shield from the logic board; remove it and lay it aside. *Be careful: this shield is easily damaged!*

Figure 7-10: Key sites on the PRO-46

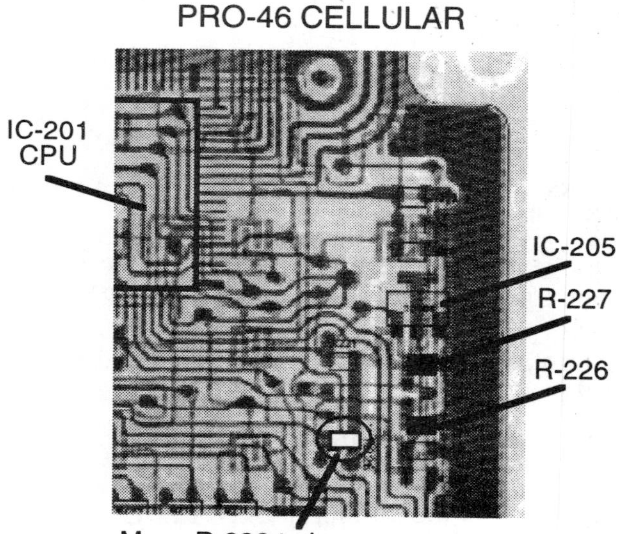

PRO-46 CELLULAR

IC-201 CPU

IC-205

R-227

R-226

Move R-226 to here

Cellular: Hold the unit so the speaker is down, and look along the right edge of the logic board.

Locate IC-205, a 3-pin device about a third of the way down from the top.

Now look below IC-205 for the first two chip resistors (actually chip jumpers) marked R-227 and R-226 on the PCB.

These two components will have a "0" imprinted on them. Carefully remove them both.

Now look about .5" to the left of where R-227 was removed to find R-221.

The right end of R-221 connects to a short PC strip that runs up and down about .5". To the left of that PC strip are two empty jumper pads.

Solder one of the removed R-227 or R-226 to the upper of the two pads and to the PC strip to which the right side of R-221 is soldered.

Reassemble the unit in reverse order of Steps 1-4 above.

PRO-2027— (Moan)

Cellular: Remove bottom panel (4 screws).

Locate diode D35 located behind the <Enter> key. This is a surface-mount component that resembles a tiny black rectangle.

Desolder and remove D35.

This is done by gently prying up the component with a pin or tweezers while touching one leg with a soldering iron. Don't apply much heat for very long at one time.

Wrap it up; party's over. Operate normally.

LAST WORDS!

1. Be careful and patient.

2. Keep the manual in front of you.

3. Don't illegally listen to cellular – it's boring, anyway (or so I'm told). I helped you put fuel injection on your hot rod, but that doesn't mean you have to speed, right?

4. REPORT BACK! Get on the BBS and share your experience with me and everyone else trying to optimize their scanners. The best way for you to learn about a new hack is to support an environment where everyone shares information.

COMPUTER INTERFACES

If it's an Ultimate Scanner, it's wired to a computer...

NO LONGER A LUXURY

It's as obvious as tomato juice on a white shag carpet that scanners with lots of channels *need* automated computer programming. The Cosmic Light will inspire you the first time you punch in 400 channels only to discover an error on #47.

If you've done my 1,600 to 25,600 channel Extended Memory Mods, that Light will sear your retinas.

GENESIS OF COMPUTER INTERFACES

Would you believe that computer interfacing of a scanner is nothing new? Years ago, an ad in *Monitoring Times* offered plans for a Commodore 64/128/PRO-2004 interface.

I mentioned this to Lin Burke, a digital guru, who whipped up a functional interface for the Radio Shack Color Computer II. He went on to modify it and its associated BASIC program for my Apple IIe of the time. Then came a design by Miles Abernathy for the Macintosh computer. We converted that design and its BASIC control

program for my Apple IIe. They all programmed a scanner's memory by automated means.

Next came a commercial, universal interface kit from RW Systems, and an MS/DOS-specific interface package including software from Datametrics, Inc. The kit from RW Systems held a lot of promise because (1) it was universal for most computers and (2) computer-specific software was not required to run it. It needed only a serial communications port and a plain telecom program – and it worked. Unfortunately, RW Systems either didn't sell as many interfaces as they expected, or else they weren't patient enough to wait around for the idea to catch on. RW Systems went out of business (to the best of my knowledge), though their interface did a good job with a variety of computers and software.

EVOLUTION

The Datametrics Interface package is still available at this writing, probably because it comes complete, ready to install in any MS/DOS-based computer with 640k RAM and a parallel port. The

Datametrics interface works only in IBM/clones and is driven by proprietary software. The interface is easy to install and virtually foolproof in operation.

The RW Systems kit supports any of the PRO-2004/5/6 series, while Datametrics specifies theirs to be for the PRO-2006 only. After looking it over, I think it is a safe bet that it will work just fine in the PRO-2005. and can be easily adapted to the PRO-2004, but Datametrics actively supports only the PRO-2006.

Enter "Professor Peabody," occasional columnist for the monthly *World Scanner Report.* That fine fellow and his able assistant, "Sherman," concocted a do-it-yourself computer interface for the PRO-2004/5/6 and presented it in great detail in still-available back issues, V2N2-V2N6.

Professor Peabody's "FatMan" interface was distinguished by its ability to work from most any computer with unsophisticated software, and it controlled every function of the PRO-2004/5/6. People are still building the "FatMan" today.

Rather than take space to repeat it here, I refer interested builders to those issues of the *World Scanner Report* where the instructions reside in all their splendor and glory and where the ol' Professor still helps those who need tech support.

Shortly after the "FatMan" appeared, HB Technologies *(now defunct)* and COMMtronics Engineering *(alive and well)* introduced the potent and awesome HB-232 Scanner/Computer Interface.

COMMtronics Engineering further evolved the interface into the CE-232, which is presented in the pages ahead as a do-it-yourself, no charge, no royalty, honest-to-goodness, "gimme." The CE-232 project is offered as the center of your Ultimate Scanner, and you paid for the right to build it when you bought this book. But there are other options...

Most recently, Optoelectronics, Inc. introduced their OptoScan 456 Interface for the PRO-2005 and PRO-2006. Its basic principle is to replace the scanner's CPU in controlling the receiver's PLL circuits.

Installation is reported to be fairly easy, with not too many snags. The OptoScan 456 comes complete, albeit with a somewhat minimal software control package, which led to the emergence of third-party software products that are available to properly complete the project.

WHAT'S OUT THERE TODAY

For more information about commercially available interfaces, contact:

```
Datametrics, Inc.
2575 South Bayshore Drive, Suite 8A
Coconut Grove, FL 33133
    (no phone available at this time)

Optoelectronics, Inc.
5821 NE 14th Ave.
Fort Lauderdale, FL 33334
800-327-5912

COMMtronics Engineering
POB 262478
San Diego, CA 92196
BBS and FAX: 619-578-9247
    5:30pm-1:30pm Pacific Time, only
```

WHAT A PROPER INTERFACE DOES

Before you even think about buying an interface, or rolling your own, you should know more about scanner/computer interfaces in general.

Focus nowadays is correctly on a TWO-WAY interface, one that not only can program the scanner's memory banks and control the scanner remotely from the PC, but that can also acquire and pass data from the scanner to the computer for logging and processing of active frequencies, duration of transmissions, dates, times, and much more. This means data acquisition *and* control.

A well-designed two-way interface between scanner and computer can perform great deeds, and you don't even have to be there!

The most important function of an interface is probably to program memory banks, sparing us drudgery and opportunity for error.

An important secondary function is data logging and processing, which produces a database of your specific area of interest.

Half the fun of scanning is listening to what's going on; the other half is the accumulation of knowledge and understanding.

An interface that can pass data from the scanner to the computer for logging, processing, and storage produces a long-term benefit with long-term implications. In comparison, actual monitoring is relatively short-term fun.

Therefore, both sides of a scanner/computer interface are important and useful, but some interfaces go only one way. Be demanding!

CAPTURING SCANNER DATA

There are perhaps one or two ways to obtain data *from* the scanner. The CE-232 Interface introduced the only practical technique for the casual hacker: decoding the data that flows from the scanner's CPU to the Liquid Crystal Display (LCD).

That data stream contains most everything pertinent to scanning with the exception of time/date, and the computer can provide that. The system decodes data that flows from the scanner's CPU to the LCD, but some of that data is superfluous and has to be removed. The required data going to the LCD includes the following:

Frequency digits	Manual (On/Off)
Channel number	Search step (5, 12.5, 30, and 50kHz)
Mode (AM/NFM/WFM)	Search direction (up/down)
Delay (On/Off)	Bank (0-9)
LockOut (On/Off)	Priority (On/Off)

Missing – but useful – are time, date, duration of transmissions, and squelch status. There are other potentially important data that would be nice to have captured by an interface with an S-meter, such as center-tuning or frequency errors, and the status of other mods you may have done, such as Extended Memory Blocks, Extended Delay, Automatic Tape Recorder Switch, and more.

The ideal interface, then, will capture and send to the computer not only the normal data that appears in the display, but also a variety of other data that relates to the scanner, and to the session.

SCANNERS ARE NON-ERGONOMIC!

The design of one of the most user-friendly scanners I've ever seen has not been replicated to date: the PRO-2004. Whether or not it's deliberate, it's a fact that scanners seem *designed* to be operated and monitored from a distance. The keyboards are densely congested and designed for fingers about the size of toothpicks. An ideal interface will allow full operation and control of the scanner from the computer's keyboard where even pickles for fingers can hit the right keys at the right time.

Scanner displays don't seem designed for human eyes. Readouts are small, poorly illuminated, and often must be viewed from very narrow angles. A good interface presents an image of the scanner's display on the computer's monitor, so you can see all the information, from a distance.

MY PRESCRIPTION

Let's talk about either rolling your own high-performance scanner/computer interface or acquiring one for the least possible effort and cost. Many CE-232 Scanner/Computer Interfaces (and its predecessor, the HB-232) have been successfully tested and used by hobbyists and commercial interests for several years.

The following project offers a lot to most owners of the PRO-2004/5/6, and of certain other scanners such as the PRO-2035, PRO-2022, PRO-43, PRO-39, PRO-37, and PRO-34.

Now, with the PRO-2004/5/6 scanner series passing into history, I am literally giving you the design of the CE-232 –*it's here, complete, in this book*. It's too powerful and wonderful a tool to keep as a strictly commercial venture.

If you have knowledge of electronics and general hacking skills, you can build the CE-232 for yourself at modest cost.

LEGALESE

Of course, there are a few catches to this deal...

CATCH 1: The design and assembly instructions for the CE-232 as presented herein are copyrighted ©1992 by COMMtronics Engineering and Bill Cheek, and may not be used for any commercial purpose or application without the express written permission of, and license granted by, the author.

License is freely given and permission freely granted for individual use of the design, drawings, and instructions solely to readers of this book for strictly hobby applications.

You may not, under this license, use the material presented herein to produce kits or finished products for resale nor for use in any commercial enterprise.

CATCH 2: The CE-232 Scanner/Computer Interface requires software expressly designed for it. This software is not simple or easy to show in print, and it will not appear in this book. If you desire to build the interface but not write your own software, for the cost of disk duplication and shipping I'll send you an IBM/PC-compatible control program, plus supporting programs and files for the CE-232. If you elect to write your own software, I'll help by *giving* you the Developer's Kit, but cannot take responsibility for, or directly assist, your work.

The materials that I provide are *"copyrighted freeware,"* which means the package is freely available for individual, non-commercial use for only my cost of duplicating and shipping.

This software package is "complete" and powerful, so there is little reason or need for you to develop your own software unless you enjoy that sort of thing.

This complete software package is available for $9.95, ppd (USA), only on a high density, 3.5" floppy disk in MS-DOS 3.1 and up format and compatibility. Add $5 special handling for 5.25" disk. Payment in US Funds, check, money order, MC/VISA, to: COMMtronics Engineering, PO Box 262478, San Diego, CA 92196 or (619) 578-9247 (1:30-5:30pm, Pacific Time). Foreign shipping and handling add US$10.

CATCH 3: The CE-232 as presented herein is strictly for the PRO-2004/5/6 scanner series. Other scanners are supported, but you must contact me privately or on my BBS for that information.

CATCH 4: The CE-232 is known to work with virtually all modifications that can be made to the PRO-2004/5/6 with one important exception: It will NOT work with scanners that have been speeded up by means of a faster crystal. The standard diode speedups are okay, however.

All other mods of which I am aware will work just fine with the CE-232, though some may require slight alterations regarding where or how they are installed.

CATCH 5: I support strictly IBM/PC compatible computers, but third parties have written software that lets Macintosh computers control the CE-232, so if you need software for the Mac check the resources listed in this chapter or on my BBS. Formats for other computers are not available.

Other third parties that have written shareware or commercial control programs for the CE-232 Interface are identified on my BBS.

READ THIS FIRST

These instructions are geared for PC-compatible computers with MS/DOS 3.1 or higher, and a minimum of 512k RAM, though 640k is recommended. Operation of the CE-232 is possible from a floppy disk, but a hard drive with 2 MB free is better.

This version of the CE-232 Scanner/Computer Interface is expressly for the PRO-2004/5/6 scanner series.

It will work, as shown herein, for certain other scanners at reduced capability (1-way interface), but special add-on software and hardware are required. These other scanners include, but are not limited to, the following: PRO-2035, PRO-2022, PRO-2021, PRO-34, PRO-37, PRO-39, and the PRO-43.

Features and functions of the 2-way CE-232 Interface are:

♦ *AutoPrograms* scanner's 400 memory channels in 8 minutes (typical)

♦ *Remote-Controls* scanner keyboard functions from the PC

♦ *AutoLogs* contents of scanner's display ("hits") to a text file or a printer

♦ *AutoLooksUp* and displays your frequency data when a "hit" occurs

♦ *AutoRejects "birdies"* and undesirable frequencies – *no false stops!*

♦ *Script* feature allows unlimited automated control

♦ *User Switches;* status and control registers for generic purposes: data acquisition and control

♦ *Proved technology;* reliable and effective

CONNECTIONS

The CE-232 Scanner/Computer Interface connects between a PC/XT/AT-compatible computer and the scanner. A standard serial cable connects the CE-232 to the computer's COM1 or COM2 port.

The CE-232 can be installed inside the scanner for a tidy package, or it can be built into a small project box, with a short cable and plug to mate with a receptacle mounted on the scanner.

External installation allows a CE-232 to be used with more than one scanner. The scanner is not appreciably modified by either approach; rather, approximately 20 wires go from the CE-232 to various points in the scanner.

Absolutely no scanner features or performance are altered or sacrificed to gain the automated features.

FEATURES / FUNCTIONS

From a functional viewpoint there are no compromises whatsoever. The system has the following features and capabilities:

AutoProgram; in about 8 minutes it will insert up to 400 frequencies of your choice into the scanner's memory channels, along with custom settings of DELAY, MODE, and LOCK-OUT.

Try to program 400 channels by hand in under an hour or two... and what if you find a mistake with the channels out of sequence back on Ch-30? The AutoProgrammer uses plain ASCII text files, by the way.

View and control all standard scanner keyboard functions from the computer. The monitor displays a monochrome or color facsimile of the scanner's keyboard and LCD. Whatever shows in the scanner's LCD at any time is simultaneously displayed on the Monitor.

Press M on the computer keyboard for MANUAL, press S for SCAN, or press P for PRGM. All of the control keys of the scanner's keyboard are active at your computer's keyboard.

The scanner operates directly from the computer keyboard exactly as it operates from its front panel. In fact, you can operate from either location alternatively or simultaneously at any time.

AutoLogs to a handy text file the details about every "event" seen by the scanner. For example, the AutoLog mode senses when the SQUELCH breaks (a signal comes in).

It then commands the computer to write and append a line of data to a text file, containing channel number or SEARCH Bank, frequency, MODE setting (NFM, AM, or WFM), DELAY status (On or Off), LOCKOUT status, SEARCH Mode and STEP increment (if applicable), Date, Start Time, and Duration of transmission.

This file is "comma-delimited" to make it easy to load into a database manager for more processing and sorting as desired.

A text editor is provided with the CE-232 Program for a handy way to review and edit your AutoLogged Files. The CE-232 AutoLogger files its data in the same format as needed by the AutoProgrammer.

AutoLogged files of newly found frequencies in a SEARCH mode can be programmed back into the scanner's memory for a SEARCH and STORE function.

This process can be automated to eliminate duplicates and common frequencies. A dot-matrix or daisy-wheel printer can be selected to print AutoLogged data in real time as it is acquired.

The CE-232's **Lookup** function works when the scanner stops on an active frequency. It displays a line of text for that frequency on the monitor from your file. This reference file can be the SAME file used to AutoProgram the scanner. Great for signal identification.

An **Anti-Birdie** function compares a frequency "hit" to the contents of a "REJECT" file, and instantly resumes SCANning or SEARCHing, if that frequency is found in the file. It will not AutoLog these momentary "birdie" stops.

This superb feature is not limited to just "birdies"; you can put up to 32,000 undesired frequencies in the "REJECT" file, such as for pagers, computer data channels, continuous tones, encrypted signals, and other frequencies that you don't want the scanner to stop on or to AutoLog.

There are easy ways to automate the collection of undesirable signals for the REJECT file. The REJECT function can be turned on and off by the user or automatically commanded by a Script function.

The CE-232 has a powerful script or macro function to allow the automation of virtually any process that would normally be done by hand.

A Script can produce a file of what's been programmed into the memory channels (CHANNEL DUMP), or set a time limit for stops on various frequencies or channels, or lock-out every frequency found in a SEARCH session to avoid duplicate log entries.

The CE-232's microprocessor is programmed by your computer every time you run the program.

No expensive "hard programming" or firmware on the MPU chip.

Not only can low cost upgrades be done, but the CE-232 has attracted third-party developers who have produced many useful tools for the hacker, including superb support programs, utilities, and hardware.

The next few pages will present an overview followed by graphic details of how to build and install the CE-232 Scanner/Computer Interface. We start with the overview in *Figure 8-1*, and progress into the gory details, stage by stage and step by step.

This is the path to the Ultimate Scanner!

Figure 8-1: The big picture!

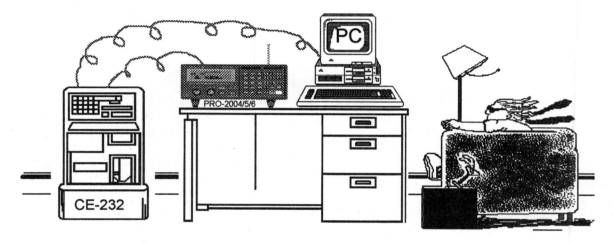

But, just in case you're blown away by all this technology.................

External Installations

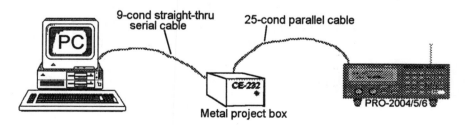

And for those who really need to (KISS) Keep It Simple, Stupid, then................

Internal Installations

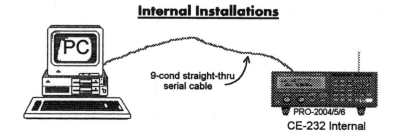

HERE'S THE PLAN

Okay, bear with me. Whether you're a new hacker or have been around for many years, this is really important.

This is Chapter 8, and by now you've had to plow through a lot of cautions, caveats, and warnings to "be patient," "have a plan," "lay out the parts and tools," and more. So why should I do it again?

Two reasons. First, if I do it enough, eventually you'll figure out that I *really mean it* – in the most friendly way. Just like a paint job, if you prepare properly the work is a lot easier.

The second reason is that a lot of you will get the book and instantly flip to the chapter that interests you the most. Therefore, I've splattered my warnings quite liberally throughout this book.

Well, here we go again... step-by-step, this time.

1. Examine, assess, and inventory parts, materials, tools, and documents. Make a list of needed parts, materials, and tools that you don't have in stock...

   This will save you time, trouble, and headaches.

2. Acquire, install, and pre-test the CE-232 program and software...

   A confidence builder, and you've got to do it eventually. No sense in building the CE-232 without software.

3. Purchase, acquire, make all needed parts, materials, and tools...

   This more or less ices down the preparatory stages and ensures your readiness to launch.

4. Review documents and procedures...

   Final preparations before the ultimate commitment.

5. Build the CE-232 circuit or acquire one.

6. Install CE-232 board.

A. Inside scanner (*74HC4050 Buffer optional but recommended*).

B. In an external metal box. Build and install the 74HC4050 buffer circuit inside the scanner as close to the logic/CPU board as possible.

If (A) above, connect a straight-through serial cable between the computer's COM1 or COM2 serial port and the input to the CE-232.

If (B) above, connect a straight-through serial cable between the computer's COM1 or COM2 serial port and the input to the CE-232, *and* a 25-cond parallel cable between the CE-232 and the scanner.

Inspect and double check all your work, ensuring no mistakes and clean work. To reduce my workload, check it one more time.

Set up and run the CE-232 software.

You're finished!

MANUAL

The formal manual for the commercial CE-232 Kit occupies more than 100 pages.

The following pages present a compromise, with sufficient detail for the technologist and experienced hobbyist.

There is no missing key information. If you are interested in this project but have doubts, the formal *Assembly, Installation, and Operation Manual for the CE-232* is available, as are a printed circuit board, parts, software, and even a packaged kit, ready to assemble for those who want the least hassle.

You can even download the full manual from my BBS, *free.* The end of this chapter will discuss the options available to you.

Table 8-1A is a list of all the materials that you must have on hand *before* you start, and *Table 8-1B* lists the nice-to-have stuff.

Table 8-1A: CE-232 parts, materials, and supplies – mandatory

Qty √	Circuit Symbol	Circuit Description	All parts numbers are DigiKey or Radio Shack unless noted Source and Part #
__1	Program	Current program and files (from the author, 3rd parties, or your own).....	COMMtronics Eng
__1	DOC	At least this book, ideal to have the full manual...............................	COMMtronics Eng
__1	PCB	Printed Circuit Board, ready to assemble (author's or yours).................	COMMtronics Eng
__1	XU-3	PLCC 68 pin Leadless Chip Carrier Socket for IC-3..........................	A419-ND
__1	IC-1	MAX232CPE RS-232 Receiver/Transmitter (AD-232 is okay)............	MAX232ACPE-ND
__1	IC-2	TL7757C or MC34064P-5 Undervoltage Sensing Integrated Circuit.......	*
__1	IC-3	MC68HC11F1FN Microprocessor Unit, or XC68HC11F1FN..............	*
__4	IC-4,5,6,7	74HC4066 Quad Bilateral Switch..	MM74HC4066N-ND
__1	IC-8	78L05 Voltage Regulator, +5V @ 100mA.......................................	AN78L05- ND
__1	IC-9	74HC4050 Hex Non-inverting buffer	MM74HC4050N-ND
__4	C-1,2,3,4	Capacitor, electrolytic, 22µF/35 WVDC...	RS# 272-1026
__6	C-5 thru 10	Capacitor, monolithic, 0.1µF/50 WVDC...	RS# 272-109
__1	C-11	Capacitor, electrolytic, 4.7µF/35 WVDC..	RS# 272-1024
__2	C-12,15	Capacitor, electrolytic, 1.0µF/35 WVDC..	RS# 272-1434
__2	C-13,14	Capacitor, monolithic, 22pF/50 WVDC..	RS# 272-806
__8	D-1 thru 8	Diodes, switch, silicon, 1N914 or 1N4148......................................	RS# 276-1620
__1	R-1	Resistor, 10Ω, 1/4-watt...	RS# 271-1365
__1	R-2	Resistor, 100Ω, 1/4-watt..	RS# 271-1311
__4	R-4 thru 7	Resistor, 47kΩ, 1/4-watt..	RS# 271-1342
__2	RN-1,2	Resistor Network, 10 pin w/bus, 10kΩ...	Q9-103-ND
__1	RN-3	Resistor Network, 8 pin w/bus, 10kΩ...	Q7-103-ND
__1	RN-4	Resistor Network, 6 pin w/bus, 4.7kΩ..	Q5-472-ND
__1	X-1	Crystal, quartz, HC-18, 8MHz...	CTX-056-ND
__1	PC	PC/compatible, 512k RAM (min), w/9600-baud COM1 or COM2 port and MSDOS 3.1/up	
__1	MAN	Service Manual for your scanner: call Tandy National Parts (800) 442-2425	

* These parts are hard to find. Try Future Active at (800) 757-9438 or COMMtronics Engineering

Table 8-1B: CE-232 parts, materials, and supplies – "nice-to-have," or useful

Qty √	Circuit Symbol	Circuit Description	All parts numbers are DigiKey or Radio Shack unless noted Source and Part #
___1	J-1	DB-9 jack, male, mates w/W-1 below	RS#276-1537 or 276-1538
___2	J-2	DB-25 jacks, female, mate w/W-2 below	RS#276-1548
___1	LED-1	Light Emitting Diode (LED), choice of color	RS# 276-1622
___1	R-3	Resistor, 1kΩ, 1/4-watt	RS# 271-1321
___1	W-1	Serial cable, 9 conductor, straight-thru (not null-modem), w/female DB-9 on one end (see text)	
___1	W-2	Parallel cable, 25-conductor, shielded, DB-25 male-todB-25 male	RS#26-249
___1	XU-1	IC Socket, 16 pin, DIP, Low Profile Best is DigiKey	RS# 276-1998 AE-7216
___4	XU-4,5,6,7	IC Socket, 14 pin, DIP, Low Profile RS# 276-1999, Best is DigiKey	AE-7214
___4'	Misc	Wire, insulated, 22 gauge, stranded, best are wires salvaged from cable –>	RS #278-776
___2	Misc	Mounting studs	RS# 276-195
___4	Misc	Pin-line sockets, see Chapter 3	A-208
___1	Misc	Metal project box	RS# 270-253

More hack than factory!
This PRO-2004 has an (early) CE-232 interface, S-meters (analog and LED) 25,600 channels, Data/Tone Squelch, SCA decoder, and much more.

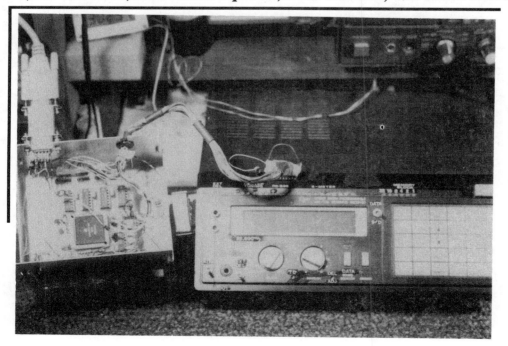

Figure 8-2: CE-232 System Block Diagram

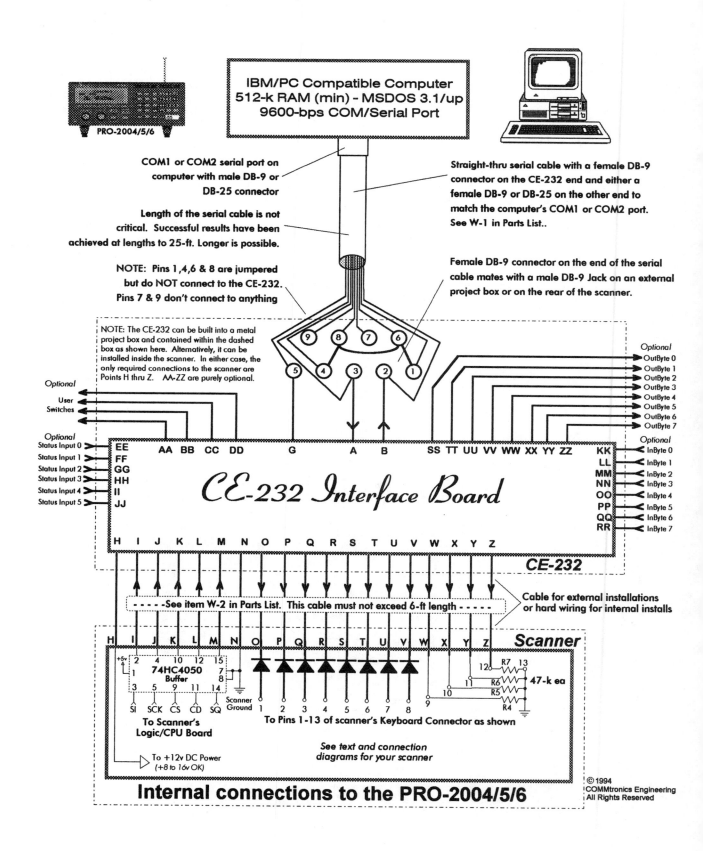

Internal connections to the PRO-2004/5/6

Figure 8-3: CE-232 schematic

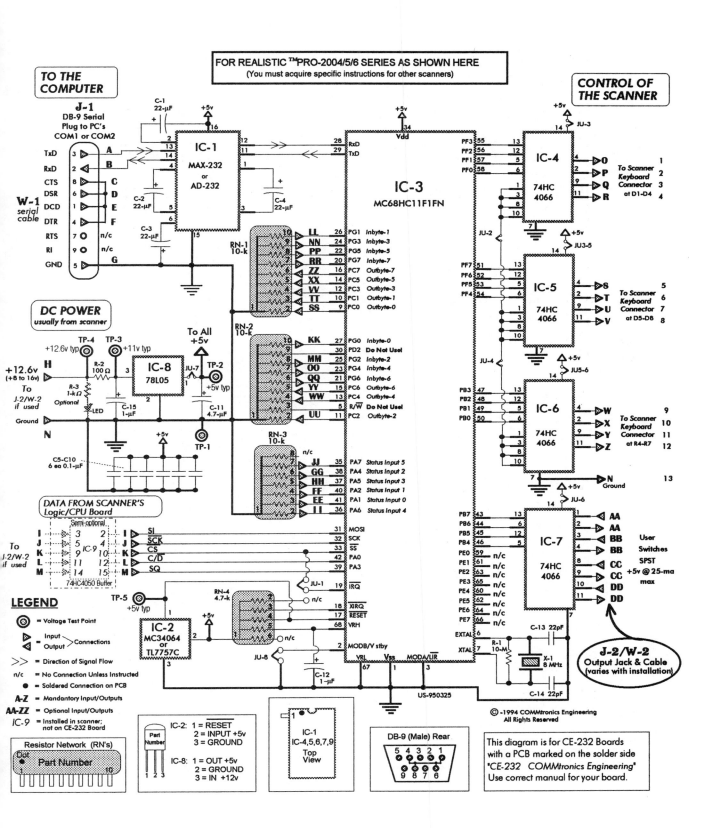

Figure 8-4: CE-232 circuit board – component side

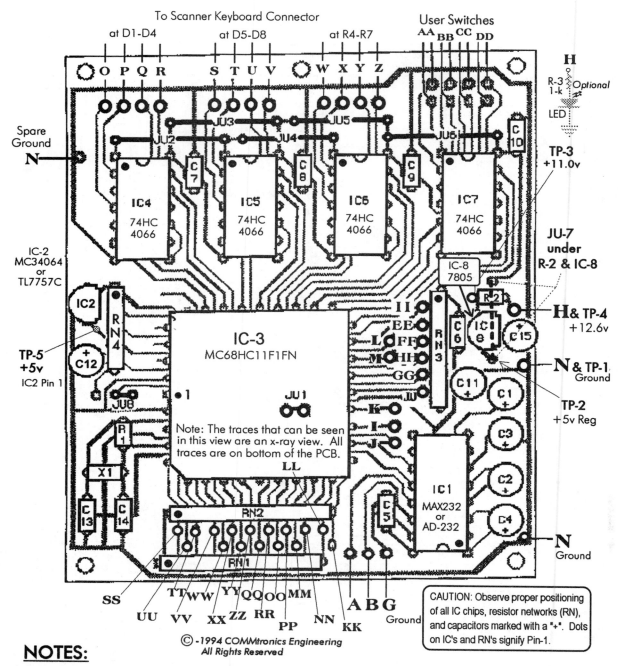

© -1994 COMMtronics Engineering
All Rights Reserved

CAUTION: Observe proper positioning of all IC chips, resistor networks (RN), and capacitors marked with a "+". Dots on IC's and RN's signify Pin-1.

NOTES:

1. Input/Output points are designated by letters A,B,G,H through Z, and AA through ZZ. C thru F are on the DB-9 connector.
2. Input/Output points can be hardwired to their destinations, but use of PinLine Sockets & Plugs is highly recommended.
3. Input/Output points EE thru ZZ are non-essential and can be disregarded during assembly. PinLine Sockets are suggested however.
4. Test Points: TP-1 is ground. TP-2 is regulated +5v. TP-3 is DC input to IC-8. TP4 is +12v In to R2. TP-5 is special +5v to IC-3.
   Current drain of the CE-232 is calculated by: (((Volts at TP-4) — (Volts at TP-3)) ÷ R2) = typical: 1.6v/100 = 16 ma (13-18 ma OK)
5. Voltage at TP-5 is critical. If the microprocessor IC3 is ok, expect +5v. If any problems with X-1 or IC-3 circuits, TP-5 will be 0-v.
6. THIS DIAGRAM is for CE-232 boards distributed AFTER 1/1/95. This board is marked on rear: "CE-232 COMMtronics Engineering"
   Previous versions of this board are marked "HB-232" and "9217" on the rear. Use the right manual for your version of the board.

Figure 8-5: CE-232 circuit board — solder-side

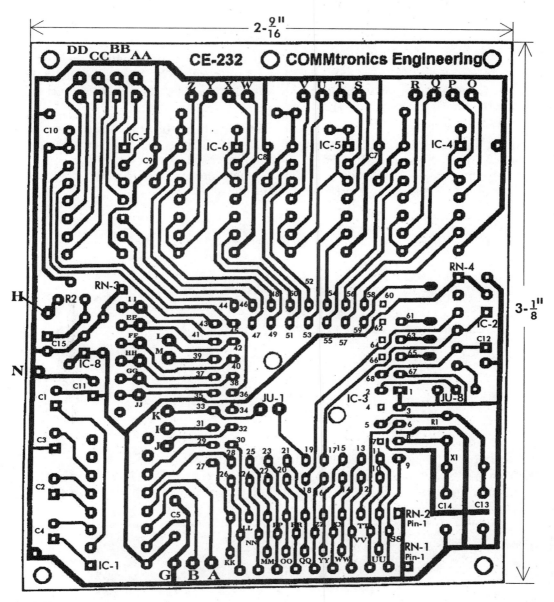

NOTES:

1. Square pads are Pin #1 for IC's and RN's and (+) leads of capacitors.
2. IC Pin Spacing in the vertical and horizontal planes is 0.1"
3. Mounting holes and IC-3 access holes are 1/8" dia.
4. CAUTION: This pattern is NOT to scale, but is accurately proportioned.
   It will be just right if reduced to where IC pin centers are spaced exactly 1/10-inch apart,

FOLLOW INSTRUCTIONS

Before we get into the detail of this project, I want to tell you a (true) story. When my daughter, Ali, was a 15-year-old 10th grader, I gave her a draft copy of the Parts Layout with these instructions. With no other special preparation or guidance, she was able to obtain all the correct parts from our component bins and successfully assemble the first production HB-232 board. *It worked the first time out!*

She made no errors, and the only input I gave her was at the end when I insisted on pressing the microprocessor chip into its socket myself (I should have let her do it). The point is that I gave her no real help, and from the few questions that she raised I was able to make these instructions even clearer and to the point.

For a painless assembly of the PCB, you need only follow the diagrams and instructions. The procedure is a proved method and should be clear even to those not highly experienced with this line of work, like my daughter used to be.

NOTES: A mention of *"No Polarity"* in these assembly instructions means the component can be installed either way. Inspect for solder blobs and bridges after every step. Leave all IC's and the microprocessor chip in their original packing until needed.

Don't forget!

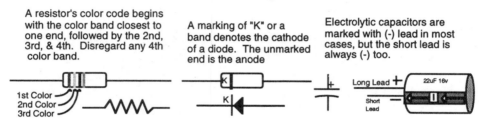

A resistor's color code begins with the color band closest to one end, followed by the 2nd, 3rd, & 4th. Disregard any 4th color band.

1st Color
2nd Color
3rd Color

A marking of "K" or a band denotes the cathode of a diode. The unmarked end is the anode

Electrolytic capacitors are marked with (-) lead in most cases, but the short lead is always (-) too.

Long Lead +   22uF 16v
Short Lead

Pushing the limits
Here's the Intercept Technologies Voice Activated Digital Electronic Recorder (VADER) for use with the CE-232 Interface. 16 Mb of audio RAM for 1 hour of continuous recordings, perfectly synchronized with the CE-232 activity log file.

PARTS ID — A REVIEW

The banded end of a diode is the cathode. The unbanded end is the anode. The cathode is schematically represented as the bar while the anode is the triangle.

A 10MΩ resistor is color coded Brown-Black-Blue, a 1kΩ resistor is Brown-Black-Red, a 100Ω resistor is Brown-Black-Brown, and 47KΩ resistors are Yellow-Violet-Orange. Zero through nine goes: black - brown - red - orange - yellow - green - blue - violet - gray - white.

Resistor Networks (RN's) are identified with a dot or a bar at the end where pin 1 resides.

Pin 1 of most IC chips is identified from the top by a dot or hole next to a notch at one end of the chip. Pin numbers increase in a counterclockwise direction around the perimeter of the chip, as viewed from the top.

Capacitors C5-10 and C13-14 are non-polarized and may be installed either way. The eight little (usually yellow) capacitors look alike at first glance – it's up to you to keep them apart.

The rest of the capacitors are electrolytics, clearly marked, and must be installed with the proper polarity. The negative (–) lead of these capacitors is marked on the side next to the lead.

PROCEDURE

A. Install and solder the 68-pin Microprocessor Socket, XU-3.

B. Solder all except those few pins that dead-end to no traces or pads. Use a thin-tipped soldering pencil, and position the tip so that entry is from ABOVE the pin, not from the side. This will minimize chances of solder bridges from one point to the next.

    After all pins have been soldered, examine each with a strong light and a magnifier to ensure that each solder joint has "taken" properly and that there are no bridges or blobs between pins.

    Do not skip this Quality Assurance procedure!

C. Install and solder all eight jumper wires on the PC board. Note the short jumper (JU-8) near IC-2.

JU-1 is on the BOTTOM (solder) side of the PCB. JU-2,3,4,5, and 6 are near the ends of IC4,5,6 and 7. JU-7 is near IC-8 and R-2.

Use #22 to #30 gauge solid copper wire for jumpers, OR you can use snipped component leads. Make the jumpers neat and clean. Avoid shorts between pads and traces. Snip excess wire from all jumpers.

D. Install IC sockets for IC-1,4,5,6, and 7, observing the proper locations of all pins #1. Insert one socket at a time, and solder the #1 pin of each to its pad.

    Then, pushing down on the socket from above the board, melt the solder at pin 1 so that the socket slips in and seats flush with the top of the board.

E. When all sockets have been seated, solder the remaining pins of each to their respective pads on the bottom of the board. Snip...

    By the way, a strip of 3 pin-line sockets makes a good socket for IC-2 and IC-8. Purists will solder these and all other IC's with exception of IC-7, though. Sockets are best for the novice hacker.

F. Install Resistor Networks, RN-1, 2, 3, and 4. Be sure the #1 pin of each resistor network is properly positioned before inserting into the holes.

    Pin 1 is designated by a dot toward one end of the "chip." Figure 8-4 shows the proper orientation of each resistor network. Snip...

G. Pin-line strips:

    Install a 6-socket strip in the Input/Output holes for Points EE-JJ next to RN-3.

    Install a 9-socket strip in the Input/Output holes for Points SS, TT, VV, XX, ZZ, RR, PP, NN, and LL next to RN-2.

    Install a 2-socket strip for Points L and M.

    Install a 3-socket strip for J, I, and K.

    Install a 5-socket strip in the Input/Output holes for Points WW, YY, QQ, OO, and MM next to RN-1.

    Install single sockets in the spots for UU and KK next to RN-1.

    Install 4-socket strips in the spots for O-R, S-U, and W-Z.

Install 2-socket pairs for each of AA, BB, CC, and DD.

Install a 3-socket strip for A, B, and G.

Install single sockets for Point H and all Points N.

PIN-LINE NOTES:

1. PIN-LINE sockets are available from DigiKey, (800) 344-4539, Part # A-208. Another source of low-cost pin-line sockets is HOSFELT Electronics, 2700 Sunset Blvd, Steubenville, OH 43952, (800) 524-6464, Part #21-151 (10 pin), #21-128 (16 pin) and #21-161 (20 pin). Hosfelt Electronics may also have other configurations of pin-line sockets.

2. Use of pin-line sockets is optional. You can later hard-wire to all the points if you wish. Pin-line sockets are a touch of class, however, that make future work, such as troubleshooting, a heck of a lot easier.

3. If you are not going to use pin-line sockets, then skip this step altogether. Hard-wiring will come later.

H. Install two capacitors C-13 and 14 (22pF), possibly marked "220" and "A1J" on one side; disregard markings on the other side.

Do not confuse these capacitors with C5-10, which look exactly like them except for the markings. No polarity. Snip...

I. Install six capacitors C5-10 (0.1µF), possibly marked "104" and "C1K" on one side; disregard markings on the other side. No polarity. Snip excess leads.

J. Install C-12 (1µF/35V) near pin 6 of RN-4, observing the (+) polarity. The (+) terminal is not marked, but is the LONGER lead of the two. The (−) lead is shorter, identified by a wide stripe with a (−) and a ">" on the stripe.

K. Install C-15 (1µF/35V) near IC-8, observing the (+) polarity. The (+) terminal is not marked, but is the LONGER lead of the two. The (−) lead is shorter and is identified by a wide stripe with a (−) and a ">" on the stripe.

L. Install C-11 (4.7µF/35V) near RN-3, observing the (+) polarity. C-11 looks

exactly like C-12 and 15, but is marked differently. Refer to Steps H and I above for the method to distinguish the proper polarity.

M. Install C1, 2, 3, and 4 (22µF/16V), the capacitors near IC-1. Observe (+) polarity using the method in Steps H and I. Snip...

N.

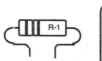

Install R-1 near pin 6 of RN-4, no polarity, standing on end or laid flat with the leads properly bent, as shown in the sketch above. R-1 = 10MΩ (Brown-Black-Blue). Flat is preferred. Snip....

O. Install R-2 near C-15. It MUST go flat and bridge over JU-7. It is okay to raise R-2 above the board a little because each end is a Test Point at which you'll measure voltages. Ease of access to the ends of R-2 is a big consideration here.

One pin-line socket soldered to each end of R2 makes a nice Test Point. Take a look at the drawing below.

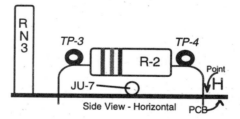

P. Install X-1, an 8MHz crystal, no polarity. Partially insert its two leads into the holes provided and then bend X-1 back 90° so that it lies flat on top of C13 and 14.

Pull the leads tight from underneath the board and solder. Snip excess leads.

This method offers minimum vertical clearance but X-1 can also be installed straight into its two holes, flush with the board, otherwise.

The latter method is technically best for the sake of shortest leads, but X-1 is the tallest item on the CE-232 board and could interfere in tight installations.

Q. Install IC-2 near RN-4 (looks like a 3-lead transistor), observing the proper polarity of the 3 leads. (Flat side faces RN-4.) Snip...

Install IC-8 near RN-3 (also looks like a 3-lead transistor), observing the proper polarity of the 3 leads. The rounded side faces RN-3. Snip...

It's decision time now; the moment of reckoning is at hand. You have to decide the course of the rest of your scanner's life: internal or external installation.

I'll help. The next few pages present a standard wiring scheme for *whichever* way you decide. Those pages offer insight to the final steps of the: connection of the CE-232 PC board to the scanner, and either way, the concepts are similar.

Step R waits for you to make up your mind. Just consider these next few pages before jumping.

STANDARDIZED WIRING SCHEMES

The first years of distribution of the CE-232 taught us several lessons, the first of which is that our instructions are good. Most hackers are successful the first time out.

But there have been a few problems that stand out in our notes, and they will be shared with you. These errors occur in the wiring and point-to-point connections.

The first four editions of the Interface and *Manual* left the wiring up to the hacker, and for most that was sufficient but a few had trouble.

This procedure will standardize point-to-point wiring to reduce errors during installation. Regarding the CE-232 Wiring Plan, *Tables 8-2* and *8-3*, you may disregard if you see fit.

If you stick to it and run into trouble, I will be better prepared to assist with remedial measures; call it "both playing to the same sheet of music."

Whether you choose to install your CE-232 inside the scanner or in a metal project box, at leaast 19 wires are to be connected between the scanner and the CE-232 printed circuit board.

That's a lot of wires to keep track of, and to trace down later if/when something doesn't work. Actually, there's not much to say about internal installations except that the color codes I

recommend will help keep things consistent – *if* you will adhere to them. If you won't, then wire up one point at a time and one wire at a time, making sure that each wire originates and terminates at the right places. Also, tag each wire (in lieu of color code) so you can troubleshoot if necessary.

When questions are thrown at me, I am much friendlier when I find your compliance with standardized wiring procedure.

USE STANDARD PARTS

External installations can make it tough to track things, which is where our CE-232 Wiring Plan shines. It's standardized.

The first step is to use female DB-25 connectors, one mounted on the rear panel of the scanner and the other on the rear panel of the CE-232 box. This allows interconnection with a cheap and commonly available shielded parallel cable, with male DB-25 connectors on each end, cost of which is about $10 anywhere. Do NOT under any circumstances, use "ribbon cable" for remote installations, and preferably not for internal installations, either.

PROCEDURE

Now that the cable question is out of the way, the rest is a lot easier. Before you physically mount the female DB-25 connectors on the scanner and metal project box, you'll be wise to lay the two loose female connectors side by side and prewire each one so they're exactly alike in color codes.

Each wire bundle can be cut and trimmed to the approximate correct length after mounting the connectors. Then, when you install the DB-25's, mount them so the SPARE unused pins face up and are accessible for future use.

After the DB-25's are installed, then and only then, route and solder the wires to their respective termination points.

ALTERNATIVE ONE

If the idea of installing DB-25 connectors doesn't appeal to you, there is another way to keep things smart and still simple. Buy two shielded 25-conductor parallel cables, one with male DB-25 on each end and the other with female DB-25's on each end. After that, it's almost intuitive.

Lay aside the one with the male DB-25; it will be your interconnecting cable later. Now cut the female cable a certain distance from each end to have enough length to use as "pigtails."

That is, you'll drill a ³/₈" hole in the back of the scanner and another in the back of the CE-232 project box.

Now slip a cut female cable into one of the holes, cut off excess cable, strip enough of the insulation for the individual wires to flare out and go to their respective termination points.

Make a note of color codes: one color for each CE-232 Wire or Point, and use the same color code at each end to keep things straight.

I'll show you , and you can choose.

Look at *Table 8-2.*

Figure 8-6: Wiring the computer to the scanner

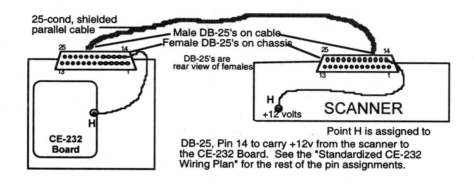

Table 8-2: **The** Standardized *CE-232 Wiring Plan*

Wiring from CE-232 Box or PC Board to Terminations in Scanner

CE-232 DB-25 Pin No	CE-232 Wire/Point I.D.	Wire Color Codes for Inside CE-232 Box/Scanner	Termination Points Inside the Scanner, or Notes & Function	PRO-2005/6 | PRO-2004 - Pin No
1	Z	White	Row-4	CN-501 | CN-502 ----- Pin 12
2	Y	Black/White	Row 3	CN-501 | CN-502 ----- Pin 11
3	X	Brown/White	Row 2	CN-501 | CN-502 ----- Pin 10
4	W	Gray/White	Row 1	CN-501 | CN-502 ----- Pin 9
5	V	Green/White	Column 1	CN-501 | CN-502 ----- Pin 8
6	U	Blue/White	Column 2	CN-501 | CN-502 ----- Pin 7
7	T	Violet/White	Column 3	CN-501 | CN-502 ----- Pin 6
8	S	Tan/Orange	Column 4	CN-501 | CN-502 ----- Pin 5
9	R	Yellow/Orange	Column 5	CN-501 | CN-502 ----- Pin 4
10	Q	Orange/White	Column 6	CN-501 | CN-502 ----- Pin 3
11	P	Pink/White	Column 7	CN-501 | CN-502 ----- Pin 2
12	K	Tan	CS - Chip Select	CPU
13	O	Red/White	Column 8	CN-501 | CN-502 ----- Pin 1
14	H	Red	+12 to +14 volts, DC	
15			*spare*	
16			*spare*	
17	I	Gray	SI - Serial Data	CPU
18			*spare*	
19	M	Blue	SQ - Squelch	CPU
20			*spare*	
21	*DD (1)*	*Yellow (Demo of a User Switch)* --	*User Switch 4: Beep Vol: DD(2) ground*	
22	*JJ*	*Green (Demo of a Status Input)* ---	*Status Input 6: Squelch Break Indicator*	
23	L	Violet	C/D - Command Data	CPU
24	J	Brown	SCK - Serial Clock	CPU
25	N	Black/Yellow	GND - Ground	CN-501 | CN-502 --- Pin 13

Wiring Between the CE-232 DB-9 Input Jack and the CE-232 PC Board

DB-9 Pin #	CE-232 Wire/Point ID	Wiring Color Codes	Notes/Function
1 •	E	Bare Jumper	*No Connect to CE-232*
2>	B	>GREEN	>RxD - Receive Data
3>	A	>PINK	>TxD - Transmit Data
4 •	F	Bare Jumper	*No Connect to CE-232*
5>	G	>Black/Orange	>PC Ground to CE-232
6 •	D	Bare Jumper	*No Connect to CE-232*
7	none	*No Connection*	*No Connect to CE-232*
8 •	C	Bare Jumper	*No Connect to CE-232*
9	none	*No Connection*	*No Connect to CE-232*

NOTES: The unused User Switches (AA, BB, CC) can be wired to any of the above SPARE pins on the DB-25 connector, if and when you need them.

The 8 OUTBYTE, 8 INBYTE and five of the six INPUT STATUS registers are not wired to anything. These functions are up to you to implement and use as desired. See Manual.

Status Input (JJ) goes to IC-2, Pin 13 in the scanner through a 4.7-kΩ limiter/safety resistor.

User Switch (DD) shown here is used to turn the BEEP on and off. It wires straight thru to the BEEP line: (PRO-2005/6 is CN-3, Pin 8) (PRO-2004 is CN-504, Pin 7). Use CTRL+F4 for On/Off.

• Pins 1,4,6,8 are jumpered, but go nowhere.

Interesting views of cobbled-up scanners. Can you tell which are prototypes (my fault) and which were sent to me for "help?"

A massive assault on a PRO-2006. The bottom are of the 2004/5/7 and the 2035 can be stuffed! Shown here, left to right, are: Remote Control, Extended Delay, LED Center Tune and S-Meter, and a computer interface! Note the DB-9 connector where the AC cord once entered the chassis. And there's still room for more down there...

A PRO-2004 with 6,400-channel Extended Memory and Keyboard Memory Block Controller. Old-style SRAM, but still works!

Figure 8-7: Connectors and cables

CONNECTORS & CABLES

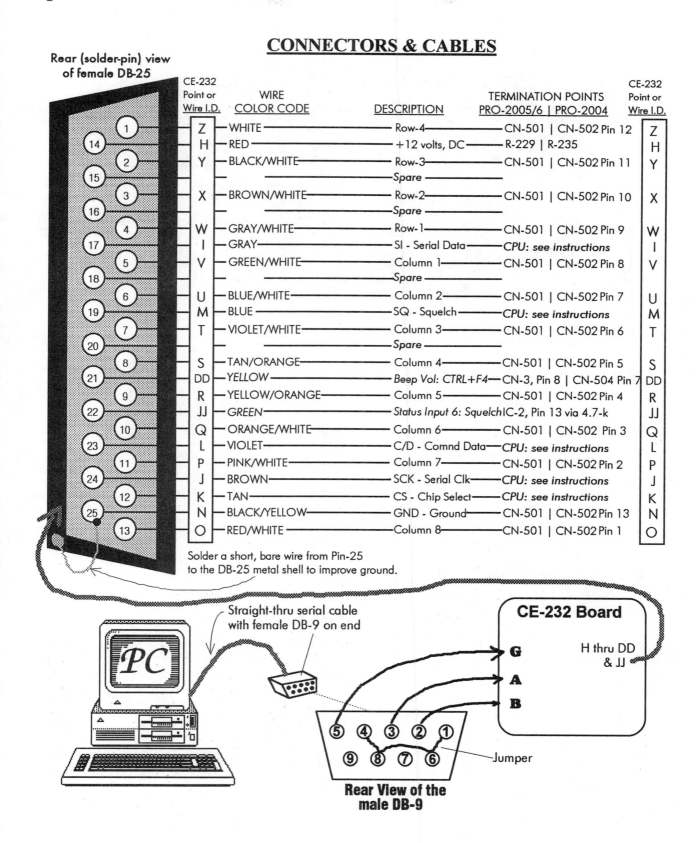

Rear (solder-pin) view of female DB-25

CE-232 Point or Wire I.D.	WIRE COLOR CODE	DESCRIPTION	TERMINATION POINTS PRO-2005/6 | PRO-2004	CE-232 Point or Wire I.D.
Z	WHITE	Row-4	CN-501 | CN-502 Pin 12	Z
H	RED	+12 volts, DC	R-229 | R-235	H
Y	BLACK/WHITE	Row-3	CN-501 | CN-502 Pin 11	Y
		Spare		
X	BROWN/WHITE	Row-2	CN-501 | CN-502 Pin 10	X
		Spare		
W	GRAY/WHITE	Row-1	CN-501 | CN-502 Pin 9	W
I	GRAY	SI - Serial Data	*CPU: see instructions*	I
V	GREEN/WHITE	Column 1	CN-501 | CN-502 Pin 8	V
		Spare		
U	BLUE/WHITE	Column 2	CN-501 | CN-502 Pin 7	U
M	BLUE	SQ - Squelch	*CPU: see instructions*	M
T	VIOLET/WHITE	Column 3	CN-501 | CN-502 Pin 6	T
		Spare		
S	TAN/ORANGE	Column 4	CN-501 | CN-502 Pin 5	S
DD	*YELLOW*	*Beep Vol: CTRL+F4*	CN-3, Pin 8 | CN-504 Pin 7	DD
R	YELLOW/ORANGE	Column 5	CN-501 | CN-502 Pin 4	R
JJ	*GREEN*	*Status Input 6: Squelch*	IC-2, Pin 13 via 4.7-k	JJ
Q	ORANGE/WHITE	Column 6	CN-501 | CN-502 Pin 3	Q
L	VIOLET	C/D - Comnd Data	*CPU: see instructions*	L
P	PINK/WHITE	Column 7	CN-501 | CN-502 Pin 2	P
J	BROWN	SCK - Serial Clk	*CPU: see instructions*	J
K	TAN	CS - Chip Select	*CPU: see instructions*	K
N	BLACK/YELLOW	GND - Ground	CN-501 | CN-502 Pin 13	N
O	RED/WHITE	Column 8	CN-501 | CN-502 Pin 1	O

Solder a short, bare wire from Pin-25 to the DB-25 metal shell to improve ground.

Straight-thru serial cable with female DB-9 on end

CE-232 Board

G
A
B

H thru DD & JJ

Jumper

Rear View of the male DB-9

Figure 8-8: CE-232 board, assembled – two views

Examine these illustrations, which show component location and orientation. Note the liberal use of pin-line connections to increase flexibility and permit quick disconnect, etc.

STANDARD CE-232 WIRING PLAN

The final steps of this section help you connect a wiring harness to the CE-232 board. How that's done depends on your choice of installation, internal or external. No matter which way, the preferred starting point is to install a pin-line socket strip at each group of Input/Output Points on the CE-232 board so that the female sockets are exposed.

This facilitates making your own connectors for the CE-232 board using identical pin-line sockets as on the board, with the male plugs exposed and wires soldered to the female sockets. They mate perfectly and allow for quick connects and disconnects. See *Figure 8-7.*

YOUR CHOICE

If you don't understand this concept, or don't want to bother with it, then go ahead and solder wires to each In/Out point. Refer to the wiring guides and diagrams.

The wire length should be kept to a minimum for your choice of installation. For instance, if the CE-232 is installed inside the scanner, the wire bundle from the board to the destination points should be kept short consistent with neatness and ease of routing.

For external installations, the wiring will consist of two phases:

(1) wiring the I/O points on the CE-232 to a DB-25 connector installed on the metal box, and

(2) wiring a DB-25 connector on the back of the scanner to its termination points in the scanner.

In either case, choice of wire is critical. Do not use the stiff, single or multi-strand hookup wire from Radio Shack. Ribbon cable is not recommended. The best choice is to pull the color-coded wires from Radio Shack's "25-conductor LAN cable," #278-776, if you can find some.

WIRING, CONTINUED

Review the wiring layout shown in *Figures 8-4 and 8-6,* and study *Table 8-2* before performing Steps R – Y. The guide provides some alternative ideas, and you must make a commitment one way or the other.

No matter which installation you choose, Steps R–Y are a guide only.

R. Solder wires A, B, and G to their respective termination points or pin-line plugs.

S. Solder wires J, I, and K to their respective termination points or pin-line plugs.

T. Solder wires M and L to their respective termination points or pin-line plugs.

U. Solder wires H and N to their respective termination points or pin-line plugs.

V. Solder wires O, P, Q, and R to their respective termination points or pin-line plugs.

W. Solder wires S, T, U, and V to their respective termination points or pin-line plugs.

X. Solder wires W, X, Y, and Z to their respective termination points or pin-line plugs.

Y. Solder wires AA, BB, CC, and DD to their respective termination points or pin-line plugs.

Z. Solder wire JJ to its respective termination points or pin-line plug.

AA. Install all IC's in their sockets now – IC1 and ICs 4-7 first.

BB. The pins of these IC's are probably spread a little too far apart to fit your sockets. Grasp the ends of each chip's body between your thumbs and forefingers with the pins away from you and lay the chip against a flat, hard surface.

Pushing downward, force the chip body toward the bottom row of pins lying on the flat surface. This will cause the row of pins to flatten a little.

Flip the chip over and repeat the procedure to the other row of pins. Then compare the pin alignment with the pins of its socket. If they match, press the chip into the socket, ensuring proper orientation of pin #1. Repeat this procedure for all five IC's: 1, 4, 5, 6, and 7.

CC. CAREFULLY unwrap the foil packaging from the Microprocessor Chip, IC-3. Avoid touching its pins on the perimeter (sides) of the chip. Hold it between thumb and forefinger on its top and bottom, not the sides.

Facing the TOP side of the chip, look for one of the four corners that has a tiny flat corner instead of a sharp one. This flattened corner must mate with the corresponding flattened corner of the leadless chip carrier socket on the CE-232 board. The flattened corner of the chip will be next to the crystal, X-1.

DD. Carefully lay the microprocessor chip into the open area of the chip socket, but don't force it in, just lay it there so that it rests with the flattened corners aligned. Jiggle the chip a little

with something like a small screwdriver so that it settles into the chip carrier socket slightly. It won't actually go all the way in because of back pressure from the pins of both the socket and the chip. Just make it lie in the opening as flat as possible, with all pins aligned.

EE. Now grasp the CE-232 board with the four fingers of each hand on the bottom of the board and your two thumbs resting on the top of the microprocessor chip.

Begin exerting an even pressure on the top of the chip to force it down into the chip carrier socket.

Be gentle at first, ensuring that the chip remains relatively flat. Increase pressure gradually, watching the chip as it is pressed into the socket.

If one edge of the chip suddenly drops in a little more than its opposite side, then exert more pressure on the opposite side to even things up again. Avoid a "bending" pressure on the chip.

FF. In this manner, with careful application of force, the chip will "pop" down into the chip carrier socket. Continue applying increasing pressure until the microprocessor seats solidly into the carrier and can go no farther.

Examine the chip carefully with respect to the carrier.

When properly seated, the top surface of the µP chip will be about 0.5 to 1 mm *below* the top edge of the carrier socket.

GG. Use a good light and magnifier to inspect all pins of the MPU to ensure that none got crumpled or torqued out of alignment.

There are two 1/8" holes on the standard PCB boards, for the purpose of pushing out the MPU chip from the bottom, if ever necessary.

Radio Shack now sells the proper extraction tool: #276-2101, which is a better way to remove the MPU.

This concludes the basic fabrication and assembly of the CE-232 Printed Circuit Board.

At this time, inspect ALL your work, and especially the solder-side of the board, with a strong light and a good magnifier.

Inspect for solder blobs, bridges, and unsanitary-looking solder joints. Correct all problems and investigate all suspicious looking oddities. When you are sure your work is perfect, go have a cup of coffee.

When you come back, check it thoroughly yet one more time, and only then proceed to the following instructions.

INSTALLATION INSTRUCTIONS

Study all the wiring diagrams and illustrations to develop a good understanding of the big picture.

Select a COM (serial) port (COM1 or COM2) on your PC to drive the CE-232. Acquire a standard, straight-thru serial cable with the appropriate connector on one end that mates with your PC's COM port. The other end should have a female DB-9 to mate with the male DB-9 input connector on the CE-232.

Determine whether your CE-232 Installation will be internal or external. We suggest external for a variety of good reasons including ease of maintenance and installation, and the fact that an *external* CE-232 can be used to drive other scanners, too, provided they are appropriately wired. One at a time, of course.

If you choose an internal installation that's fine, but you can be on your own here since the job is mostly mechanical (see Chapter 4). Just follow the wiring diagrams and pictorials and read the remainder of this section, which is geared for external installations, but which will also be applicable in terms of wiring between the CE-232 and scanner.

POWER SUPPLY REVISITED

This is my last chance to convince you to take an important step. It will open space for future modifications, improve scanner reliability, and more. Please do it!

Regardless of how you install the CE-232: *REMOVE THE POWER TRANSFORMER*, T-801, and power your scanner with a source of external DC to the coaxial power plug on the rear of the scanner.

External power will let the scanner run much cooler and thereby preserve its life. If you remove T-801, you'll have plenty of room in which to mount the CE-232. The suggested external power

source should be rated at 12V @ 500mA at a minimum with 12V @ 1A preferred. The following Radio Shack power supplies and AC/DC adapters will work just fine with the PRO-2004/5/6: #22-120, #22-127, and 273-1653. WARNING: Radio Shack's #273-1652 has been found to be inadequate, despite its specs.

You could use the A/C power cord and a removed T-801 in the design of your own external power supply. T-801 heats up the rest of the scanner, and that's not good. Do something about it.

PRO-2004 ONLY (Internal)

The CE-232 board can fit in the PRO-2004 quite handily, on the back of the keyboard panel. Velcro strips will hold it there just fine. Another possibility is in the area just forward of the power transformer, on either the top or the bottom of the scanner.

If you insist on retaining an internal supply, it may be useful to move the power transformer, up or down and/or to the REAR slightly, to make more room.

T-801 is mounted to the chassis side wall with two locking nuts and bolts, so drilling two more holes is all that's needed to move it a little.

Again, I suggest you remove T-801 entirely and power the scanner from an external DC supply.

PRO-2005 and PRO-2006 ONLY (Internal)

Space is very limited in these rigs and you need a lot of it for other modifications and gizmos, so I strongly urge an external installation of the CE-232. If you insist on keeping it internal, there are two possibilities.

One is to move T-801 a bit up or down and to the rear to make space for the CE-232 on the side opposite the direction in which you move T-801. T-801 is mounted to the chassis side wall with two locking nuts and bolts, so drilling two more holes is all that's needed to move it somewhat.

Again, we suggest you remove T-801 entirely, and power the scanner with external DC.

Another possibility is on top of the two small shielded compartments just behind the keyboard on the top right side of the scanner. That's where I install 'em.

A very thin layer of insulation should be placed on the top of these two compartments and/or on the bottom of the CE-232 board. Clear acetate will do, or any thin plastic. *Beware:* snipped solder joints on the bottom of the CE-232 board are very sharp and can penetrate plastic.

I have done many of these, however, and a layer of acetate with Velcro between the CE-232 and the plastic will do nicely. You might also scope the bottom area of the scanner over that large cutout in the metal chassis. As I said, possibilities are limited.

You decide, but keep in mind the likely future need for maintenance, modifications, and general access.

Figure 8-9: CE-232 internal installation guide

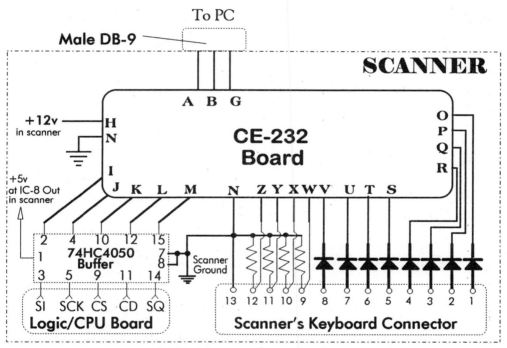

See text and connection
diagrams for your scanner

INTERNAL INSTALLATIONS

1. Build CE-232 Board
2. Install a male DB-9 on rear of scanner
3. Make a wiring harness for CE-232 Board: A, B, G, H-Z, DD, JJ
4. Install CE-232 Board somewhere in scanner
5. Fabricate and mount the 74HC4050 Buffer circuit
6. Fabricate and mount the diode/resistor group to keyboard connector
7. Connect 5 wires to Points I-M on scanner's Logic/CPU Board
7. Connect Wires I-M from scanner's Logic/CPU Board to Buffer as shown
8. Connect CE-232 Wires O-Z to diode/resistor group as shown
9. Connect CE-232 Wires I-M to Buffer as shown
10. Finish wiring: Buffer +5v, CE-232 +12v, grounds, etc.

CONNECTIONS

If you choose an *internal* installation, a male DB-9 connector should be mounted on the rear of the scanner and wired as previously shown to points A, B, and G on the CE-232. Examine *Figure 8-9.*

The rest of the points on the CE-232 will be terminated within the scanner at places discussed just ahead and in the specific sections for your scanner.

The remainder of the installation involves point to point wiring for the most part. Most of the rest of this discussion will be focused on external installations, but the basic principles – and the actual connections (what point connects to what) – will apply to internals as well.

Fabricate a short multi-conductor wire bundle for the CE-232's Input-Output points. *(You might have done this in Steps P-Y)* A minimum of nineteen (19) wires are needed here.

Cut the cable to desired length for whichever installation you choose: if external, then long enough to go from the CE-232 board to the DB-25 connector; if internal, then long enough to go from the CE-232 board to the termination points in the scanner.

EXTERNAL INSTALLATION

Install the CE-232 in a suitable Project Box –metal (for shielding) is strongly suggested. The CE-232 board can be mounted on two or four metal standoffs in the box.

Install the CE-232's DB-9 connector on the back panel of the Project Box. Install the CE-232's DB-25 connector on the back panel of the Project Box.

Refer to the CE-232 Scanner/Computer Interface Schematic Diagram *(Figure 8-3),* the Component Location Diagram *(Figure 8-4),* and the Wiring Plan from CE-232 board to Scanner *(Figure 8-10)* as guides to the designated wiring points on the CE-232 board.

Use a VOM/DVM (or wire color codes) to keep track of which wire is used at any given point.

Make a record of pin numbers and color codes. Solder or bolt the ground wires N and G on the CE-232 board to the box's chassis.

Install a prewired female DB25 connector on the back panel of the scanner.

PRO-2004 – PRO-2005 – PRO-2006 DIFFERENCES

While the PRO-2004/5/6 are all pretty much the same scanner (electronically), there are mechanical differences among them, notably their logic-display boards.

The PRO-2004's logic-CPU board is all by itself on the bottom of the main chassis, well away from the separate display board tucked inside the front panel. The PRO-2005 and PRO-2006 are alike with a single logic-CPU-display board mounted inside the front panel.

The PRO-2005/6's logic-display board is installed vertically in the front panel, and that can be very intimidating to those who don't know how to get it out. It's not *that* difficult, and I'll guide you through it.

Meanwhile, since the PRO-2004 differs from the PRO-2005/6, they will be discussed separately. Watch for the header titles that apply to your scanner.

PRO-2004, PRO-2005, and PRO-2006

These specific wiring instructions are for the PRO-2005/6, followed by those for the PRO-2004. The instructions for each calls for some splicing, or soldering wires to other wires. This is largely for simplicity of verbiage, and you can (and should) devise your own scheme with pin-line connectors wherever that helps connecting one wire to another.

If you must solder the wires directly use good splicing techniques, including a bit of heat shrink tubing inserted over one of the wires before it is soldered to the other one. The heat shrink tubing is pulled over the solder joint and heated briefly with a heat gun or butane lighter until it shrinks down tightly to insulate the connection. DON'T USE TAPE!

I recommend the mini-connector technique, and one way this can be done is by use of break-apart pin-line sockets. You'll need two strips of 25 to make one 25-pin male/female combination.

You may have better ideas, depending on what's available in your area. Just don't use large jack/plug combinations because space is cramped and you need room not only for the CE-232 but also for other modifications in the future.

Therefore, use proper splicing techniques if other ideas fail you and if you don't like my pin-line socket idea. Splicing is a good technique for all-round use, with the singular liability that quick-disconnects/re-connects are not possible.

PRO-2005 and PRO-2006 ONLY

FRONT PANEL DISASSEMBLY

> *NOTE:* Cable connectors and ground straps should be disconnected from the main circuit board and chassis, *not* from the logic/CPU board.

1. Disconnect the PRO-2005/6 from main power. Remove the internal Memory Retention Battery. Remove the top and bottom cases from the chassis.

2. Disconnect all wires and cable bundles that go from the front panel assembly to the main circuit board. There are six (6) cable bundles and connectors to be disconnected from the top side of the scanner, and one cable bundle and connector on the bottom side of the scanner.

   Disconnect the two ground straps that go from the logic/CPU board to the bottom side of the scanner chassis.

3. Remove 4 (2 on each side) countersunk machine screws from the sides of the front panel that secure it to the main chassis. Gently, pull the front panel assembly away from the chassis until it's free.

4. Desolder the bare ground wire from the chrome metal shield that goes to the area by the VOL control and push this wire out of the way towards the VOL and SQUELCH controls.

5. Remove the six small screws that secure the logic/CPU/display board to the front panel.

6. Face the inside of the front panel as it is placed in an upright position, and locate the white, 13-pin connector (CN-501) at the upper left corner of the printed circuit board.

   This connector doesn't have any wires and doesn't look like a connector at first, but that's what it is. Insert a small flat blade screwdriver under the edge of that connector and gently pry upward.

   The entire logic/CPU/display board should then slip up, away from the plastic front panel and come loose in your hands. Handle it by its edges and be very careful, but don't let paranoia make a critical error.

> CN-501 is a female connector for 13 long pins (CN-601) that protrude up from the keyboard panel underneath, where you can't see it easily.
>
> Friction grips the CN-601 male pins tightly in CN-501, but the logic/display board separates easily enough from these pins.
>
> Use caution and protect those connectors!

Figure 8-10: CE-232 external installation

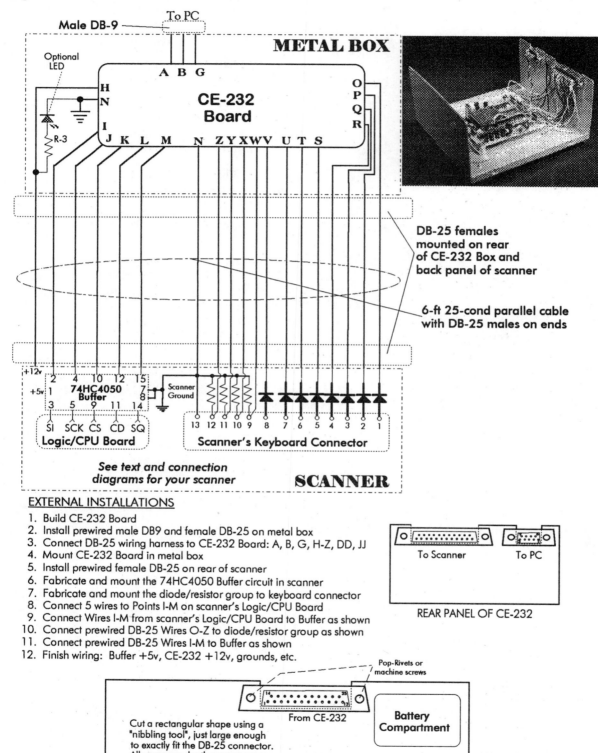

EXTERNAL INSTALLATIONS

1. Build CE-232 Board
2. Install prewired male DB9 and female DB-25 on metal box
3. Connect DB-25 wiring harness to CE-232 Board: A, B, G, H-Z, DD, JJ
4. Mount CE-232 Board in metal box
5. Install prewired female DB-25 on rear of scanner
6. Fabricate and mount the 74HC4050 Buffer circuit in scanner
7. Fabricate and mount the diode/resistor group to keyboard connector
8. Connect 5 wires to Points I-M on scanner's Logic/CPU Board
9. Connect Wires I-M from scanner's Logic/CPU Board to Buffer as shown
10. Connect prewired DB-25 Wires O-Z to diode/resistor group as shown
11. Connect prewired DB-25 Wires I-M to Buffer as shown
12. Finish wiring: Buffer +5v, CE-232 +12v, grounds, etc.

To Scanner   To PC

REAR PANEL OF CE-232

Pop-Rivets or machine screws

From CE-232

Battery Compartment

Cut a rectangular shape using a "nibbling tool", just large enough to exactly fit the DB-25 connector. Allow excess depth so rear cover lip can clear the DB-25. Also allow clearance for speaker, etc.

REAR PANEL OF PRO-2004/5/6 SCANNER

Figure 8-11: Details of connection points on PRO-2005/6 logic board

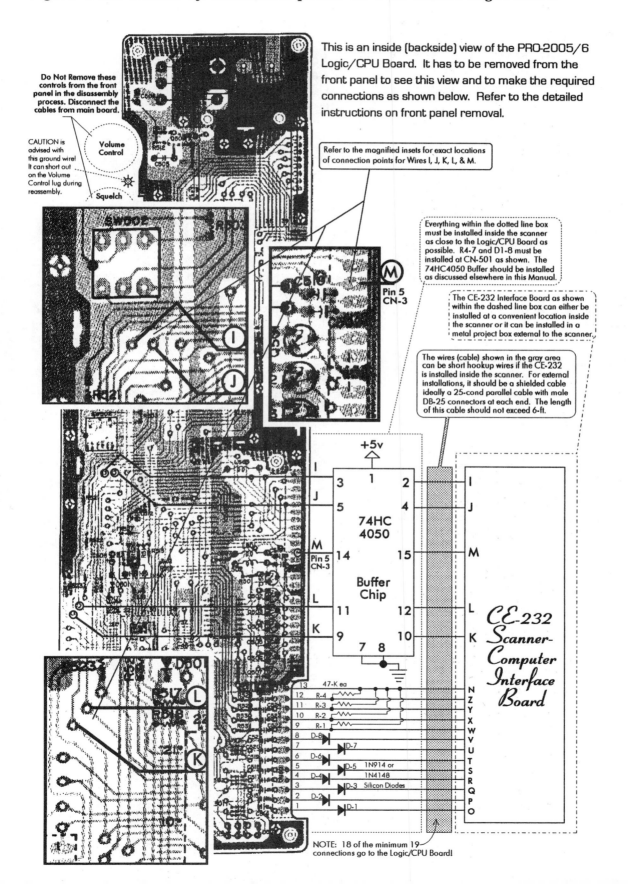

This is an inside (backside) view of the PRO-2005/6 Logic/CPU Board. It has to be removed from the front panel to see this view and to make the required connections as shown below. Refer to the detailed instructions on front panel removal.

Do Not Remove these controls from the front panel in the disassembly process. Disconnect the cables from main board.

CAUTION is advised with this ground wire! It can short out on the Volume Control lug during reassembly.

Volume Control

Squelch

Refer to the magnified insets for exact locations of connection points for Wires I, J, K, L, & M.

Everything within the dotted line box must be installed inside the scanner as close to the Logic/CPU Board as possible. R4-7 and D1-8 must be installed at CN-501 as shown. The 74HC4050 Buffer should be installed as discussed elsewhere in this Manual.

The CE-232 Interface Board as shown within the dashed line box can either be installed at a convenient location inside the scanner or it can be installed in a metal project box external to the scanner.

The wires (cable) shown in the gray area can be short hookup wires if the CE-232 is installed inside the scanner. For external installations, it should be a shielded cable ideally a 25-cond parallel cable with male DB-25 connectors at each end. The length of this cable should not exceed 6-ft.

M Pin 5 CN-3

+5v

74HC 4050

Buffer Chip

Pin 5 CN-3

CE-232 Scanner-Computer Interface Board

47-K ea
R-4
R-3
R-2
R-1
D-8
D-7
D-6
D-5 1N914 or
D-4   1N4148
D-3 Silicon Diodes
D-2
D-1

NOTE: 18 of the minimum 19 connections go to the Logic/CPU Board!

HOOKUP TO THE CE-232

7. Refer to the pictorial for the PRO-2005/6 logic-display PCB, *Figure 8-11,* and solder 5 short (6") color-coded wires to the back side of the logic-display board to points I, J, K, L, and M, as shown in the pictorial. Make written notes of which wire goes to what point. You don't want to forget what went where, so a drawing should go into your notebook.

8. Flip the logic-display board over so that the side with the chrome metal shield is exposed. Solder the anodes (unbanded ends) of 8 silicon switching diodes (1N914/1N4148) to the solder pads for pins 1 through 8 of CN-501. Solder a short wire (2") to pins 9, 10, 11, and 12 of CN-501. Dress up the 8 diodes and these 4 wires so they point up and out from the board and clip the ends so that all 8 diodes and 4 wires are of equal length. About 1/4" of cathode lead on the diodes will be about right.

NOTE: You can solder in a 13-pin strip pin-line socket to the 13 holes just beneath CN-501, so the female side is exposed.

Then prepare a mating 13-pin male strip to plug into that permanently soldered female strip. The 8 diodes and 4 short wires can be soldered to the removable "plug."

9. Replace the logic-display board back into the front panel, being observant of the 13 male pins on the keyboard that have to be lined with CN-501. Press the logic-display board partly down onto these 13 pins and then dress and route the newly-installed 5 wires over the bottom edge of the board so that they are free

and accessible. Press down on CN-501 again until the logic-display board solidly seats in the front panel.

You might have to jiggle the board a little to work the SOUND SQUELCH and DIMMER/LIGHT switches through their holes in the panel. Replace and tighten the 6 Phillips screws.

10. Resolder the bare ground wire near the VOLUME and SQUELCH controls back to the chrome metal shield, taking great care to see that it does not short against one of the lugs of the VOLUME Control. Reinstall the front panel to the scanner chassis. Plug in all previously removed connectors.

11. Solder the 5 wires I, J , K, L, and M from the logic-display board to their corresponding wires in the parallel cable. Solder Wire N of the parallel cable to the chrome metal shield of the logic-display board (Ground). Solder Wire H to the left end of R-229 as you face the front panel of the PRO-2005/6.

NOTE: Use of the 74HC4050 buffer is optional but highly recommended for internal installations; it is mandatory for external installations.

12. Identify and separate Wires O through Z from the bundle out the parallel cable. Refer to *Figures 8-10* and *8-11* and solder Wire O to the cathode of D-1 (at pin 1 of CN-501).

Complete the wiring to the 7 remaining diodes and 4 short wires as shown in the diagrams and pictorials.

This completes the PRO-2005/6 detail section.

Figure 8-12: PRO-2005/6 74HC4050 buffer connections

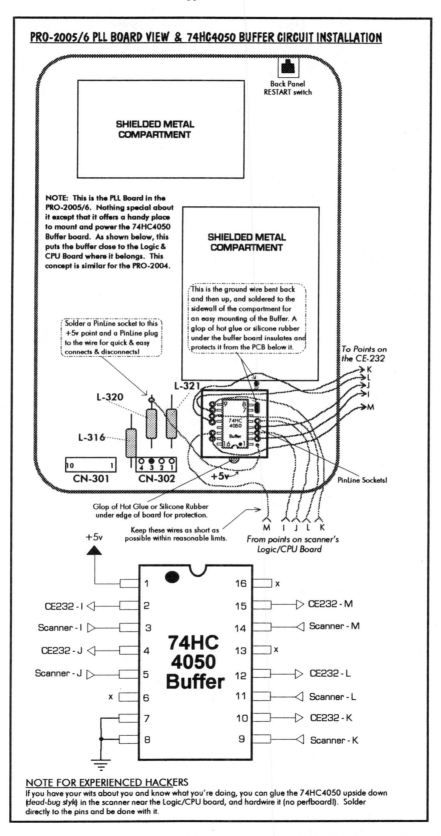

PRO-2005/6 PLL BOARD VIEW & 74HC4050 BUFFER CIRCUIT INSTALLATION

Back Panel RESTART switch

SHIELDED METAL COMPARTMENT

NOTE: This is the PLL Board in the PRO-2005/6. Nothing special about it except that it offers a handy place to mount and power the 74HC4050 Buffer board. As shown below, this puts the buffer close to the Logic & CPU Board where it belongs. This concept is similar for the PRO-2004.

SHIELDED METAL COMPARTMENT

This is the ground wire bent back and then up, and soldered to the sidewall of the compartment for an easy mounting of the Buffer. A glop of hot glue or silicone rubber under the buffer board insulates and protects it from the PCB below it.

To Points on the CE-232
K
L
J
I
M

Solder a PinLine socket to this +5v point and a PinLine plug to the wire for quick & easy connects & disconnects!

L-321

L-320

74HC 4050 Buffer

L-316

PinLine Sockets!

10   1
CN-301

4 3 2 1
CN-302

+5v

Glop of Hot Glue or Silicone Rubber under edge of board for protection.

Keep these wires as short as possible within reasonable limits.

M   I   J   L   K

From points on scanner's Logic/CPU Board

+5v

1	16 x
CE232 - I ◁ 2	15 ▷ CE232 - M
Scanner - I ▷ 3	14 ◁ Scanner - M
CE232 - J ◁ 4	13 x
Scanner - J ▷ 5	12 ▷ CE232 - L
x 6	11 ◁ Scanner - L
7	10 ▷ CE232 - K
8	9 ◁ Scanner - K

74HC 4050 Buffer

NOTE FOR EXPERIENCED HACKERS

If you have your wits about you and know what you're doing, you can glue the 74HC4050 upside down (dead-bug style) in the scanner near the Logic/CPU board, and hardwire it (no perfboard!). Solder directly to the pins and be done with it.

PRO-2004/5/6... PROTECTION

I have recommended an external installation because it has so many advantages, but I waited till now to tell you about the single electrical disadvantage. In this case, the pluses outnumber the minus by a huge margin. But, the minus has to be taken care of because it's a potential killer.

The CPU needs an electrically clean environment. If you do an external installation for the CE-232, you need a simple little circuit to protect the scanner's CPU from external noise, spikes, and static generated by nearby or connected hardware.

Since the CE-232 connects directly to the CPU at several points (I, J, K, L, and M), the CPU is susceptible to being zapped.

Provided with my Kit is a 74HC4050 High Speed CMOS Hex Non-Inverting Buffer, a 16-pin DIP standard IC. If you're rolling your own, get one.

The 74HC4050 isolates outputs from inputs and still cleanly transfers signals. Up to six signal lines can be protected with one 74HC4050. You will need a piece of perf board on which to mount the chip and a 16 pin DIP IC socket.

This little board is installed in the scanner near where Wires I-M terminate at the logic/CPU board. The closer the better.

PROCEDURE

Build the protection circuit on a tiny piece of perf board – I use a piece that's 8 holes by 10 holes with pin-line sockets for the chip's inputs and outputs to make connections easier and to aid troubleshooting when required.

Use an IC socket to avoid direct soldering of the chip.

Loop a stiff copper wire (18 gauge) through two holes in one corner nearest pins 7 and 8 of the 74HC4050 and bend/pinch and solder the loop so that it is tight and about 1 inch of the copper wire protrudes away from the perf board.

Solder pins 7 and 8 of the 74HC4050 to this ground wire.

Solder this 1" stiff copper wire to any chassis or PCB ground in the scanner near where Wires I-M from the CE-232 terminate. This wire not only serves as a ground, but also as a mount.

The idea is to install the 74HC4050 buffer circuit close to the scanner's logic/CPU board.

Connect the wire from Point "I" on the scanner's logic/CPU board to pin 3 of the 74HC4050. Connect the Wire "I" that goes out to the CE-232 to pin 2 of the 74HC4050.

Repeat this procedure as shown above for Wires/Points J, K, L, and M as shown in *Figure 8-12*. Connect pin 1 of the 74HC4050 to a source of regulated +5V, as shown in *Figures 8-12* and *8-14*.

PRO-2004 ONLY

You guys have it easier in *some* ways.

Disconnect *just* CN-501 from the left-rear corner of the logic-CPU board. Now, remove the seven screws that hold the logic-CPU board to the main chassis. Gently, flip this subassembly up and over toward the front of the scanner so you can work on the bottom side. *You do not need to remove any other connectors.*

Refer to the Installation Guide just ahead to see where to make your solder connections. 18 of the required 19 wires go to easy spots on this board, so relax and do the job carefully.

Fabricate and mount the simple 74HC4050 Buffer assembly you built onto that small perf board.

Solder 4 short wires from each of the solder pads for CN-505, pins 5, 6, 7, and 9, to the Input pins of the 74HC4050 Buffer, 3, 5, 9, and 11, respectively.

Study this 11-pin connector carefully from the top first, so that you can identify its eleven solder pads. At first glance, pin 1 doesn't look like a pin pad.

Make sure you can identify pin Pads 5, 6, 7, and 9 before soldering. Pin 1 doesn't look like pin 1 from the bottom, but you can tell by looking from the top.

Solder a short wire from pin 9 of CN-504 to Buffer Input pin 15. Easy enough. Again, make sure you *correctly* identify CN-504, pin 9.

Solder the anodes (unmarked ends) of 8 diodes, D1-D8, to CN-502, pins 1-8. Clip the anode leads to about 1/4" before soldering.

Correctly identify CN-502, pins 1-8. Then solder the four 47kΩ resistors, one each to CN-502, pins 9-12. The free ends of these resistors go to ground.

Figure 8-13: PRO-2005/6 main PCB - source of +12V for CE-232

Figure 8-13: PRO-2005/6 main PCB - source of +12V for CE-232

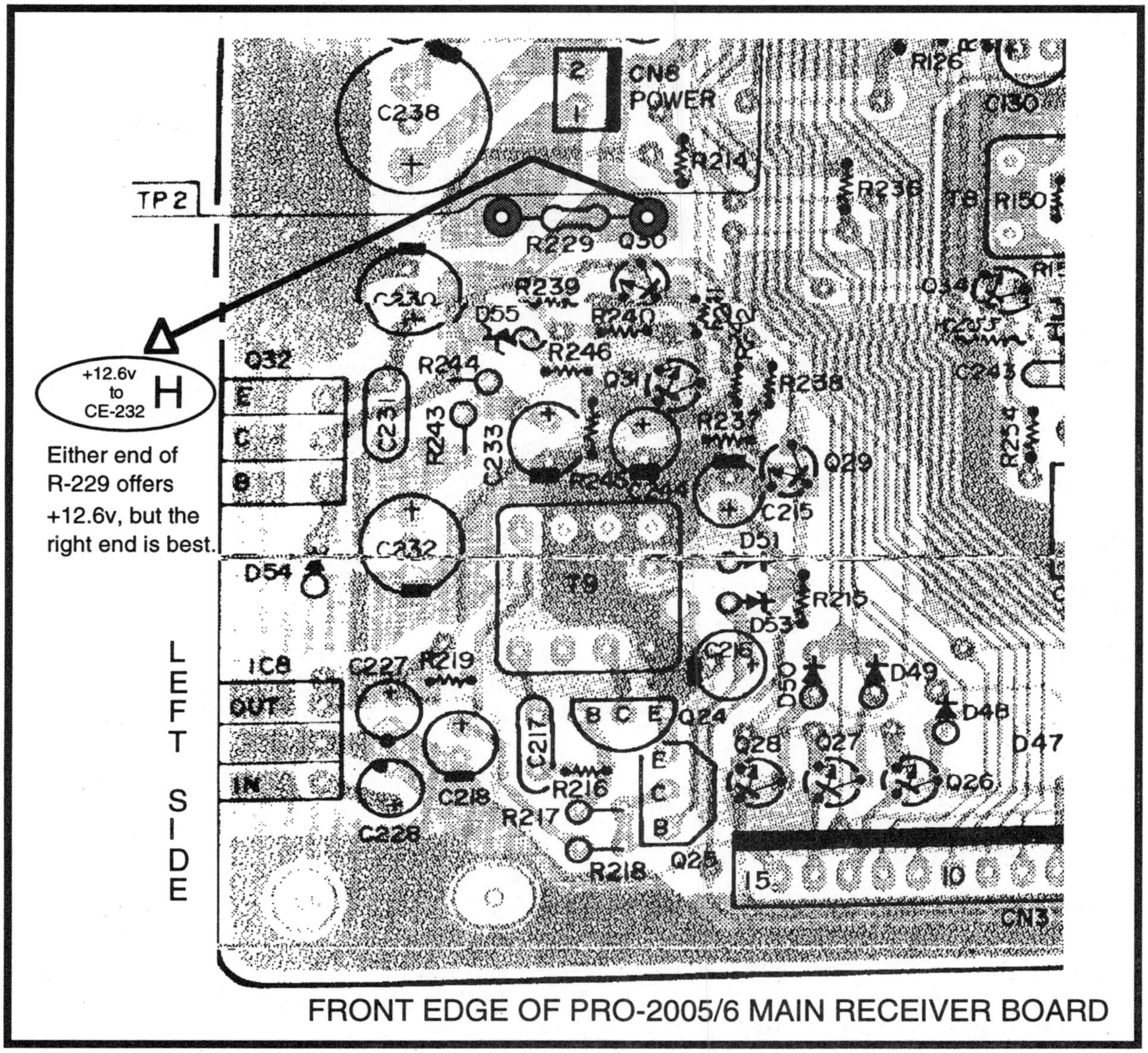

Solder 5 short wires (2") to CN-502, pins 9-13. Dress up the 8 diodes and these 5 wires so they point out from the board and clip the ends so that all 8 diodes and 5 wires are of equal length. About 1/4" of cathode lead on the diodes will be about right.

Make a diagram of the pinout or coding of these 19 wires so you don't have to remove this board again, and then reinstall the logic-CPU board back onto the chassis standoffs and replace the 7 screws. Reconnect CN-501.

NOTE: You can be slick at this point and solder in a 13-pin strip pin-line socket to the 13 solder pads of CN-502 so that the female side is exposed.

Then prepare a mating 13-pin male strip to plug into that permanently-soldered female strip. The 8 diodes and 4 short wires can then be soldered to the removable "plug;" a "pro" flourish here.

The socket can be superglued to the board, and hot-glued for strength after checkout.

Figure 8-14: PRO-2004 detail

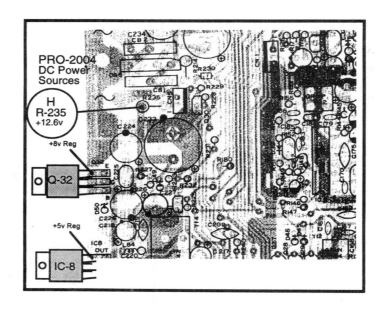

PRO-2004 CONTINUED

Solder Wire H from the CE-232 board to the exposed end of R-235 on the top-rear of the main board. See *Figure 8-14* for the location of R-235.

It's a good idea to solder or bolt a ground wire from the metal shells of any DB-9 or DB-26 connectors to the chassis/frames of the scanner and any external metal boxes.

Point N on the CE-232 board should also be connected to the chassis or frame in which it is mounted.

Figure 8-15: PRO-2004 key locations – note 74HC4050 buffer

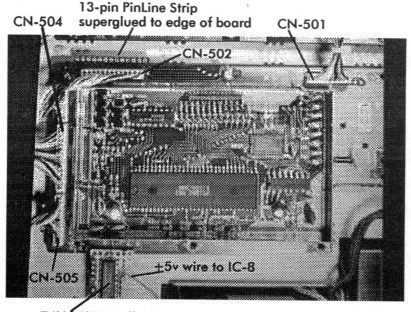

Figure 8-16: Connections to logic/CPU board

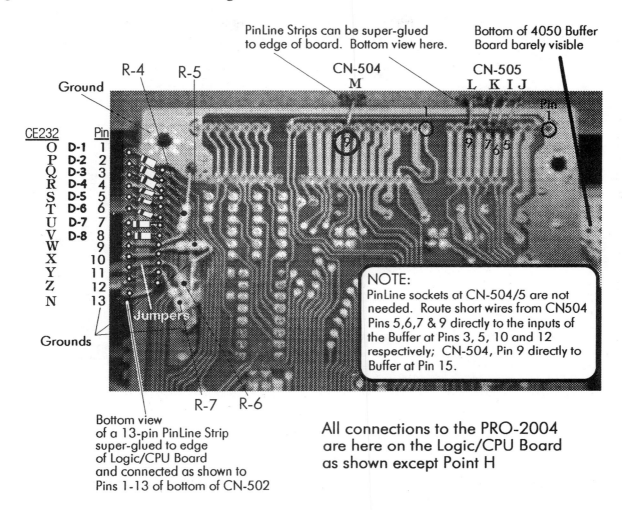

PinLine Strips can be super-glued to edge of board. Bottom view here.

Bottom of 4050 Buffer Board barely visible

R-4   R-5

Ground

CN-504
M

CN-505
L K I J

CE232		Pin
O	D-1	1
P	D-2	2
Q	D-3	3
R	D-4	4
S	D-5	5
T	D-6	6
U	D-7	7
V	D-8	8
W		9
X		10
Y		11
Z		12
N		13

Jumpers

Grounds

NOTE:
PinLine sockets at CN-504/5 are not needed. Route short wires from CN504 Pins 5,6,7 & 9 directly to the inputs of the Buffer at Pins 3, 5, 10 and 12 respectively; CN-504, Pin 9 directly to Buffer at Pin 15.

R-7   R-6

Bottom view of a 13-pin PinLine Strip super-glued to edge of Logic/CPU Board and connected as shown to Pins 1-13 of bottom of CN-502

All connections to the PRO-2004 are here on the Logic/CPU Board as shown except Point H

Solder the five Output Points (I, J, K, L, and M) from the Buffer Circuit to their corresponding wires that go to the CE-232 board.

Identify and separate Wires O through Z from the bundle that comes from the CE-232 board. Refer to the diagrams and pictorials and solder Wire O to the cathode of D-1 (at pin 1 of CN-502). Complete the connection of Wires P-Z to the seven remaining diodes and pins 9-12 of CN-502 as shown in the diagrams and pictorials.

This completes the portion of the project that is specific to the PRO-2004.

Figure 8-17: Keyboard matrix wiring

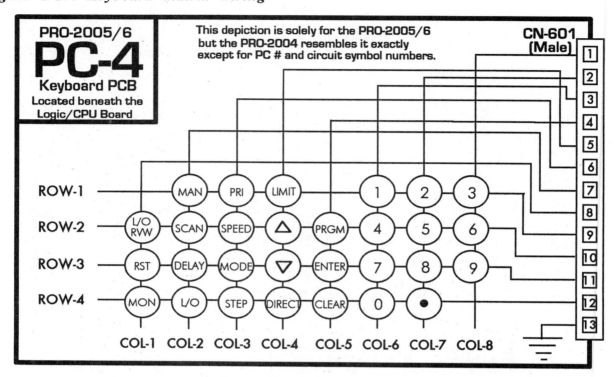

KEYBOARD MATRIX PCB (ALL)

Figure 8-17, above, shows the stock PRO-2005/6 Keyboard Matrix PCB and its associated male connector, CN-601. This information applies to the PRO-2004 also.

The configuration is not easily understood until the logic-display board is removed from the front panel for the work that must be done to it, at which time everything will become clear.

Figure 8-18 shows how to connect the 13 wires from the CE-232 to CN-501.

You can fabricate a connector to mechanically mate with CN-501 by soldering a 13-pin strip of

pin-line sockets to the 13 plated-thru (unused) holes just behind CN-501.

The males of another 13-pin pin-line strip will then mate with the exposed females of the previously soldered pin-line strip.

The diodes and resistors can be soldered to the removable strip for a convenient quick-disconnect arrangement, and it keeps the board looking neat.

A bit of the chrome metal shield over that end of the logic-display board has to be "nibbled" away to make more room for the new connector. Watch any sharp edges, and look out for metal filings.

Figure 8-18: CE-232 to CN-501 wiring details

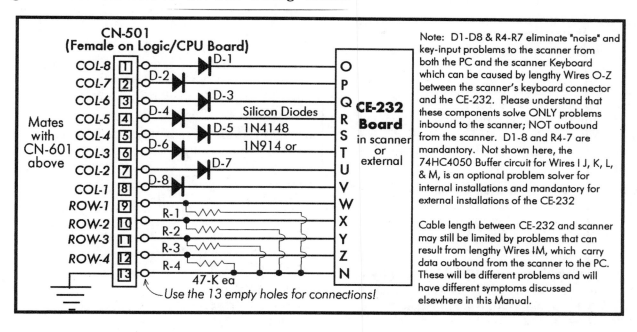

WHAT IF YOU RUN INTO TROUBLE?

You won't, if you follow my instructions to the letter. But, to quote CE-232 Murphy... "anything that goes will probably be inaccessible." Keep your dynamite handy.

If you encounter trouble, it will be due either to a failed component or to an error on your part. I'll help with a bit of guidance, and the first thing you need is an understanding of how the CE-232 functions. Let's walk through the circuit...

1. IC-8 accepts a range of +8 to +16V input and generates a regulated, steady +5V to power the CE-232.

2. The computer sends data or control signals to the CE-232 down Wire "A". The CE-232 sends data back to the computer on Wire "B". Wire "G" is the common or ground between the two.

   IC-1 is a dual RS-232 receiver + transmitter that lets your PC and the CE-232's microprocessor, IC-3, "talk" to each other.

3. The CE-232 receives data from the scanner on Wires I-M, with Wire N the common or ground (same as Wire G)

   Wires I-M have nothing to do with data or control signals sent to the scanner.

4. The CE-232's MPU sends data to and/or controls the scanner via IC-4, 5, and 6 and Wires O-Z with Wire N as common or ground. IC-4, 5, and 6 and Wires O-Z have nothing to do with what the scanner sends to the PC.

5. IC-3, the MPU, processes both data from the scanner as well as data or control signals to the scanner.

6. IC-2 won't let the MPU operate until DC power has stabilized after turn-on. The CE-232 will not operate till pins 1 and 2 of IC-2 are stable at +5V, ± 0.15V.

7. IC-7 is the User Switch Bank and is controlled by the MPU independently of everything else.

Whether or not everything works, this information will help you understand the unit. If you do have problems, this will help you define them when you seek help or troubleshoot on your own.

TROUBLESHOOTING

The CE-232 Interface has different circuits and signal flow paths, of which one is the Scanner Control section and another, Data Acquisition.

Trouble is less likely in the data acquisition side than in the control side, but it is important that you understand each physical path to avoid wild goose chases.

DATA ACQUISITION SIDE

Data Acquisition is the opposite of the "scanner control" that electronically presses the scanner's keys, from the AutoProgram or Keyboard Control functions.

Data Acquisition reads and processes the scanner's LCD data for replication on your monitor. It also acquires and processes scanner data for AutoLogging, LookUp, and Birdie Reject functions as well as for portions of the Script function.

The Scanner Control section consists of one half of IC-1, portions of IC-3, and most of IC-4, 5, and 6. Scanner control begins in the computer with signals sent to the CE-232 via Wire/Point "A".

Those signals are coded into MPU format by IC-1 (pin 13) and sent to the MPU from pin 12. The MPU (IC-3) processes control signals and operates IC-4, 5, and 6 to emulate keypresses on the scanner's keyboard via Wires/Points O through Z. The CE-232 Scanner Control section is shown in detail in *Figure 8-16*.

Data Acquisition begins in the scanner with sampling of display, clock, and squelch activity data at Points I, J, K, L, and M on the scanner's logic/CPU board.

The data are buffered (copied and isolated) and passed through our protective 74HC4050 Buffer and fed directly to the CE-232's MPU at pins 31, 32, 33, 39, and 42.

The MPU continuously processes the scanner data and transfers it out pin 29 to IC-1, pin 11 where the data are encoded into computer format and outputted as RS-232 serial data from pin 14 through Point "B" into the serial cable and on to your computer's COM1 or COM2 ports.

The Data Acquisition section is neither complicated nor trouble-prone and does not need further treatment here.

Figure 8-19 depicts the signal paths that were described above. It is useful to know something about them in the event your CE-232 ever develops problems.

Figure 8-19: Scanner Control section

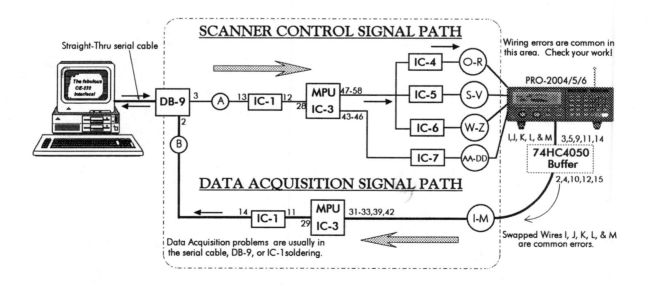

IN CASE OF (SERIOUS) DIFFICULTY

Many HB-232's and CE-232's have gone into service since August, 1991, when the first few were Beta tested. All bugs and glitches have since been worked out of the design, and the software is quite robust and not buggy.

If your CE-232 fails to perform properly, you will waste a lot of time with an attitude of *"I checked everything three times."* You simply have to check everything a fourth time.

Or more – because the problem is in the execution or in a part failure, but not in the design.

About the only realistic possibility of a problem not within your responsibility will be a defective part.

There are no known instances of this having occurred, but I suppose it could happen.

One fellow told us he replaced X-1 (8MHz crystal) with a new one and it worked. We don't know if he damaged the original or if it was defective from the factory. There have been very few cases of user-damaged parts, so components are not the primary focus for problem resolution.

On the other hand, after providing Technical Support for nearly three years, I do know something of where problems occur in those rare cases when it happens.

Let me give you the benefit of that experience.

PREPARING FOR TROUBLESHOOTING

Resistance and voltage measurements are of limited value when the problem is a wiring error, but voltage measurements at the test points are often informative. You should record these measurements for future reference, whether or not you have a problem at the beginning, and then use that information if a problem comes up in the future. Fill out and retain *Table 8-3*.

Table 8-3: Test results – your record

Attach the BLACK (-) lead of a voltmeter to any PCB ground or TP-1. Measure the voltage at each of the test points and record the results below:

#	Location	Nominal Or Typical	Your Test #1	Your Test #2	Your Test #3	Your Test #4	Your Test #5
A	TP-5	+ 5.0v ±0.1v					
B	TP-4	+12.6v ±3.4v					
C	TP-3	* 11v					
D[1]	B– C	1.6v ±0.3v					
E	TP-2	+5.0v ±0.1v					
F[2]	(D ÷100)(1000)	16-ma ±3-ma					

* *Absolute value is not as important as is the difference from (B) with 1.6v difference being typical. See (D)*

1. Subtract (C) from (B) and record the difference in (D)

2. Divide (D) by R-2 (100-0hms); multiply by 1000 and write the result in (F). This applies Ohm's Law to calculate current drawn by the CE-232. If the calculation is not less than 10-ma, nor more than 20-ma, there will not be a serious problem with the unit. If greater than 25-ma, shut off power immediately and troubleshoot the problem. NOTE: R-2 can burn out under current greater than 50-ma.

Table 8-4: Trouble history – learning from the mistakes of our fellow scannists

The assigned number tells you something about history, and therefore the likelihood of a specific area causing a problem

0 = No problem history at all...
1 = Rare
2 = Occasional
3 = More frequent

PROBLEMS AT THE PC, OR BETWEEN PC and CE-232:	**1** (avg)
Defective or incorrectly configured COM1 or COM2 port on the PC	1
Defective or incorrect type of serial cable	2
Reversed wires or errors in wires A, B, and/or G	1
Incorrect installation of the software	1
Misunderstanding of how to operate the software	2
PROBLEMS ON THE CE-232 BOARD:	**2** (avg)
Wires soldered to the wrong spots on the printed circuit board	2
Cold or defective solder joints on the printed circuit board	2
Reversed/swapped parts on the printed circuit board	1
Solder blobs/short circuits/open circuits on printed circuit board	2
Defective part on the printed circuit board due to User error	1
Defective part	0
Reverse installed IC's	2
Reverse installed polarized capacitors or resistor networks (RN1-4)	1
PROBLEMS BETWEEN CE-232 BOARD and SCANNER	**1** (avg)
Defective or incorrect type of cable	0
Defective wiring of connectors	1
Broken wire	1
PROBLEMS INSIDE THE SCANNER	**3** (avg)
Keyboard Connector Installation	*2* (avg)
Reversed polarity diodes, D1-8	1
Defective diodes (if from Radio Shack)	1
R4-7 installation errors	1
Wiring errors, Wires/Points O thru Z	3
Logic/CPU Board Wiring errors	*3* (avg)
Wires/Points I thru M	3
74HC4050 Buffer errors	1
DC Power	*0*
Wire H error	0
Wire N Error	0
Scanner failures associated with CE-232 Installation (errors)	1
Due to CE-232 (does not impact or alter scanner's performance)	0

TIPS - HINTS - IDEAS FOR TROUBLESHOOTING

Startup problems will usually be caused by one or more of the following. Check each carefully.

– solder-blobs and bridges between pins and traces (*short-circuits*)

– cold solder joints (*open/intermittent circuits*)

– reversed wires, wires soldered to wrong spots

– erroneous component installation, location

– incorrect polarity (+ and –) of diodes and electrolytic capacitors

– improper pin alignment of the integrated circuits, IC sockets, and resistor networks.

Double and triple check for correct soldering and parts locations on both sides of the CE-232 board BEFORE you install it in the metal box or scanner. If you just give the board a casual *"eyeball"* before installing it, then STOP HERE! GO BACK. DO IT RIGHT.

You need a strong light and magnifier to properly check the soldering of the CE-232 board. Solder joints should be bright, shiny, and smooth in appearance. It's easy to get solder bridges between those tightly spaced IC pins. You must not take your work for granted, even if you think you're an expert.

The microprocessor chip socket, if installed wrong, will get the chip in wrong – and it *will* blow! Check all other IC's for proper installation on the board, also. It's easy to get 'em *bass-ackwards*. I know. I'm the guy who has fixed a boatload of these where the only problem was a reversed chip.

LIKELY WIRING ERRORS, AND DIAGNOSTICS

The greatest potential for error will be the wiring of the CE-232 to the scanner. There are at least 19 output wires, and any could be miswired to the wrong spot or cross-wired, either on the CE-232 board, or at the termination points in the scanner.

If some keyboard functions work from the computer, but not others, you will find a pair of reversed wires in the O-Z group, probably one in the O-V group and one in the W-Z group. A quick study of the scanner's Keyboard Matrix Diagram in *Figures 8-17* and *8-18* may disclose which pair(s) may have been reversed.

For instance, if PRGM, ENTER, and CLEAR along with MANUAL, PRIORITY, LIMIT, 1, 2, and 3 don't work, you'll find wires R and W to be reversed.

If all functions "happen," but two or more don't work according to the specified keypresses, then you have one or more miswired pairs in the range of O-V or W-Z, but not both as would be the case if some functions worked and others didn't. For example, if pressing PRGM, ENTER, or CLEAR results in functions L/O RVW, RESET, or MONITOR, it's obvious that wires R and V are reversed.

If there is no computer keyboard control of the scanner but the Monitor gives a faithful reproduction of what's going on in the scanner, then an error or defective solder joint could exist in the vicinity of IC-6.

Also, be sure the INPUTS to the CE-232 are properly connected between the DB-9 connector and the CE-232 board. This includes the jumper between pins 1, 4, 6, and 8 on the DB-9 which do NOT go to the CE-232 board.

Pins 7 and 9 of the DB-9 have no connection at all. Pin 3 goes to Point A, pin 2 goes to Point B, and pin 5 goes to any ground Point G or N on the CE-232.

Other variables include the quality and type of your serial cable and/or your COM port. The serial cable must be the "straight-thru" variety, *not a null-modem cable*. If your cable is a null-modem type, you can invert it back to the straight-thru type with a "null modem adapter," commonly available at all computer outlets and Radio Shack.

A null-modem adapter on a null-modem cable turns it back into a "straight-thru" cable. If all else fails and you're just not sure of what kind of serial cable you have, try a null-modem adapter, just for the hell of it.

Now let's look at your COM port, which could be faulty. Cheaper serial I/O cards and old computers are sometimes only marginally capable of the 9600-bps serial data speed that's required by the CE-232 to keep pace with the scanner.

The bottom line is that your serial port, serial cable, and serial input (DB-9) wiring to the CE-232 must be proper. I would expect COM port problems to be more common with some of the el-cheapo or older PC/compatibles.

Finally, be sure that you have selected the correct COMport for the CE-232 – don't mistake COM2 for COM1, etc., and forget COM3 and COM4.

WHAT ELSE?

We worked hard to make the CE-232 both foolproof and simple enough to be handled (and operated) by the casual scannist. Yet, the CE-232 is a very sophisticated tool, and that sophistication increases complexity, creating more and more opportunities for Murphy to toot his whistle.

Knowing this, I have done everything but fire bullets and flame throwers at the CE-232. It works, and it goes right on working. If yours should fail to work, the first thing to do is RELAX – go have a cup of coffee or one cold beer. No doubt, that work took a lot out of you, so get away from it for a while.

When you come back, do so with the idea that the problem is going to be found on a few square inches of circuit board, either at the CE-232 or in the scanner.

No magic. No mystery. Just a little game of hide and seek awaits you. And you're gonna win!

CRYSTAL SPEEDUPS?

Several users had problems that frustrated me until I learned their scanners had been accelerated with a new crystal reference. Sorry, the CE-232 does not work with crystal-accelerated scanners. "Clip-or-add-a-diode" speedups are okay, but not crystal speedups.

Another scannist had me going for a couple of weeks until I learned he was trying to make his CE-232 work from an ancient Wang computer. Sorry, that old Wang and other historic computers may not be "PC/compatible." Another tried to get his to work with 256k RAM; nope, you need 512k minimum, with 640k better.

Another user went bananas for weeks, saying he'd checked everything dozens of times. Finally he sent me his CE-232 board. Wow, what a cobbled up mess! Repair of two defective solder joints and a general straightening up of things on the board resulted in perfect operation. *Yet, he swore upon all that was holy that there were no errors or bad solder joints on the board.*

A few hackers sent us the chips from their CE-232 Kits to test when nothing else at their end seemed to point to a solution. In most cases, the chips proved okay. Two users out of hundreds managed to zap their MPU chips (IC-3). Static discharge, mostly likely.

HELP ME HELP YOU!

If you run into trouble, can't find your way out, and gotta have Technical Support, help me by providing useful measurements, and a logical assessment from the procedures coming next.

Even if you have no trouble at the start (which is the case for the majority), you should make the measurements anyway so as to establish a base line for future troubleshooting, should it be required. Remember, even after you do everything in this book there's another dozen or two mods coming down the pike. So keep notes. You may never need them. But if you don't keep notes, it's certain that Murphy will step in.

SPECIFIC TESTS – RECORD THE RESULTS

For your records, and when invoking Tech Support (if needed):

1. Does the scanner receive signals normally?

If everything works just fine except that the scanner does not receive any signals, there will be a problem in Wires I, J, K, L, or M, or in the circuits at either end of these five wires.

If reception at the scanner is drastically affected and you find no errors in Wires I, J, K, L, or M, or in the respective circuits at either end, then you can suspect a blown MPU chip, IC-3, which we'll be happy to test for you.

You can do one additional test before suspecting this, however: remove the MPU from its socket and test the receiver again. If it works, the MPU could be blown. If the scanner still doesn't receive with the MPU pulled, then the problem is elsewhere and the MPU is likely okay.

2. Test the User Switches

Check by operating CTRL+F1, CTRL+F2, CTRL+F3, and CTRL+F4. Observe the

OUTPUT STATUS window in the upper-left of the computer's display to see that the zeroes change to 1's and back to 0's as the switches are operated. This test affirms the ability of the CE-232 and its MPU to respond to PC keyboard commands in general. It does not test the status of IC-7 itself, nor the status of your interconnecting wiring other than Wires A, B, and G

3. Test IC-7 and the User Switches

Connect the leads of an ohmmeter to Wires AA. High (almost infinite) resistance should be noted if User Switch #1 is OFF. Press Ctrl+F1 once, at which time the resistance should go low, down to 35-80 ohms or so. Press Ctrl+F1 again, and the resistance should go back high. This test can be repeated for Wires BB, CC, and DD (Ctrl+F2-F4) to test the integrity of IC-7. This test proves up the status of IC-7 and the ability of the CE-232 and its MPU to respond to PC keyboard commands in general.

User Switch errors are limited to Wires A, B, G, AA thru DD, and/or IC-7, only. Proper operation of the User Switches conclusively proves two-way communications between the computer and the CE-232. If other aspects of the CE-232 do not work, this is strongly suggestive of errors in your work.

NOTE: This test can be used to check the status of IC-4, 5, and 6, by plugging these chips into the socket for IC-7 and repeating the above tests.

4. Test the Data Acquisition side

Observe the display of the scanner's LCD functions on the Monitor. If the display on the Monitor is a faithful reproduction of the scanner's LCD, then Wires I, J, K, L, and M are proved good and the data acquisition mode is proved good.

You can go on to test the *AutoLogger, LookUp*, and *BirdieReject* functions if you like, but these tests are not necessary at this time.

Erratic or improper display in the Monitor is suggestive of errors associated with Wires I, J, K, L, and/or M, and/or the 74HC4050 buffer.

5. Test the CE-232 Scanner Control Circuit

Operate all the 29 normal scanner key functions from the keyboard of your PC. For instance, press MANUAL : SCAN : MANUAL. Does the scanner go into Manual mode, followed by Scan, and then Manual again?

Test all 29 scanner key functions in this manner. Make a table of those that work and those that do not. I like this sequence of keypresses: <M>anual : 1234 : <M>anual (*Error*) : <Backspace (Clear)> : <M>anual : 5678 : <M>anual (*Error*) <Backspace (Clear)> : <M>anual : 9000 : <M>anual (*Error*) <Backspace (Clear)> : <S>can followed by all other functions.

Problems with operation of the scanner from the computer keyboard when everything else is okay suggests faults or errors associated with Wires or Points O-Z, diodes D1-D8, resistors R4-R7, and/or IC-4, 5, and 6. You may as well verify proper voltage of +5V on pins 14 of each of IC-4, 5, 6, and 7, and IC-1, pin 16. An incorrect voltage at any of these supply pins may suggest a defective solder joint or PCB trace problem.

Since IC-4, 5, 6, and 7 are the same kind of chip, you can use the above test for IC-7 and the User Switches to check IC-4, 5, and 6 by swapping them around with IC-7, and repeating the AA-DD resistance checks.

6. Software installation and operation problems

This is a different animal altogether. The best checks and tests are to simply follow the directions for installation and operation of the CE-232 program and reinstall or continue working with it any number of times until you get it right.

We have observed that some Users are unfamiliar with the MS-DOS operating system, especially with hard and floppy disks and directory and subdirectory concepts.

Unfortunately, my job is not to teach you how to use your computer and I can't go to lengths over this kind of problem. Learning how to operate your computer and how to work under MS-DOS is your job and that's where it will stay. This is not to say that I won't help, because I will, but at my convenience and time. You can bet that I don't have the time to teach computing by mail.

But if you can work a BBS and send e-mail, then you know your way around the computer well enough to get help.

RESISTANCE AND CONTINUITY CHECKS

There isn't much else that can be dynamically tested. If all else fails at this point, the next logical step is to perform relevant point-to-point continuity checks with an ohmmeter. This method can be used to detect faulty solder joints and wire/trace paths, if close visual inspection doesn't arouse your suspicions.

Here's an example: Note in *Figure 8-3* that there is a direct connection between and among IC-4, 5, and 6, pins 1, 3, 8, and 10. If you were to put one lead of a VOM on pin 1 of IC-4, on top at the chip, you should measure virtually zero resistance to:

IC-4, pins 3, 8, and 10
IC 5, pins 1, 3, 8, and 10
IC-6, pins 1, 3, 8, and 10.

If a measurement of more than 1Ω is detected, that's a sign of trouble somewhere. You can perform a lot of continuity tests using *Figure 8-3* as a "roadmap." Just make sure all power to the CE-232 is off before doing resistance/continuity measurements.

TEST EQUIPMENT TIP

Here's a little tip for your VOM: use the kind of test leads that have *alligator clips* or *"mini hook clips"* on the business end. Get a large sewing needle, about 2-3" long, and wrap the eyelet end with tape to build up an insulated handle. Two pieces (with a gap for the alligator clip) of thin heat shrink tubing is even better, and let it extend to within a millimeter or so of the tip.

The idea is to make a very slender and very sharp test probe for the RED (+) lead of the meter. Grip the alligator or hook clip to the body of the needle when making a measurement. Benefits are hard to describe, but they'll be clear after you use "fat" test probes that come with most meters nowadays.

The sharp sewing needle allows entry into cramped areas to "dig" into solder spots and traces for quick tests. The thin insulated probe ensures that your test is "isolated," and touches exactly the right spot and nothing else.

Also, it's sharp and doesn't slide off the test points as easily as standard (blunt) test probes. Keep several of these "needle probes" handy.

RUMINATIONS

IC-3 cannot be tested and you really should not attempt to make any measurements at its pins. If all else fails and you think IC-3 has gone south, I can test it for you for a nominal shipping and handling charge.

Consider this a contingency to lean upon if you draw a blank on other options available to you. Statistically, one out of 500 Users may blow the MPU chip. Careful handling will reduce the risk.

If diodes D1-8 are connected backwards, the unit will have no keyboard control of the scanner, but no harm will be done; just reverse them. If the electrolytic capacitors are installed backwards, chances are that they will be damaged. Radio Shack carries them.

Unless you physically damage one, it is most unlikely that the monolithic capacitors will ever fail. R-2 is subject to failure by overheating if the CE-232 circuit ever draws too much current. In this context, R-2 serves as a protective fuse for IC-8 and the CE-232 in general, not to mention an easy way to calculate current drain.

R-2 will probably burn up (and turn black) with a current above about 50mA. If R-2 ever burns up, something else will have caused it. Like R-2, R-1 is unlikely to ever fail unless there's another problem somewhere else.

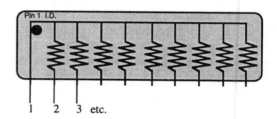

Resistor networks, RN-1, 2, 3, and 4, will never fail unless you do something that destroys them.

A resistor network is internally like the drawing above. The resistor networks can be tested with an ohmmeter by measuring the resistance between pin 1 and each of the remaining pins in the network. See the diagram here for how they're laid out.

Replacements can be done with conventional resistors installed into the holes for pins 2, 3, 4, etc., and the upper leads all soldered together and routed back to the hole for pin 1, as shown above.

IDIOSYNCRASIES

My 2006 won't AutoProgram...

A few PRO-2006's have surfaced in which everything except the AutoProgram function works perfectly. Slower settings of the time constant won't stop the "error" messages in the scanner's display.

RELAX: There is an immediate and easy fix for this problem: use the 20045V13.PER file in the Basic Setup for the CE-232 Program. Just go back and redo your configurations, selecting the PRO-2004/5 setting instead of that for the PRO-2006.

This problem is rare and we've not seen it on the bench, but some PRO-2006's are afflicted with this oddity.

We suspect this phenomenon are caused by internal variances of devices within the scanner, which are not considered by the Program's 2006V13.PER file. So use the one for the PRO-2004/5 and you'll be all set with no handicap or limitations.

In fact, scanners with this odd problem will AutoProgram somewhat faster under the 2004/5V13.PER file than "normal" PRO-2006's with the standard setup. So except for the momentary adrenaline it's really an advantage.

What if it won't stop?

We've seen this problem in a few PRO-2004's, but it could appear in any, so I developed a sure-fire fix.

The problem shows up in CE-232s that work perfectly in all respects, but the scanner won't STOP even on strong signals when in the SCAN or SEARCH modes. Yet, if you MANUAL-step to a known signal, reception is just fine.

The cause of this problem is an oddity associated with the cable or wiring between the CE-232 and the scanner.

The culprit will be found to be in the area of Wires I, J, K, L, and/or M, and can sometimes be alleviated by shortening or rerouting the wires between the scanner and the CE-232. But in a few cases, nothing longer than 1 foot works.

We'd let it go at that, except that some people really need a longer cable than that.

For them, I designed a simple add-on circuit to permit any reasonable length and method of routing of the interconnect cable, to at least 6 feet or more.

So take your choice: shorten the cable until it works, or add a 74HC4050 buffer circuit for Wires I, J, K, L, and M as discussed earlier in this chapter. Install that buffer, anyway, if you know what's good for you and your scanner.

TECHNICAL SUPPORT

It's costly when hobbyists do their own work and then need Tech Support. To control that expense, there are restrictions that I must impose, and they are not flexible.

The most important is: *absolutely no voice tech support whatsoever.* The preferred method is to log on to my BBS (619) 578-9247 after 5:30pm and before 1:30pm, Pacific Time, where you will be guided to the forum for the CE-232.

This forum has a nice backlog of tech support messages and support files, and is electronically networked to other BBS's around the world.

IF you have read the backlog and did not find the information you need, ask for help!

The bottom line is that I provide accurate and to-the-point support for the CE-232, but to get it you must help me do it cost-effectively. If you do, you're assured of my assistance if you need it.

Now, *please* scan through Chapter 1 again.

SPECIALIZED HELP RESOURCES: BBSs

Regarding the HB-232, you can also reach me (and others who know a lot about the design and its operation) via the HB-232 message base on any of the following BBS's.

Incidentally, most of these BBS's have some dedication to radio, so you may find them interesting for other reasons than just CE-232 Tech Support.

For instance, all carry my generic radio engineering and hacking conference called RADIO-TEK.

That's where you can find answers to general technical questions about my books and their contents, and lively discussions of other things, too.

Table 8-5: BBS support for the CE-232

Telephone	ST	City	SySop	BBS Name
*619-578-9247	CA	San Diego	Bill Cheek	Hertzian Intercept
206-750-9703	WA	Vancouver	Leroy Pluard	Powers Of Two
315-425-5580	NY	Syracuse	Jim Bernier	SBE Syracuse
319-556-4536	IA	Dubuque	Pat Powers	Tri-State Data Exchg
319-583-6462	IA	Dubuque	Mike Donovan	Spec-Com
504-886-2157	LA	Sun	Nolan Lee	WSTPC
513-297-0250	OH	Dayton	Dan Hughes	Intercept Technology
619-278-7361	CA	San Diego	Brenda Donovan	PRI Wildcat. BBS
619-669-0385	CA	Indian Springs	Joe Nicholson	The General Alarm
810-478-4284	MI	Farmington Hills	Pat Richard	Enterprize
816-627-6366	MO	Kirksville	Forrest Joyner	NEMO Wildcat. BBS
908-245-6614	NJ	Roselle	Marv Shelton	The Micro Room
909-984-9580	CA	Ontario	Larry Files	Teleterm Amiga West
914-342-4585	NY	Wawayanda	Steve Fleckenstein	Red Onion Express
916-577-4438	CA	Lake Tahoe	Frank Gaude	HighSierra Online
297-8-56851	Aruba	Matividiri	Gerardo Oduber	Hack on The Beach

* Hours of operation: 5:30pm-1:30pm, Pacific Time, weekdays, 24-hrs/weekends/holidays

OPERATING THE CE-232 INTERFACE

If you choose to write your own software then you'll have to write operating instructions that comply with that software. If you use a third-party control program or the program that I supply, the operating instructions will be on disk for you.

Therefore, not much space is required here for instructions on operating the system, but I will tell you about a few things to pique your interest and to keep the flame alive.

The AutoProgrammer is one of the strong suits of the CE-232 because it takes the drudgery and errors out of your channel programming.

Basically, you push a button, and the computer finds the file and loads it through the CE-232 into the scanner's memory.

The AutoProgrammer file is a plain ASCII, comma-delimited, text file with the extension of .APF.

My home is near Miramar Naval Air Station, here in San Diego. That's the (former) home of Top Gun training. Every year we have a truly major military air show, which invariably features many historic airplanes and exhibits.

It is also a showcase for our Navy's flight demo team; the Blue Angels. Their comm is a standard package, with specific frequencies allocated to the team, not to the location. It's fun listening to them as they rehearse and perform. With the CE-232 it's *more* fun.

Here is a ***portion*** of one of my *.APF files for the Blue Angels air team. The file is called BLUEANGL.APF

Table 8-6: BLUEANGL.APF

```
,161,121.900,    ,D,,Blue Angels - Ground Support
,162,123.400,    ,D,,Blue Angels - Common Airshow
,164,142.000,    ,D,,Blue Angels - Maintenance Alfa
,168,143.000,    ,D,,Blue Angels - Maintenance Bravo
,169,241.400,am,D,,Blue Angels - Air to Air Channel
,160,250.800,am,D,,Blue Angels - Air to Air Channel
,171,251.600,am,D,,Blue Angels - Demonstration
,172,263.350,am,D,,Blue Angels - Flight Line common
,174,275.350,am,D,,Blue Angels - Comm 1 Lead and Formation
,175,302.100,am,D,,Blue Angels - Comm 2 Talkback
,176,302.150,am,D,,Blue Angels - Comm 3 Solos
,177,307.700,am,D,,Blue Angels - Comm 2 Formation talkback
,179,360.400,am,D,,Blue Angels - Comm    Solos
```

(Yes, I know there are many more Blue Angel frequencies. This is a "portion.")

The AutoProgram function allows the user to program the scanner's channels from a plain text file that's been organized and structured to a specific format.

When selected, a Dialog Box pops up to allow selection of the file. Choose the desired file by highlighting it and press Enter. If you change your mind and don't want to load a file just press ESC. Additional data may be requested depending upon the option selected.

NOTE: The file must be a text file with data in the format shown below. The AutoProgrammer requires the delimiters (commas) to be present. The field sizes shown are maximum values.

The AutoLogger generates text files in exactly the same format as required by the AutoProgrammer, so the description will apply to both:

The first field is blank (not important here).

The next sets channel 160 to be programmed with 250.800MHz, AM mode, Delay set, no LockOut, and a brief description of the assignment.

The AutoProgrammer ignores the description. Easy as 1-2-3 when you examine it.

Table 8-7 shows the exact structure of an APF and LOG file, and descriptions of each element follow that.

Table 8-7: APF and LOG file structure

1 Filter	2 Chan	3 Freq	4 Mode	5 D	6 L	7 Ops	8 Step	9 Date	10 Time	11 Duration	12 Anything
aaaaaaaaaaaa,	BBB,	CCCC.CCCC,	DDD,	E,	F,	GGG,	HHHH,	IIIIII,	JJJJJJ,	KKKKKK,	xxxxxxxxxxxxxxxx
a	B	C	D	E	F	G	H	I	J	K	*your data*
12	3	9	3	1	1	3	4	6	6	6	255 chars/line
Commas distinguish one						<------ These fields, if sent to the ------ >					
field from the next						<------ CE-232, are *ignored* by the ------ >					
						<------ AutoProgrammer ------ >					

Now, here's what that all means...

A – Reserved field consisting of one character that is always logged blank by the AutoLogger, used by the AutoProgramming function only and can be up to 12 characters.

B – Up to three characters (0-400) represents the **channel #** or **search bank #**.

C – This field is the **frequency** and consists of nine characters (including the decimal point).

eg: 1234.6755 (MHz)

D – **Receive Mode (WFM, NFM, AM)** – three characters

E – **Delay** – (**blank** = delay off , "D" = delay on) – one character

F – **Lock-out** – (**blank** = lockout off , "L" = lockout on) – one character

The AutoProgrammer ignores everything after the 6th comma or Field "F".

The following fields are not used by the AutoProgrammer, but are generated by the AutoLogger.

G – **Op Mode** – Scanner Operating Mode: three or four characters as shown below:

SrUp – Search up

SrDn – Search down

Prgm – Program

Man   – Manual

Scan – Scan

H – **Step Size** – one to four characters, including decimal: 12.5, 5, 50 or 30 *(kHz)*

I – **Date** – six characters: YYMMDD

J – **Start Time** of signal – six characters – 24 hour format: HHMMSS

K – **Duration Time** of signal – six characters – 24 hour format: HHMMSS

Table 8-8: Typical AutoLogger output

Filter	Chan	Frequency	Mode	Dly	L/O	OpMde	Step	Date	Time	Duration
,	283,	450.2875,	nfm,	,	,	Scan,	,	950303,	164538,	000007,
,	320,	173.3750,	nfm,	,	,	Scan,	,	950303,	164549,	000006,
,	310,	857.6750,	nfm,	,	,	Scan,	,	950303,	164605,	000014,
,	306,	455.7125,	nfm,	,	,	Scan,	,	950303,	164626,	000010,
,	310,	857.6750,	nfm,	,	,	Scan,	,	950303,	164641,	000009,
,	307,	455.5000,	nfm,	,	,	Scan,	,	950303,	164656,	000044,
,	320,	173.3750,	nfm,	,	,	Scan,	,	950303,	164750,	000005,
,	320,	173.3750,	nfm,	,	,	Scan,	,	950303,	164801,	000010,
,	288,	161.7600,	nfm,	,	,	Scan,	,	950303,	164822,	000002,

NOTE: Maintain your frequency records in a database manager program. Most database programs can import and export comma-delimited ASCII text files in the formats above.

MORE DOCUMENTATION — FREE!

Gosh, there are a hundred other things I could tell you about that are in the documentation. The CE-232 documentation package is available for free download from my BBS.

The downloadable doc file is CE232MAN.ZIP. For now, go back and review the features and functions of the CE-232 as described in the beginning of this section.

Detailed operating instructions are available on the disk that I provide, and in the downloadable CE-232 file, and in the hard copy Manual.

WHO ELSE SUPPORTS THE CE-232 INTERFACE?

PerCon Corporation supplies frequency data on CD-ROM and floppy disks straight from the FCC's records. Yeah, so do others (they say), but PerCon is unique. For one, their prices are low, and they are the prime contractor to the FCC to produce CD's, so you don't get any more direct than that.

But the slickest thing of all is that most PerCon CD databases come with a function that produces CE-232 Autoprogrammer (*.APF) files, all ready to feed into your scanner, hands off.

That's right! You need only query the master database for records of interest, and when the query is complete you press a button to have the records compiled into CE-232 Autoprogrammer format. Not only that, but these *.APF files are keyed to serve as the CE-232's LookUp files as well.

What a package!

PerCon offers a variety of products, one or more of which are probably tailored to meet your needs and the needs of your CE-232 Interface, including a full line of FCC frequency databases, ham and repeater, and FAA Frequency/Aircraft/Pilot and Airport Databases. Write or call:

PerCon Corporation
4906 Maple Springs/Ellery Rd
Bemus Point, NY 14712
Voice (716) 386-6015, fax 386-6013

Intercept Technology makes the mother of all enhancements for the CE-232, a solid-state **V**oice **A**ctivated **D**igital **E**lectronic **R**ecorder, called VADER. Imagine, if you will, a tape recorder with no moving parts that records signals from your scanner as controlled by the intelligent CE-232 Interface.

VADER works independently from the CE-232 otherwise, but records a special log file just like the AutoLogger does, and synchronizes all recorded sound to this log file. VADER is better called an intercept analyzer.

When your recording session is finished, you can play back the material as you would with a normal tape recorder, but there is much more.

For instance, you can selectively play back by channel or frequency, skipping everything else. After an all-night recording session, you can actually follow the events and conversations in sequential order. You can play back hand-selected intercepts or automatically by channel, frequency, groupings of identical frequencies, time of day, and duration.

VADER offers sound processing and convenient controls for instant lookup and playback, including repeats and partial repeats. There's a lot more, so you've got to get the data sheet and brochure for yourself.

VADER is basically "plug and play" and quite easy to install and set up. VADER is an AT-size plug-in board that works in most AT/compatible computers, 286 and up. Mine has worked well in a 386SX/16, 486DX/50, and in my Pentium. VADER's secret is the 16 MB of low-cost on-board audio RAM that stores up to an hour's worth of continuous audio.

This normally means several hours to several days of recording time, depending on the density of activity and the number of channels or bandwidth that you SCAN or SEARCH with VADER.

The audio stored in VADER's memory can be transferred to your hard disk at any time, and can even be converted to *.WAV files for playback and processing through other multimedia accessories. Perhaps for sound enhancement?

VADER will run from MS-DOS™, Windows™, or Windows 95™ and offers tremendous power to your monitoring capabilities. For more information, write to

Intercept Technology
74 Western Ave.
Enon, OH 45323

or log on to their BBS at (513) 297-0250. Detailed information is available in their BBS Conference Area #2 and you can download a demo VADER file from File Area #1. Intercept Technology is a high tech company with a sideline in hobby radio.

They cannot deal with casual hobby inquiries by voice phone, but once you're a customer, they'll do everything but fly out to your location to make sure you get up and running. Good guys there!

If you use a Macintosh computer and are interested in the CE-232 Interface, there may be hope. While I don't know a Mac computer from a Mack truck, at least two Mac developers have produced software for the CE-232 and the Mac computer.

If you want more information, send me a business-sized SASE with the incoming envelope clearly marked, "CE-232/Mac Info" and I will be happy to put you in touch with Mac people.

You can also send me e-mail or log onto my BBS for the information.

THIRD-PARTY PC SOFTWARE

There are third party control IBM/PC programs for the CE-232, but either I have not been authorized to release their particulars, or their programs are still in the beta testing phases.

The control program that I provide for the CE-232 is very powerful and fully functional, but these other guys have worked to make theirs even better. You can log onto my BBS for the latest.

IF YOU DON'T WANT TO ROLL YOUR OWN........

THIS SECTION WAS INTENDED AS A SERVICE, NOT AN ADVERTISEMENT, BUT YOU ARE AUTHORIZED TO BECOME INDIGNANT IF YOU MUST.

The CE-232 is available as a Kit of Parts, Program Disk, and detailed Instruction Manual for the PRO-2004/5/6. Selected other scanners are also supported at extra cost.

The Basic Kit includes a printed circuit board, microprocessor with socket, 9 IC's, 4 resistor networks, 1 crystal, 7 resistors, 8 diodes, 15 capacitors, and a partridge in a pear tree.

NOT supplied are: computer, scanner, serial cable, common IC sockets, wiring, lugs, connectors, pin-line sockets, tools, solder, project box, and optional items.

The kit is functionally complete. Whether you use it or gather the parts yourself, the disciplines are the same. Assembly and installation require basic soldering skills, patience, and the ability to read and follow directions.

Installation, whether in a project box or inside the scanner, is a mechanical task. The CE-232 has been beta-, gamma-, and market-tested by hundreds of hobbyists, from entry level to expert.

Construction and installation typically requires 6-12 hours. For a hobbyist, the best results are obtained if the work is broken into segments of 2-3 hours each.

IF YOU CAN'T FIND ALL THE PARTS...

But you still want to roll your own CE-232 Interface, then you can get the most critical ones from me, independent from the kit offered above. There are only two parts that have been an occasional problem: IC-2 and IC-3.

IC-2 is called an "Undervoltage Sensing Circuit," the purpose of which is to prevent the MPU (IC-3) from operating when the supply voltage is too low. This is a critical part and cannot be substituted or eliminated.

Part numbers known to be viable are the Motorola MC34064 and the Texas Instruments TL7757C. I don't know of others. The MPU is a Motorola 68HC11F1FN and there are no substitutes. A good independent source of either IC-2 or IC-3 is Future-Active Electronics, (800) 757-9438.

If they are out of stock, and you can't find an alternative retailer, write, or call my BBS for a price. DigiKey Corporation is a reliable supplier of all the rest of the parts required for the CE-232.

For that matter, you can get most of the resistors, capacitors, and connectors from Radio Shack. You can even special order most of the chips and the crystal from Radio Shack.

If you prefer, I can usually provide one-stop shopping for almost anything you'll need, but please understand that I am not a parts-house and cannot price-compete with the big guys. Please don't expect me to sell a chip for the same price as the company that sells a few thousand a month.

Therefore, I do not provide common components on a piecemeal basis. *Table 8-9* is a list of what I *can* supply, should you have supplier problems.

Table 8-9: What I can provide...

Item	Description
CE-232K1	CE-232 Kit of Essential Parts, Program Disk, detailed Manual
CE-232K2	CE-232 Assembled/Tested Board, Program Disk, detailed Manual
Program1	Current CE-232 program, and supporting files/docs: 3.5" disk
Program2	Current CE-232 program, and supporting files/docs: 5.25" disk
PCB	Etched/Printed Circuit Board, ready to assemble
IC-3	MC68HC11F1FN Microprocessor Unit
XU-3	PLCC 68-pin Leadless Chip Carrier (LCC) Socket for IC-3
IC-1	MAX232CPE or AD-232 RS-232 Receiver/Transmitter (I/O)
IC-2	TL7757C or MC34064P-5 Undervoltage Sensing IC
IC-4,5,6,7	74HC4066 Quad Bilateral Switch, 4 each
IC-8	78L05 Voltage Regulator, +5V @ 100mA, TO-92
IC-9	74HC4050 Hex Non-inverting Buffer
RN-1-4	Resistor Networks, 4 each
X-1	Microprocessor Crystal, quartz, HC-18, 8MHz
R1-7	Resistors, all required, 7 each
C1-15	Capacitors, all required, 15 each
D1-8	Silicon switching diodes, 8 each
CE-DOC	The complete Assembly, Installation, and Operation Manual for the CE-232
XU-1,4-7	IC Socket Kit, 1 each, 16 pin DIP, and 4 each, 14 pin DIP, machine pin
J-1	DB-9 jack, male
J-2	DB-25 jack, female
W-1	Serial cable, 9-cond, straight-thru, w/female DB-9 and your choice of other end
W-2	Parallel cable, 25-cond, shielded, (DB-25 male)-to-(dB-25 male)
Misc	Pin-line sockets, strip of 16 (4-8 strips required)

Contact me by BBS, FAX, e-mail, or U.S. Mail for a current price list. You can also call my business office for matters of this nature, with the understanding that I'm not available by phone and that the receptionist does not offer tech support of any kind. Here are the "contact" details once again:

COMMtronics Engineering
World Scanner Report
PO Box 262478
San Diego, CA 92196-2478

BBS/FAX (619) 578-9247, 5:30pm-1:30pm, Pacific
Voice admin: (619) 578-9247, 1:30pm-5:30pm, Pacific
Internet: bcheek@cts.com
Compuserve: 74107,1176
FidoNet: 1:202/731

Table 8-10: Resource List

In no particular order of preference, the following companies are known to provide parts, materials, and other resources essential, useful, or supplementary to the CE-232 Interface:

All Electronics Corp.	PO BOX 567	Van Nuys	CA	91408	(800) 826-5432	Parts/Materials
COMMtronics	PO Box 262478	San Diego	CA	92196	*(619) 578-9247	CE-232 Source
Derf Electronics	37 Plain Ave	New Rochelle	NY	10801	(800) 645-5030	Parts/Materials
Digi-Key Corporation	701 Brooks Ave So.	Thief River Falls	MN	56701	(800) 344-4539	Parts/Materials
Electronic Salvage Parts	706 Middle Country Rd	Centereach	NY	11720	(800) 645-5030	Parts/Materials
Fordham Radio	260 Motor Parkway	Hauppauge	NY	11788	(800) 645-9518	Test Equip/Tools
Future-Active Electr	41 Main Street	Bolton	MA	01740	(800) 757-9438	Parts/Materials
Hosfelt Electronics, Inc.	2700 Sunset Blvd	Steubenville	OH	43952	(800) 524-6464	Parts/Materials
Intercept Technology	74 Western Ave	Enon	OH	45323	#(513) 297-0250	Vader
JameCo Electronics	1355 Shoreway Rd	Belmont	CA	94002	(415) 592-8097	Parts/Materials
Jensen Electronic Tools	7815 S. 46th Street	Phoenix	AZ	85040	(602) 968-6231	Tools/Supplies
MCM Electronics	858 E. Congress Park Dr.	Centerville	OH	45459	(800) 543-4330	Parts/Materials
Mouser Electronics	2401 Hwy 287 No.	Mansfield	TX	76063	(800) 346-6873	Parts/Materials
Newark Electronics	5308 W. 124th ST	Alsip	IL	60658	(312) 371-9000	Parts/Materials
Parts Express Intnti	40 E. First Street	Dayton	OH	45402	(800) 338-0531	Parts/Materials
PerCon Corp	4906 Maple Springs	Bemus Pt.	NY	14712	(716) 386-6015	FCC DB
Tandy National Parts	900 E. Northside Dr.	Ft. Worth	TX	76106	(800) 442-2425	Parts/Svc Manuals

On my BBS – Voice 1:30-5:30pm, Pacific Time. BBS/FAX all other times

 # BBS number only – no voice

IF YOU WANT TO WRITE YOUR OWN SOFTWARE...

I'll help as much as possible.

I can provide a "developer's toolkit," with the understanding that the original developer is no longer available for support. In a word, you're on your own if you write your own software for the CE-232 Interface. On the other hand, the price for the toolkit is "right" (*free*).

But it's not that big a challenge... A number of third-party developers have successfully used the toolkit without complaint.

To get this toolkit *at no charge,* contact me on the BBS and I'll direct you to the file.

Good luck to you... and remember to share your insights with the other hobbyists who can benefit from your experience. Also, you may do a whizbang software package that really deserves to be shared with others... use my BBS for that.

SO YOU'RE COMPUTERIZED NOW...

Yes, now the nastiest part of our hobby is being done by a machine that doesn't know the meaning of the word "boring."

Your scanner will be programmed, and your files will be maintained, automatically, by that ultimate ingredient of the Ultimate Scanner – the computer!

CONGRATULATIONS!

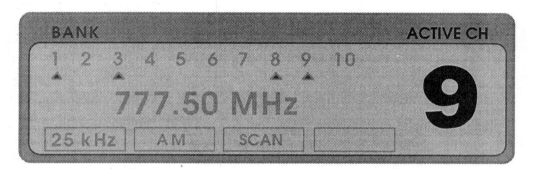

FUN STUFF

I'm sorta slipping one past you, but you're gonna love it!

YOU DESERVE A BREAK TODAY!

Hacking is fun, but now and then we hackers have to take time off "work" for a little relaxation and serious couch potato-ing. Patience be damned for this section. Rush or lag all you want; make all the mistakes you want, including downright stupid ones. In fact, this is a good section to unwind before turning on your scanner.

Relax; grab a steaming cup of Jamaican Blue Mountain estate coffee, a frosty barley pop, or maybe a big ol' fat corned beef and anchovy sandwich. Put on your slippers; turn your soldering irons off. The most you'll need here is a calculator, pencil & paper, and a computer if you have one – and you should by now, right?

There is one thing, though...

WHY?

If you're serious enough about our hobby to be reading this book, then you know that no matter how "ultimate" the hardware might become, you have to know what to do with it.

Hence this chapter, where we'll pick up a bunch of loose ends, give you one or two basic tutorials, transmit a couple of remarkable tools, and talk about ways to really exploit your Ultimate Scanner.

If all you want to do is boast about how many wires stick out of your store-bought PRO-9999, fine. If all you want to hear is your neighbor's baby monitor, or the local Highway Patrol, that's up to you. Skip this chapter until your interests evolve somewhat.

However...

If you *really* want to expand your horizons (in every sense, as you will soon see), and get the most out of that incredible machine into which you've poured so many hours and dollars, then this chapter was prepared just for you.

TOOLS

The tools of radio go far beyond voltmeters, soldering irons, and radio equipment. There's a whole boatload of stuff to fill the spaces behind the scenes of radio above and beyond the mere flipping of a switch and listening to what's going on in the spectrum.

Granted, some people are interested ONLY in flipping switches and maybe twisting a couple of knobs. You're probably not one of them, given that you're reading this hardcore book.

Hacking and electronic experimenting are two distinct facets of radio that might elude the entry-level knob twister, but there are more... *oh, my goodness, a lot more!* A serious pursuit of the Ultimate Scanner dictates the addition of a few serious tools to your warbag, apart from frequencies, antennas, and coax cable. I can't lay 'em all on you in this single volume, but Jumpin' Jehosephat, do I ever have a few goodies for you more serious types... stuff you might think is magic. It's not... but it works that way.

I'll start slow and easy for you green weenies, and then I'll pop the eyeballs of even a few experts.

ELECTRONIC FACTS, FIGURES, & FORMULAS

If you already know all this stuff, then *beat it!* Get outa here. Jump a few pages where I will knock the socks off of even the crustiest hackers. This first segment is for those who are a little green

around the gills and not sure of the difference between a resistor and a resister. This is a reference section for the kinds of things you'd remember if they were used every day instead of just on Saturdays. Like me for instance... I keep a *Hammer & Nail* chart on the wall in one corner of my shop. It shows the difference between the hammer and the nail. *Ahem...* you think *you* have problems...?

Immediately ahead is an electronic symbol chart for quick reference if you don't have a lot of experience following a schematic diagram. Electronic symbols are fairly universal, but don't get too hung up on my depictions of what's what. You may see others. I will try to stick to what's in the chart, though. It pretty much follows service manual schematics, too, so you'll be okay for the most part.

Next comes some basic electronics math, followed by a bit of advanced math and then a rousing crescendo. Check it out now or later, as suits your fancy, but don't omit it completely from your scanner training. It's good material.

This section was designed to be monstrously rewarding in the long run but you can ignore it for a while without missing a lick. You say you're ready *now?* Okay, break out your slide rule and abacus, and let's get to it. It's not *all* fun... there might be a little work in there, also.

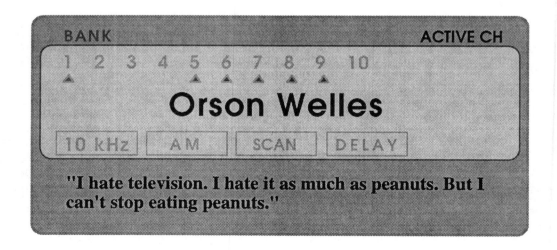
"I hate television. I hate it as much as peanuts. But I can't stop eating peanuts."

Figure 9-1: Standard (more or less) electronic schematic symbols

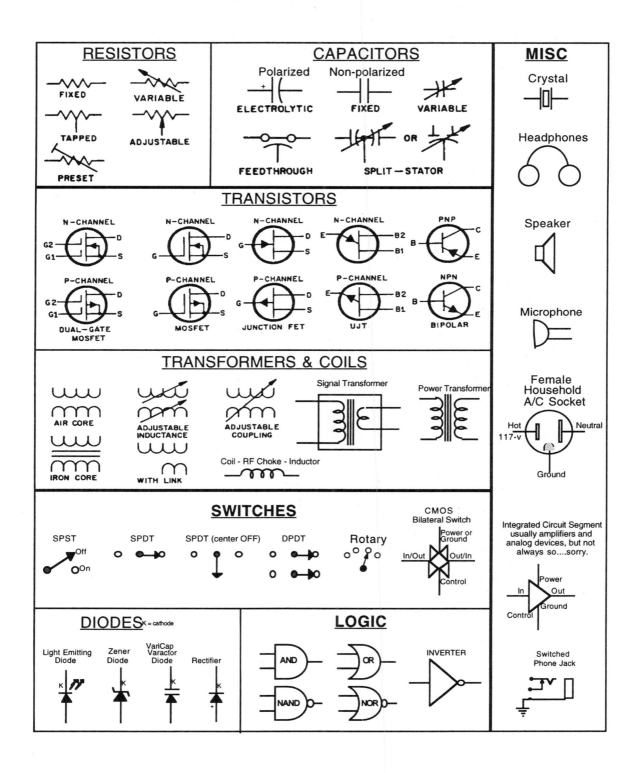

ELEMENTARY ELECTRONICS MATH

Let's learn Ohm's Law once and for all! It's a key ingredient of any electronic stew:

Eye equals eeeeee over arrrrr

$$I = \frac{E}{R} \quad \text{and} \quad R = \frac{E}{I} \quad \text{and} \quad E = I \times R$$

where:
I   =   current, **amperes**, *item, (sackful of electrons)*
E   =   voltage, **volts**, *a force (pressure)*
R   =   resistance, **ohms**, *an obstacle, (friction)*

Ohm's Law – taken to a second level, is almost as simple as the previous one:

$$P = E \times I \quad \text{and} \quad E = \frac{P}{I} \quad \text{and} \quad I = \frac{P}{E}$$

where:

P   = Power, watts, *energy (horsepower)*

$$P = I^2 R \quad \text{and} \quad R = \frac{P}{I^2} \quad \text{and} \quad I = \sqrt{\frac{P}{R}}$$

$$P = \frac{E^2}{R} \quad \text{and} \quad E = \sqrt{P \times R} \quad \text{and} \quad R = \frac{E^2}{P}$$

Other useful formulas follow. They're worth noting because the technician working with radio frequency (RF) circuitry must refer to them frequently.

Inductive Reactance	*Capacitive Reactance*	*Resonant Frequency*
$X_L = 2\pi F L$	$X_C = \dfrac{1}{2\pi F C}$	$F_O = \dfrac{1}{2\pi \sqrt{LC}}$

where: X_L =   Inductive reactance, ohms
            X_C =   Capacitive reactance, ohms
            L   =   Inductance, henries
            C   =   Capacitance, farads
      F and F_O =   Frequency, Hz

LOGARITHMS

Are logarithms a problem for you? Use this general solution as a reference and I'll try to clarify the issue:

where we have the general form of $B^X = Y$

then: $X = Log_B Y$

Examples: $10^2 = 100$ therefore $2 = Log_{10} 100$
            $2^3 = 8$ therefore $3 = Log_2 8$

Pronounced: *"Two is the logarithm in the base 10 of 100, and three is the logarithm in the base 2 of 8."*

The logarithm is a useful tool to the engineer because once the concept is learned, manipulation of even extremely complex numbers becomes both easier and faster.

In particular, logarithms are important to the compleat scannist and dedicated hacker because of the all-important unit of measurement called the *decibel*. Decibels are logarithms and are very easy to handle and to understand – with just a little practice. A brief historical note here...

The decibel is actually one-tenth of a *Bel*, a unit of measurement named after Alexander Graham Bell, best known for his invention of the telephone.

In his day, however, Bell was widely known and acclaimed for his work with sound and the deaf. Nowadays, the *decibel* has become a standard unit throughout science, physics, and especially radio.

Here we go:

A LOGARITHM IS AN EXPONENT

That's all... an exponent. Look at $B^X = Y$ again. X is the logarithm of Y to the base B. The most common base is 10. There are others, but we won't need them in this book.

Unless specified differently, logarithms here are Log_{10} which means *"Logarithm to the base 10."*

Some Logs are easy to determine at a glance. Like "100" for instance. $100 = 10^2$. So the Log_{10} of $100 = 2$. Easy! Log_{10} of $10 = 1$ and Log_{10} of $10,000 = 4$. Log_{10} of $1,000,000 = 6$.

All those are easy. But what about this one: *Log_{10} of 50 equals what?* It is 1.698970004, that's what, ($10^{1.698970004} = 50$), but how to find out?

Well, when I was first whacking out logarithm-based solutions, we had to look them up in monstrous tables in very boring books, or perhaps use our slide rules if accuracy was not too important.

Nowadays, you just enter "50" into your calculator, and hit the **LOG** key exactly like I did to find the logarithm of 50. I'm not sure I ever learned how to manually calculate a logarithm, or if I did, I forgot. Even mathematicians and engineers of the olden days did not manually calculate their logarithms. We looked them up in tables.

We *still do,* but now those tables are embedded into most calculators and all computers. Use the **LOG$_{10}$** key on your calculator to find logarithms unless they're the easy ones.

Here is a practical example for the use of logarithms to simplify a hairy calculation:

Suppose you were given the opportunity to work for 31 days, earning a penny the first day, two cents on the second, four cents on the third, doubling each day, for 31-days?

What would be your wages for the 31st day?

That's easy: it's 2^{30}.

A penny on the first day is 1¢, doubled to 2¢ on the 2nd with 30 days to go: that's 2^{30}.

But who wants to sit there and multiply out 2×2×2×2×2... 30 times? A better way is to enter "2" into your calculator and hit the LOG key to see 0.301029996. Now multiply that logarithm of 2 by 30 to get: 9.030899871.

We're almost there.

That big number means $10^{9.030899871}$. If that number is still in the display of your calculator, then just hit the **10^x** key on your calculator to get: 1,073,741,827.

Now remember – we're getting paid in pennies, so divide that by 100 to get dollars: $10,737,418.27 will be our wages on the 31st day of work.

Yes, I will accept that deal!

But you see my point here?

Logarithms make calculation a lot easier. Logarithms are a Way of Life in electronics and radio, so you may as well pick up a working knowledge of their use.

Many hobbyists don't, and they miss a great deal of the real magic of radio. Logarithms are a key ingredient of the Ultimate Scanner, because without logarithms you can't do decibels, and cannot develop a useful understanding of what's going in your system.

A DECIBEL IS A RATIO

That's all, a ratio – a comparison of one value to another, both with the same unit of measurement.

For instance, an amplifier with one-watt input, puts out 100 watts. The ratio of output power to input power is $^{100}/_1$ or simply, 100. Not watts. Not volts. Not apples. Just the pure, raw number of 100.

Ratios are always pure numbers, with no units.

A DECIBEL IS A SPECIAL KIND OF RATIO

With respect to the measurement and comparison of power (watts),

$$dB = 10 Log_{10} \frac{P_1}{P_2}$$

where P_1 is power, *out or in*, while P_2 is power, *in or out*, respectively.

The amplifier gain example above would be calculated as follows:

$$dB = 10 Log_{10} \frac{P_1}{P_2}$$
$$dB = 10 Log_{10} \frac{100}{1}$$
$$dB = 10 Log_{10} 100$$
$$dB = 10(2)$$
$$dB = 20$$

Therefore, it can be said that the amplifier has a *"gain of 100,"* or better still, *"20dB."* Now, let's take it one step farther, but in the opposite direction: suppose I input 100 watts, but only 1 watt comes out?

That ratio may be stated as $^1/_{100}$ or 0.01. Using the above formula, we find the logarithm of 0.01 is –2 and when multiplied by 10, we find a *"gain of –20dB"*... or better stated, *"a 20dB loss."*

Did you notice that the gain statement has a negative value while the loss statement has a positive value?

Herein lies one of the secrets to understanding the decibel, and working with it! Keep the numbers positive as much as possible! You can legitimately do that provided that you think, talk, and write in terms of real gain and real loss.

Consider how you'd be ten dollars richer if you lost a negative ten bucks! By the same token, you'd be ten dollars poorer if you gained a negative ten bucks! See how things can get confusing?

Well, decibels can be greatly simplified by working with them in such a manner as to avoid the use of negative numbers. So long as you think and label your decibels appropriately as either gain or loss, *all* those dB expressions can be positive numbers! There are times when you'll have to assign appropriate polarities in order to perform a calculation properly, but if you think logically and get a bit of practice there should be no problem.

For instance, suppose we have a system where the sum of all gains is 10dB and the sum of all losses is 7dB.

Express the net gain *and* net loss. There are two answers here:

   The net *gain* is +3dB.

   The net *loss* is –3dB.

Conversely, if the sum of all gains in that system is 7dB and the sum of all losses is 10dB, then the net *gain* is -3dB and the net *loss* is +3dB.

I prefer to speak and to calculate in terms of whatever produces a positive number, so in the first example, **net gain of 3dB** is best, while in the second example, a **net loss of 3dB** is preferred.

You will find it it mathematically easier to put the larger of two numbers in a ratio "on top," and the smaller "on the bottom."

Logarithms really don't care which way you do it, but one way produces negative decibels while the other produces positive ones. I'll help you with such concepts so you'll see how they work.

$$dB = 10 Log_{10} \frac{100}{1} = 10(2) = 20$$

$$db = 10 Log_{10} \frac{1}{100} = 10(-2) = -20$$

Okay, let's move on...........

Ratios of power (*P*) converted to dB are always ten times the logarithm of the power ratio. But for ratios of voltage and current (*E* and *I*), it's 20 times the logarithm of the voltage or current ratio.

$$dB = 20 Log_{10} \frac{E_1}{E_2} or \frac{I_1}{I_2}$$

Don't let that snow you like it did me for a few years. Voltage is *not* power and current is *not* power: power is voltage × current!

As an example, if your directional antenna delivers 100 μV (100 microvolts) of a certain signal to your receiver and an omni antenna delivers 50 μV, then the gain of the directional over the omni is:

$$dB = 20 Log_{10} \frac{100}{50}$$
$$= 20 Log_{10} 2$$
$$= 20(.301)$$
$$= 6.02$$

So the directional has a 6dB gain over the omni. About right.

Here's a calculation to prove what I said about the relationship between logarithms and decibels, and to help you keep it straight.

$$dB = 20 Log_{10} \frac{E_1}{E_2}$$

Let's use the antenna example above and convert the microvolts to power. Go back to Ohm's Law.

$$P = \frac{E^2}{R}$$

Remember? Well, we know the voltages into the antenna and we can safely assume that its impedance is 50Ω.

Therefore:

$$P = \frac{(100\mu V)^2}{50} watts$$

$$= \frac{(100 \times 10^{-6})(100 \times 10^{-6})}{50} watts$$

$$= \frac{10,000 \times 10^{-12}}{50} watts$$

$$= 200 \times 10^{-12} watts$$

$$= 200 - \rho W$$

and...

$$P = \frac{(50\mu V)^2}{50} watts$$

$$= \frac{(50 \times 10^{-6})(50 \times 10^{-6})}{50} watts$$

$$= \frac{2,500 \times 10^{-12}}{50} watts$$

$$= 50 \times 10^{-12} watts$$

$$= 50 - \rho W$$

We have two power levels now that correspond with the two voltage levels: 200 picowatts and 50 picowatts. You can have some confidence in this, now:

$$dB = 10 Log_{10} \frac{200}{50}$$

which equals ten times the Log of 4, or 6dB! So you see, 10 times the Log of Power equals 20 times the Log of either Voltage or Current.

Our assumption of 50Ω for the antenna is valid so long as it's either manufactured to be 50Ω, or is matched and balanced to be 50Ω. If, however,

that directional antenna were a TV antenna, fitted to a 50Ω coax cable with a 4:1 (300Ω to 75Ω) matching transformer, then we'd have to recalculate using 300Ω.

The resulting 1.5-to-1 Standing Wave Ratio will introduce a bit of error (4%) into the calculation, which can be disregarded for casual comparisons.

Just remember to take into account the antenna's impedance (resistance) when converting *received power* to microvolts:

$$P = E^2 \div R$$

WHY LEARN IT?

Your understanding and enjoyment of radio will be enhanced if you acquire a fundamental understanding of logarithms and decibels. For one, the whole world of radio works in those units, and for another, once you're comfortable with them they're a whole lot easier to work with than the calculations you've been using!

Decibels are additive and subtractive, you see! A series of gains and losses in a radio system can be a nightmare to analyze, if expressed in raw numbers, but can be easily combined into a net gain or loss if expressed in decibels. You can more easily understand what's going on in a system by the use of decibels!

We're going to use the hell out of decibels in an automated fashion just a few pages ahead. I've put together a calculating engine that will do most of the work for you.

So stay relaxed... and enjoy the ride. But hold onto your hat. There's more, and it's good stuff!

HOW TO COMPUTE GEODETIC BEARINGS & DISTANCE

And get the most out of the *Ultimate Scanner,* too!

There are plenty of "Great Circle" programs out and about for hams and shortwave listeners that compute Great Circle distances and directions. These are okay for practical purposes, especially hobby work.

But they can be quirky, inaccurate, and not fun, especially if you're a modern computist who uses Windows, OS/2, Unix, or other operating system that's capable of supporting several different tasks at the same time (*multitasking and multithreading*).

Great Circle programs tend to be very specific to computer type and rather unyielding with respect to format of the output data and applications for the data outside the program.

Well, I have a great Great Circle computation for most any computer and most any environment! But first... why would a scannist using his particular Ultimate Scanner need to know how to compute bearings and distances?

Many avid scannists are interested in other areas of hobby radio, including ham, SWL, and/or Citizens Band. Each of these specialized pursuits, including scanning, can be highly enhanced with the right tools and know-how.

Knowledge of how to compute bearings (directions) and distances can add some power to the ol' radio warbag. For instance, every scannist worth his salt knows that VHF-UHF signals are "line of sight" only, right?

Yeah, they "know" that, but it ain't true.

VHF-UHF signals 'diffract' around the curve of the earth and around obstacles. Diffraction is the change or loss of coherence in a beam of RF or light energy that occurs due to self-interference, when the energy beam reaches "edges," or changes, of the surface along which it's traveling.

It doesn't happen in space, but it certainly does here on earth. And we have to take it into account.

The amount of diffraction varies considerably with many factors, including weather and atmospheric conditions. Still, even over a glass-smooth ocean, UHF signals can penetrate and be detectable at least 15% beyond the optical line of sight.

Under favorable conditions, this can go to 40% or more. Out there at those kinds of distances, though, the average scannist won't detect anything but noise.

If the Ultimate Scanner station is properly equipped with a directional beam antenna, a low noise preamplifier, low loss coaxial cable, and a finely tuned scanner, these distances can be reached.

On the other hand, a directional beam antenna can easily lose signals if it's not correctly aimed in the direction of the transmitter, because it sacrifices omnidirectionality for gain.

So there you have it... *distance and direction*. If you know how to calculate them, you have a better chance of grabbing otherwise undetectable signals.

First, let's learn how to estimate the basic line of sight (optical). It's easy:

$$\text{Distance of antenna to Optical Horizon, miles} = \sqrt{2H}$$

where H = height of antenna above ground, feet

Example: If your receiving antenna is 50 feet above ground level, then your optical horizon is equal to the square root of twice its height, or the square root of two times 50; or the square root of 100, which equals 10 miles.

Now, that's just the distance to the horizon. Radio horizon, thanks to *diffraction*, goes an additional 15% for about 11.5 miles, give or take a bit.

That's about the limit of your range of detection for transmitters that are at ground level out there on the horizon. But that distance goes farther if the transmitter antenna is above ground level.

That distance is extended by an additional $\sqrt{2H}$

at the transmitter end, you see. Therefore, if the transmitter's antenna is also 50 feet above ground, then the optical line of sight between the two can go as far as 20 miles, and the radio line of sight to 23 miles or so.

Bear in mind that the only "perfect" earth curve exists over sizeable bodies of water.

Land masses definitely alter the characteristics of the radio and optical horizons, sometimes for the better, and sometimes for the worse.

Surprisingly, the average remains that of over water and the above equation is a very good initial estimator for your range of detection.

Assuming that your antenna is about 30 ft above ground and the typical transmitter antenna is 70 ft above ground, then maximum ranges can be expected to be about 20-25 miles.

Figure 9-2 depicts this concept.

Figure 9-2: Horizons...

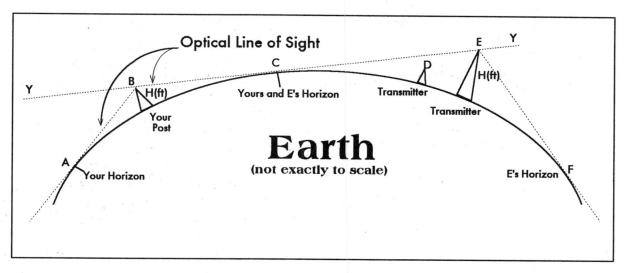

Analysis: Given your scanning post at (B), you should be able to detect most signals between the horizon at (A) and the horizon at (C). All areas from (C) to (F) will be below the horizon from your post at (B). If there were a transmitter at (D), you'd be hard pressed to detect it. However, a transmitter at (E) should be within your hearing range because it is high enough to "peek" into the line of sight from your location at (B). The transmitter at (E) should be able to cover the range between (C) and (F). Finally, any point above Line (Y) will be within optical line of sight of both stations, (B) and (E). The most cursory examination of this drawing should make the line of sight concept fairly clear.

RADIO VS OPTICAL LOSS

Don't get hung up on the additional yardage of "radio line of sight" in contrast to "optical line of sight."

The principles are much the same even though computing radio line of sight involves more variables than does optical. The compleat scannist uses optical range to assess the relative certainty of his radio range, and then factors in radio line of sight and various qualities of the station to establish a "blueprint" for his location.

It all starts with the square root of twice the height of your antenna, but it sure doesn't stop there, as you will soon find out.

COMPUTING BEARINGS AND DISTANCES

Okay, I said I had a hot one for you and here it is... well, a warmer-upper, anyway.

Rather than a clumsy program that might or might not work on your computer, I am giving you an extremely precise, easy-to-use spreadsheet model that will enable you to instantly and conveniently calculate your own Great Circle distances between any two points on earth, and more: you'll also get the bearings (directions) from one to the other!

The spreadsheet model that I'm about to lay on you was developed using Microsoft EXCEL 5.0 and tested on Microsoft Works 3.0, so it will operate fine with either. It should also be compatible with most other spreadsheets, with little or no alteration.

If it does need modification, and that depends on your choice of spreadsheet programs, the necessary changes will be slight and few.

It should work across a wide variety of computers and operating systems, from Macintosh and Apple II systems to all IBM/compatibles to Atari, Amiga, and even Commodores.

You only need to have a spreadsheet program (*Lotus 1-2-3, Quattro, Excel, MS-Works, AppleWorks, ClarisWorks, A-Lite, etc.*) and to enter the labels and formulas exactly as given. It's a very clear-cut piece of cake.

Now let me tell you a little about the model that I chose.

In 1866, a possibly deranged fellow by the name of Clarke determined that the earth is not a perfect sphere; rather it bulges slightly in the Southern Hemisphere.

The quality of his work will surprise you when you learn that the Clarke Spheroid of 1866 (his mathematical process) remains the basis for geodetic computations to this day. It is very accurate, even for engineering and surveying.

While Clarke's calculations and corrections for the elliptical deviation of the earth's shell from sphericity are rather complicated and beyond the capability of most hobbyists, I have simplified the procedure so that a 4th grader can run the model and get extremely accurate results.

The equations are built into the spreadsheet formulas that I'm about to whip on you. You need only type the formulas into a spreadsheet of your preference, character-for-character. You only have to build the spreadsheet once, and then you've got a new tool that will stay sharp for a long time.

When that's done, enter the latitude and longitude numbers for each of two sites in the blanks provided and the spreadsheet will instantly calculate and present distance in miles and kilometers between the sites, and azimuths, bearings, or headings with respect to True North for each site.

It couldn't be easier, and beats the hell out of Great Circle programs and manual calculations. You really don't have to know what you're doing.

And if you just can't stand to type, you can download the necessary file(s) from my BBS and import it into your spreadsheet, easy as you please. The filename is SPRED.ZIP. See Chapter 1 for guidance to the BBS. That file will contain the actual WORKS and EXCEL spreadsheets as well as textfiles suitable for importing into almost any spreadsheet.

SPREADSHEET MECHANICS

If you are going to type it in, then open your spreadsheet and set up for five columns by 53 rows. Columns are labeled from left to right, as A through E, while rows are numbered from top to bottom as 1-53.

The first five cells in Column A (**A1-A5**) are label headers, but **A6-A53** are math entries and interim calculations based on the formulas that you enter, so be sure to enter them, line for line, character for character, exactly as you see them. **B1, C1, D1,** and **E1** are label/header cells. **B2, B3, B4,** and **B5** are critical calculated cells, so enter the formulas exactly as you see them.

Cells **B2-B5** calculate the decimal values of the latitude and longitude coordinates that you will enter into cells **C2-C5, D2-D5, E2-E5.** More on those cells later.

Cells **C6-E6** are labels that show you where to enter your data.

Cells **B6** through **B53** are comments and labels, so you can do with them as you please, though **B52-B53** and **C51-E51** are identifier labels for the degrees/minutes/seconds results that appear in **C52-C53, D52-D53,** and **E52-E53** so you shouldn't change them.

Labels are also entered into **C47-C50** and **D47-D50** to identify distance and decimal-degree results that appear in cells **E47-E50.** Cells **C52-E52** and **C53-E53** are formulas to convert the calculated decimal bearings in **E49-E50** back into degrees, minutes and seconds. **C7-C48, D7-D48,** and **E7-E48** should be left blank for now, because we will have a mind-blowing use for them a little later.

Refer to the Technical Structure of the spreadsheet just ahead to construct the portion described above. Then you need only enter your latitude in degrees, minutes and seconds in cells **C2-E2** and your longitude in degrees, minutes and seconds in cells **C3-E3.** Enter the target's latitude in cells **C4-E4** and its longitude in **C5-E5.**

Results will instantly appear in **E47-E50** and in **C52-E52** and **C53-E53.**

It really isn't complicated at all.

SPREADSHEET MATH

You don't *really* want me to dwell on spreadsheet mathematics, but to get you oriented I will describe the first few actions that take place in the A column.

The first math entry is a constant value in cell **A6**: **1E-20.** This is spreadsheet language for scientific notation: 1×10^{-20}. This extremely small number is used at key points in the calculations to prevent errors caused by a try at division by zero.

Cell **A7, = -1*B4,** calls the contents of whatever is in Cell **B4** (the calculated decimal value of Site

B's longitude) and multiplies it by -1 to change the sign of the number. Cell A8, $=B2+A7$, combines Site A latitude with Site B latitude to get an angular difference between the two latitudes. That calculation, in Cell A8, is tested for zero in A9:

$$=IF(A8=0,A6,A8).$$

If both sites were on the same latitude, the difference in A8 would be zero, and a string of errors would result because of subsequent divisions by zero.

To prevent that, if the contents of A8 are zero, then A6 is substituted, otherwise, whatever is in A8 stays there for continued use. *A9 analysis: "If whatever is in A8 equals zero, then transfer the contents of A6 to this cell; otherwise use whatever is in A8."*

Cell A10 is a pure logic decision point.

$$=IF(A9<0,1,0),$$

reads, *"IF whatever in A9 is **less than zero**, THEN enter 1 into A10; ELSE if whatever is in A9 is zero or greater, then put 0 into A10."* Later into the calculations, the spreadsheet checks back at A10 to see if there is a 1 or a 0 and makes decisions accordingly.

Getting the idea now?

Relax, even if you don't want to become a spreadsheet expert, all you have to do is enter these formulas exactly as I show you in the Technical Structure and the arithmetic engine will do all the rest before you can yawn.

It is handy to know that personal computers do not work in *degrees*. For some mystical reason, they work in *radians*. We need to work in degrees, so all cells with trigonometric functions will include a conversion for radians to degrees.

Fortunately, there are exactly 2π radians in a circle. For instance, Cell A20 calculates the sine of an angle in A19. Without the conversion factor, the result would be the sine of that many radians.

Okay, since there are 2π radians in a circle (360°), it follows that there are $\pi/180$ radians *per degree*.

$$=SIN(A19*PI()/180)$$

serves the purpose in one fell swoop. We have an opposite situation in Cell A33,

$$=ATAN(A32)*180/PI()$$

where A32 is a tangent and must be converted back to an angle with the *arctangent* function. The correction for radians to degrees for the arc-functions is inverse that of the angle functions, so don't be confused by the 180/PI() factor in A33.

Another thing useful to know is how most spreadsheets use pi (π). It has to be spelled out followed by open and closed parentheses, PI(), no spaces, and nothing within the parentheses.

This, and an explanatory table just ahead should take care of any confusion and ambiguous meanings. Again, if you are not a spreadsheet expert, don't worry about it; just enter your formulas exactly as I show them, and there should be no problem with one exception that some spreadsheets may do things a little differently than Microsoft's.

No big deal, because any needed changes will be self-evident and can be incorporated immediately after consulting your spreadsheet documentation. Most are much alike and I tried to avoid the hairy kinds of commands that are likeliest to differ from one to the next. You'll do fine......

When you're all finished, your spreadsheet should appear a little like mine. For now, you should disregard everything shown in cells C10-C46, D10-D46, and E10-E46. We will add some great things to this section a little later.

THE NUMBERS

Warm up to spreadsheets and learn how easy it is to work with them. For Great Circle calculations, you need do no more than enter latitude and longitude in C2-C5, D2-D5, and E2-E5.

These twelve cells will always be your data input cells and you can change them at any time, of course, to instantly recalculate and show the results. Cells C2-C5 are for DEGREES only; D2-D5 for MINUTES only; and E2-E5 for SECONDS only.

In other words, you should enter ONLY data in these twelve cells. The spreadsheet will take care of everything else for you in a flash, including the calculated decimal equivalents in Cells B2-B5.

The spreadsheet cannot easily work with Lat & Lon coordinates like we enter them into Columns C, D, and E, but there's no sense in you manually converting them into decimal form when the spreadsheet can do it for you. Latitude and longitude coordinates are almost always found in the form of DDD° MM' SS", so the conversion into decimal is necessary.

By the way, the spreadsheet formulas are exceptionally accurate and produce results that agree with data taken from US Geological surveys.

You can enter fractions of seconds in **E2-E5** (assuming you know them), but this is not necessary unless you're doing serious engineering or survey work.

For instance, the latitude for Site B could just as readily be entered as: 34 09 35.459.

LATITUDE & LONGITUDE

There's meaning and facts behind all these weird numbers: there are 360° in the circumference of the earth, so each 15° of longitude represents one hour of time (15 x 24 = 360). The earth's equatorial circumference is about 24,859 miles, so 24,859 ÷ 360 = 69.05 miles per degree of longitude.

Since there are 60 minutes per degree, each minute of arc is about 1.15 statute miles, which happens to equal 1 nautical mile.

At 60 seconds per minute, each second is about 0.019 mile, or 101 feet, or a bit more than the distance from home plate to first base on a baseball diamond.

Clearly, accuracy to the second is not important. Still, my spreadsheet will give accuracy down to the distance between your ears if you input information that's sufficiently accurate.

Data entries must be all positive values for North latitudes and West longitudes; and all negative values for South latitudes and East longitudes. *When negative numbers are required, each cell data entry must be negative.*

For example, the latitude for Rio De Janeiro, 22° 57' 09"S is entered as: **−22 −57 −09**

FINDING TRANSMITTER LOCATIONS

All this stuff is self-explanatory, but the question arises as to how Lat and Lon coordinates are obtained in the first place?

The best way is direct from the FCC license database. That's available to the public thanks to companies like PerCon Corporation, which sell

CD-ROM and floppy disks with data straight from the FCC. Most radio licensees must list their transmitter site's Lat/Lon, so that's public record.

MORE SOURCES OF DATA

My BBS offers an on-line FCC database for the entire USA, which you can modem-query to download frequency files for your area. These files contain Lat & Lon data for licensees of record.

Another possibility is to use satellite Global Positioning System receivers! These GPS receivers are accurate to within about 30-300 feet, depending on whether or not a unit is deliberately limited to prevent accuracy of military value.

Still another way to acquire Lat & Lon coordinates for a station is from the FCC license that is posted in the operating area of the transmitter site. If you can't get in to see the license, you can call the station and get the coordinates.

Be polite... just tell the station manager that you're programming a missile.

MAPS

You can also get the information from US Geological Survey Topographical Maps for your region.

If you've never seen these maps, you are in for a surprise! What a work of art and beauty your tax dollars have bought! *Topo* maps come in several common sizes, but the preferred is what we call a *"7.5-minute quadrangle."*

Next best are the *"15-minute quadrangles."* Others may serve, also. The point is that topo maps are very detailed, sometimes showing YOUR house, apartment, or workplace building!

You can readily calculate your latitude and longitude coordinates from a topo map as well as those for the radio stations that interest you.

This is a fun thing to do, I might add. US Geological Survey topo maps are available from many sources, including retail map dealers in most areas, as well as from the USGS itself. Larger metro regions often have a USGS office where maps can be purchased.

The data can even be derived from Rand-McNally types of road maps where there is a marking for every degree of Lat & Lon. You won't get extremely accurate data from this source, but for many it's good enough.

You can get useful data from road maps by a little work and some simple calculations, however. *Figure 9-3* shows the mechanics of how to do it from any map that shows Lat and Lon.

Figure 9-3: Using a common road map

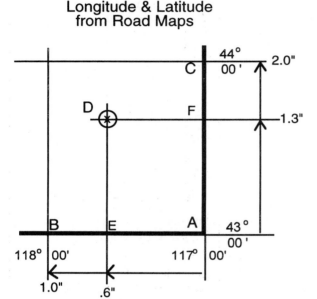

Longitude & Latitude
from Road Maps

NOTES

1. Point "D" is your location
2. Point "A" is the closest, lower right reference point to your location.

PROCEDURE

Examine *Figure 9-3*. Find your location on the map and mark it with a pencil. Label that point "D".

Now go out to the right and left margins of the map, where in small obscure text will be shown latitude tic marks.

Find and mark the latitude tics just above and just below your location at "D".

Now go to the top and bottom margins of the map where in small obscure text will be shown longitude tic marks. Find and mark the longitude tics just left and right of your location at "D".

Now draw straight lines to overlay the longitude and latitude marks you just made so that a rectangle encloses your location at "D".

Label the lower right intersection of latitude and longitude closest to you as Point "A". Label the lower left intersection of latitude and longitude closest to you as Point "B".

Label the upper right intersection of latitude and longitude closest to you as Point "C". Now measure the distance from "A" to "B", which in this example is one inch (1.0"). Next, measure the distance from "A" to "C", in this example it's two inches (2.0").

CONVERTING THE DATA

Now comes the fun part. Draw a line from your location down to intersect the line "A-B". Label that intersect point as "E". Draw another line from your location to the right to intersect the line "A-C".

Label that intersect point as "F". Measure the distance from "A" to "E", in this example, 0.6". Measure the distance from "A" to "F", in this example, 1.3".

It is a simple matter to calculate your unique latitude and longitude coordinates using simple ratio and proportion math.

The lower right reference point is the starting place where in the example, latitude is 43° 00'. The upper right reference point is latitude 44° 00', with a distance of 2" between them.

Your latitude is 1.3" above the reference, so:

Example latitude:

$$= 43 + \frac{1.3}{2.0}$$
$$= 43.65°$$

It's easy to convert that decimal of a degree to minutes and seconds, as follows:

DEGREES = (integer) = 43°

MINUTES = (decimal of a degree)(60)
= 0.65 × 60
= 39.00

SECONDS = (decimal of a minute)(60)
         = 0.00 × 60
         = 0.00

Therefore, the example latitude is: 43.65° or 43° 39' 00"

Longitude is calculated in exactly the same manner. An example follows.

$$= 117 + \frac{0.6}{1.0}$$

$$= 117.60°$$

DEGREES = (integer) = 117°

MINUTES = (decimal of a degree) × (60)
         = 0.60 × 60
         = 36.00

SECONDS = (decimal of a minute) × (60)
         = 0.00 × 60
         = 0.00

Therefore, the example latitude is: 117.60° or 117° 36' 00".

INCREMENTS

This method of interpolating your latitude and longitude coordinate from road maps is valid only if the degrees are annotated in 1° increments.

If in 30' or 2° or any other increment, the method is still valid, but you'll have to be careful to keep your references straight. Suppose the increment was 5° at 2-inch intervals, and your line were at 1" – then, you'd have to add 2.5° to the reference

to obtain that particular coordinate for your location.

It just happens that most Rand McNally and other road maps I've seen have 1° increments. *USGS 7.5 minute quadrangle topographical maps have 2.5' (0.04°) increments. You can see why they're so accurate (and fun).*

My Distance & Bearing Spreadsheet will calculate good data for you, even using road maps, but it only gets better with the more accurate latitude and longitude coordinates that you can feed it.

Anything beats laying out rulers and protractors on crumpled roadmaps.

Yuk. But *that* works, too.

USING MY DISTANCE-BEARING SPREADSHEET

It's a snap.

Type in the Site A and Site B coordinates in cells C2 through E5, and page down to the bottom of the spreadsheet where the results will be waiting for you – unless your computer is so slow that you have to blink a few times before the calculations are complete.

And that's all there is to making this baby work. It's useful, extremely accurate, and amply meets even the most serious hobbyist's needs. And it beats the socks off these bulky, cumbersome "Great Circle" programs you see floating around. And, what's more, it will be useful for what's coming next. Read on, McDuff...

Table 9-1 is a column-by-column explanation of what you need to know to build a worksheet of your own.

Table 9-1: Standardized spreadsheet symbology

Symbol Name	Typed Symbol Appearance	Keyboard Location	Meaning in Spreadsheet
Asterisk	*	Uppercase 8	Multiply by
Open paren	(	Uppercase 9	Algebraic organizer, begin
Closed paren	)	Uppercase 0 (zero)	Algebraic organizer, end
Both parens	( )	See above	Required after the PI() entry (no spaces)
Comma	,	Self-evident	Logical separator
Plus sign	+	Uppercase equal sign =	Add to or positive value
Minus sign	–	Lowercase underscore	Subtract from or negative value
Forward slash	/	Lowercase question mark	Divide by
Left caret	<	Uppercase period	Logical Is-Greater-Than
Up caret	^	Uppercase 6	Exponent; 2^4 is same as 2^4
Decimal	.	Period key	Decimal point
Equal sign	=	Left of backspace key	Equal to, or equals. Formulas begin with =
1×10^{-20}	1E-20	Standard keyboard text	Very small real number, larger than zero
Sine	SIN	" " "	Trigonometric function
Absolute Value	ABS	" " "	Changes negative numbers to positive
Cosine	COS	" " "	Trigonometric function
Arc Tangent	ATAN	" " "	Trigonometric function
Logarithm	LOG	" " "	Returns logarithm (base 10) of a number
Pi or π	PI()	" " "	Ratio of circumference to diameter of a circle
Logical If	IF	" " "	Conditional logic, IF(something,do, else)
Square Root	SQRT	" " "	Square root of a number
Truncate	TRUNC	" " "	Remove the decimal part of a number
Integer	INT	" " "	Rounds decimal down to nearest whole number

NOTE: TRUNC and INT are similar in that both return integers. TRUNC simply removes the fractional part of the number. INT rounds numbers down to the nearest integer based on the value of the fractional part of the number. INT and TRUNC are different only when using negative numbers: TRUNC(–4.3) returns –4, but INT(–4.3) returns –5, because –5 is the lower number. Either one will work for the same purpose in the spreadsheets given for the **Ultimate Scanner**.

Portions of this spreadsheet are based on the Clarke Spheroid of 1866 as published by the Coast and Geodetic Survey of the US Department of Commerce in Special Publication No. 8, **Formulas and Tables for the Computation of Geodetic Positions**, Seventh Edition.

TECHNICAL STRUCTURE OF THE GREAT CIRCLE AND
VHF-UHF PROPAGATION ANALYSIS SPREADSHEET

Open a spreadsheet and enter exactly what is shown under the **FORMULA or TEXT** column into the cell specified under the **CELL** column. Formulas begin with an *equals* (=) sign so enter exact symbols, numbers and text as shown *without spaces*. (Pure text entries may contain spaces.) Do not interpret here; take everything literally. All "0" characters in formulas are *zeroes*, except LOG, an "Oh". Shaded entries are for the Great Circle calculations. Unshaded portions (*VHF-UHF Path Analysis*) may be omitted, if desired.

CELL	FORMULA or TEXT	CELL	FORMULA or TEXT	CELL	FORMULA or TEXT
A1		B1	DECIMAL	C1	DEGREES
A2	Latitude Site "A"	B2	=C2+D2/60+E2/3600	C2	32
A3	Longitude Site"A"	B3	=C3+D3/60+E3/3600	C3	117
A4	Latitude Site "B"	B4	=(C4+D4/60+E4/3600)	C4	34
A5	Longitude Site "B"	B5	=C5+D5/60+E5/3600	C5	118
A6	=1E–20	B6	Division by 0 protection	C6	
A7	= –1*B4	B7	Change sign	C7	
A8	=B2+A7	B8	Math	C8	
A9	=IF(A8=0,A6,A8)	B9	Logic	C9	
A10	=IF(A9<0,1,0)	B10	FLAG-0 - Logic	C10	
A11	=ABS(A9)	B11	Absolute value	C11	Site A Name >
A12	= –1*B5	B12	Change sign	C12	Site B Name >
A13	=+B3+A12	B13	Math	C13	Engineer >
A14	=IF(A13=0,A6,A13)	B14	Logic	C14	Date >
A15	=IF(A14<0,1,0)	B15	FLAG-1 - Logic	C15	
A16	=ABS(A14)	B16	Absolute value	C16	
A17	=B2+B4	B17	Math	C17	
A18	=A16/2	B18	Math	C18	
A19	=A17/2	B19	Math	C19	
A20	=SIN(A19*PI()/180)	B20	Sine	C20	
A21	=A18*A20	B21	Math	C21	
A22	=A20^2	B22	A20 squared	C22	
A23	147.7397736	B23	N. America correction	C23	
A24	=A22/A23	B24	Math	C24	
A25	=+1–A24	B25	Math	C25	
A26	=COS(A19*PI()/180)	B26	Cosine	C26	
A27	=A26*A16	B27	Math	C27	
A28	=A25*A27	B28	Math	C28	Gain
A29	=1/A23	B29	1/x	C29	
A30	=1–A29	B30	Math	C30	Loss, add-on
A31	=A28/A30	B31	Math	C31	Loss, basic
A32	=A31/A11	B32	Math	C32	Loss, Free Space
A33	=ATAN(A32)*180/PI()	B33	Arc Tangent	C33	
A34	=IF(A10=1,0,180)	B34	Logic	C34	
A35	=IF(A10=1,–1*A33,A33)	B35	Logic - Change sign	C35	Loss, total
A36	=IF(A15=1,–1*A35,A35)	B36	Logic - Change sign	C36	Loss, total
A37	=A34–A36	B37	Math	C37	Loss, total
A38	=IF(A15=1,–1*A21,A21)	B38	Math & logic	C38	dB below 1-watt
A39	=(A37–A38)+180	B39	Math & logic	C39	dB below 1-watt
A40	=A39–720	B40	Math & logic	C40	dB below 1-watt
A41	=360+A40	B41	Azimuth Logic, B-A	C41	Rx Signal Level
A42	=IF(A41<0,A41+360,A41)	B42	Sine	C42	Rx Signal Level
A43	=SIN(PI()/180*A33)	B43	1/x	C43	Rx Signal Level
A44	=1/A43	B44	Math	C44	Max Line of Sight
A45	=A44*A27	B45	N. America correction	C45	Max Line of Sight
A46	=A45*69.17147736	B46	Square root	C46	Max Line of Sight
A47	=SQRT(A25)	B47	Logic	C47	Miles
A48	=IF(E50>=180,E50–180,E50+180)	B48	Math	C48	kilometers
A49	=A38*2	B49	Math	C49	Direction/Bearing
A50	=A48+A49	B50	Logic	C50	Direction/Bearing
A51	=A50–720	B51	Logic	C51	DEGREES
A52	=360+A51	B52	Azimuth, A to B (°N)-->	C52	=TRUNC(E49)
A53	=IF(A52<0,A52+360,A52)	B53	Azimuth, B to A (°N)-->	C53	=TRUNC(E50)

TECHNICAL STRUCTURE OF THE
VHF-UHF PROPAGATION ANALYSIS SPREADSHEET (Concluded)

CELL	FORMULA or TEXT	CELL	FORMULA or TEXT
D1	MINUTES	E1	SECONDS
D2	55	E2	3
D3	5	E3	44
D4	9	E4	35
D5	3	E5	30
D6	^ ENTER COORDINATES ABOVE ^	E6	
D7		E7	
D8		E8	
D9		E9	
D10	SITE INFORMATION	E10	
D11	Hertzian Intercept; San Diego, CA	E11	
D12	NOAA Weather Sta, Mt. Wilson, CA	E12	
D13	Bill Cheek	E13	
D14	3/28/1995 12:02	E14	
D15		E15	ENTER RADIO PATH DATA BELOW
D16	Transmitter Frequency (MHz) >	E16	162.550
D17	(A) Ant Height Above avg terrain (ft)>	E17	500
D18	(A) Antenna Gain (dB) >	E18	0
D19	(A) Misc Site Loss (dB) >	E19	5
D20	(B) Ant Height Above avg terrain (ft)>	E20	5710
D21	(B) Antenna Gain (dB) >	E21	2
D22	(B) Misc Site Losses (dB) >	E22	1
D23	Transmitter Power (watts) >	E23	100
D24	Height of Obstacle in Path (ft) >	E24	0
D25	Shortest Distance to Obstacle (mi) >	E25	0
D26	Notes & units of meaasurement	E26	CALCULATIONS
D27	Gain Tx Power relative to 1-watt (dBW)	E27	=10*LOG(E23)
D28	Total Gain (dB)	E28	=E18+E21+E27
D29	Disregard this Interim Calculation	E29	=IF((E24*E25*E16)>0,10*LOG(E16)+20*LOG(E24)–10*LOG(E25)–55.8,0)
D30	Shadow Loss (dB)	E30	=IF((E24*E25*E16)=0,0,IF(E29>=13,E29,EXP(((10*LOG(E16) +20* LOG(E24)–10*LOG(E25))–55.8)*(0.08534))*4.35459))
D31	Plane Earth Loss (dB)	E31	= –1*10*LOG(0.00000000000000345*((E17*E20)/(E47^2))^2)
D32	Reference ideal (dB)	E32	=36.6 + 20*LOG(E16) + 20*LOG(47)
D33	Loss, add-on, earth curve Typical (dB)	E33	=E47^(1.438001208)*0.064950355
D34	Loss, add-on, earth curve worst (dB)	E34	=0.08660047*(E47^1.438001208)
D35	Ideal Path Loss (dB)	E35	=E30+E32+E19+E22
D36	Typ Path Loss (dB)	E36	=E31+E30+E33+E19+E22
D37	Worst Path Loss (dB)	E37	=E30+E31+E34+E19+E22
D38	Ideal Rx Power (dBW)	E38	=E35–E28
D39	Typ Rx Power (dBW)	E39	=E36–E28
D40	Worst Rx Power (dBW)	E40	=E37–E28
D41	Ideal RSL (uV)	E41	=SQRT(50*(1/(10^(E38/10))))*10^6
D42	Typical RSL (uV)	E42	=SQRT(50*(1/(10^(E39/10))))*10^6
D43	Worst RSL (uV)	E43	=SQRT(50*(1/(10^(E40/10))))*10^6
D44	A to Horizon (mi)	E44	=SQRT(2*E17)
D45	B to Horizon (mi)	E45	=SQRT(2*E20)
D46	Max poss A to B (mi)	E46	=E44+E45
D47	Path Distance (mi)	E47	=A46/A47
D48	Path Distance (km)	E48	=1.609344*E47
D49	Azimuth, A to B (°N)	E49	=IF(A53<0,A53+360,A53)
D50	Azimuth, B to A (°N)	E50	=IF(A42<0,A42+360,A42)
D51	MINUTES	E51	SECONDS
D52	=TRUNC((E49–TRUNC(E49))*60)	E52	=(((E49–TRUNC(E49))*60)–D52)*60
D53	=TRUNC((E50–TRUNC(E50))*60)	E53	=(((E50–TRUNC(E50))*60)–D53)*60

NOTES: (1) Cell **E30** contains one *continuous formula* with no spaces or line breaks

(2) For MS-WORKS and other spreadsheets that do not recognize the TRUNC command, use the following instead:

C52 =INT(E49)   **C53** =INT(E50)   **D52** =INT((E49–INT(E49))*60)   **D53** =INT((E50–INT(E50))*60)

E52 =(((E49–INT(E49))*60)–D52)*60   **E53** =(((E50–INT(E50))*60)–D53)*60

VHF-UHF PROPAGATION ANALYSIS SPREADSHEET

	A	B	C	D	E
		DECIMAL	DEGREES	MINUTES	SECONDS
2	Latitude Site A	32.9175	32	55	3
3	Longitude Site A	117.0956	117	5	44
4	Latitude Site B	34.1597	34	9	35
5	Longitude Site B	118.0583	118	3	30
6	1E-20	Division by 0 protection	^ ^ ENTER COORDINATES ABOVE ^ ^		
7	-34.1597	Change sign			
8	-1.242222222	Math			
9	-1.242222222	Logic			
10	1	FLAG-0 - Logic	SITE INFORMATION		
11	1.242222222	Absolute value	Site A Name >	The Hertzian Intercept; San Diego, CA	
12	-118.0583	Change sign	Site B Name >	NOAA Weather Sta, Mt. Wilson, CA	
13	-0.9627778	Math	Engineer >	Bill Cheek	
14	-0.9627778	Logic	Date >	03/28/95 12:02	
15	1	FLAG-1 - Logic	ENTER RADIO PATH DATA BELOW		
16	0.9627778	Absolute value	Transmitter Frequency (MHz) >		162.550
17	67.0772222	Math	(A) Ant Height above avg terrain (ft) >		500
18	0.4813889	Math	(A) Antenna Gain (dB) >		0
19	33.5386111	Math	(A) Misc Site Loss (dB) >		5
20	0.5524988	Sine	(B) Ant Height above avg terrain (ft) >		5710
21	0.2659668	Math	(B) Antenna Gain (dB) >		2
22	0.3052549	A20 squared	(B) Misc Site Loss (dB) >		1
23	147.7397736	N. America correction	Transmitter Power (watts) >		100
24	0.0020662	Math	Height of Obstacle in Path (ft) >		0
25	0.9979338	Math	Shortest Distance to Obstacle (mi) >		0
26	0.8335137	Cosine	Notes & units of measurement		CALCULATIONS
27	0.8024885	Math	Gain Tx Power relative to 1-watt (dBW)		20.00
28	0.8008304	Math	Gain Total Gain (dB)		22.00
29	0.0067687	1/x	Disregard this interim calculation		0.00
30	0.9932313	Math	Loss, add-on Shadow Loss (dB)		0.00
31	0.8062879	Math	Loss, basic PlaneEarth Loss(dB)		95.86
32	0.6490689	Math	Loss, Free Space Reference ideal (dB)	114.26	
33	32.9863504	Arc Tangent	Loss, add-on, earth curve typical (dB)		50.27
34	0	Logic	Loss, add-on, earth curve worst (dB)		67.03
35	-32.98635038	Logic - Change sign	Loss, total Ideal Path Loss (dB)	120.26	
36	32.98635038	Logic - Change sign	Loss, total Typ Path Loss (dB)		152.14
37	-32.98635038	Math	Loss, total Worst Path Loss (dB)		168.89
38	-0.265966787	Math & logic	dB below 1-watt Ideal Rx Pwr (-dBW)	98.26	
39	147.2796164	Math & logic	dB below 1-watt Typ Rx Power (-dBW)		130.14
40	-572.7203836	Math & logic	dB below 1-watt Worst Rx Pwr (-dBW)		146.89
41	-212.7203836	Azimuth Logic, B-A	Rx Signal Level Ideal RSL (uV)	86.38	
42	147.2796164	Sine	Rx Signal Level Typical RSL (uV)		2.20
43	0.544439222	1/x	Rx Signal Level Worst RSL (uV)		0.32
44	1.836752311	Math	Max Line of Sight A to Horizon (mi)		31.62
45	1.473972526	N. America correction	Max Line of Sight B to Horizon (mi)		106.86
46	101.9568572	Square root	Max Line of Sight Max poss A to B (mi)		138.49
47	0.998966383	Logic	Miles Path Distance (mi)	102.06	
48	327.2796164	Math	kilometers Path Distance (km)		164.25
49	-0.531933575	Math	Direction/Bearing Azimuth, A to B (°N)		326.75
50	326.7476828	Logic	Direction/Bearing Azimuth, B to A (°N)		147.28
51	-393.2523172	Logic	DEGREES	MINUTES	SECONDS
52	-33.25231716	Azimuth, A to B (°N)-->	326	44	51.66
53	326.7476828	Azimuth, B to A (°N)-->	147	16	46.62

RADIO PATH ANALYSIS FOR VHF-UHF

This is really interesting. Imagine yourself 60-100 miles from some action that really interests you. In fact, you'd give your upper molars to be able to monitor that action on your Ultimate Scanner.

Try as you might, you just can't seem to pull in any signals from that area.

For all you know, it might be IMPOSSIBLE to receive those distant police, news media, and emergency frequencies, but basically, you don't know for sure.

Would you *like* to know? Would you like to be able to accurately estimate the requirements for VHF-UHF communications over any terrain, over any distance? Well, you might want to, if knowing in advance could save you a lot of time and dollars.

Sure... with a 200 ft tower, a massive log-periodic beam antenna, GaAsFET low noise preamplifier, and expensive hardline coax, you should be able to receive signals from Katrina's Cantina in the Ural Mountains of the former Soviet Russia. Spend enough money and you can do almost anything...

BULLINGTON?

But you don't have the money for such a hairy setup. You might be able to cough up a couple hundred bucks for a decent beam antenna, mounting mast, and preamp, but what if it doesn't work after all that expense and labor? Is the money wasted?

The only thing worse than not being able to get the job done is to spend a lot of money and *still* not have a solution!

Well, I can show you how to 'engineer' your requirements in advance, thanks to some goshawful hard work performed back in the 1940's by an engineer named Kenneth Bullington, who studied VHF-UHF radio propagation so thoroughly that he figured out how to predict and model its behavior over a wide variety of conditions and circumstances.

To follow Bullington's work isn't simple, even to this day, but thanks to the computer and other modern developments, I can show you how to use these techniques without knowing what you're doing, and still come up with some valid data

about what it takes to receive signals at Point A (your site) from a distant transmitter at Site B.

We're going to put the mathematical relationships of these calculations into a spreadsheet (call it an automatic calculation engine). Then, by simply entering the variables, the computerized engine will do all the work. Let *it* understand Bullington!

APPLYING THIS TO THE ULTIMATE SCANNER

Let's analyze some of the parameters of radio communications that are above 30 MHz, *and* that impact the Ultimate Scanner and its operator.

The threshhold of signal detection for most scanners is about $1\mu V$ (1-millionth of a volt), below which the signal is either noisy or not detectable. Some scanners are a little better; some not as good, but $1\mu V$ is the normal reference point and we will use it.

The Ultimate Scanner, though fed as good a signal as the channel can produce by an excellent antenna, good cables and connectors, remains susceptible to the losses that follow, because they occur between the transmit and receive antennas – *not* inside the electronics.

To make it simple: nothing you do to your receiver or scanner will find a signal that just ain't there. But, you know that transmitter just over the horizon is pumping out lotsa watts.

What happened?

FREE SPACE LOSS

Radio signals weaken in free space at known and predictable rates as they propagate, the first factor affecting which is the 'spreading effect' caused by the ever-expanding wavefront; same principle that makes illumination decrease, the farther away it gets from the source of light.

The rules are about the same, too. Double the distance, receive one-fourth the power.

This spreading effect is most consistent and predictable in '*free space*' where the presence of ground and other objects is not an issue. Decay of radio signals in free space is one of the most predictable physical parameters in the universe, about like free fall in gravity:

Here's what it looks like:

$$\alpha_{db} = 10Log_{10}\frac{P_t}{P_r} = 10Log_{10}\frac{4.1\times10^{12}d^2}{\lambda^2}$$

where:

α_{db} = attenuation, decibels

P_t = power transmitted, watts

P_r = power received, watts

d = distance between antennas, miles

λ = wavelength in centimeters

The above formula is complicated, but can be simplified for calculator and computer work in one of two ways, as follows:

$$\alpha_{db} = 10Log_{10}\frac{P_t}{P_r} = 10Log_{10}(4560F^2d^2)$$

or, perhaps better still:

$$\alpha_{db} = 36.6 + 20Log_{10} F + 20Log_{10} d$$

where:

α_{db} = attenuation, decibels

d = distance between antennas, miles

F = frequency, MHz

If you'd like to calculate free space attenuation of a radio wave in a spreadsheet, the procedure is as follows:

Enter frequency (MHz) into Cell E16. Remember the distance (miles) between antennas from the Great Circle calculation in E47?

Enter this formula into E32:

=36.6 + 20*LOG(E16) + 20*LOG(E47)

Cell E32 will display the free space loss, in dB, of the radio wave.

As an example, consider an aircraft 75 miles from the airport at 35,000 ft, operating on 120MHz.

Calculate the 'free space' attenuation of the radio signals:

$$\alpha_{db} = 36.6 + 20Log_{10} F + 20Log_{10} D$$
$$\alpha_{db} = 36.6 + 20Log_{10} 120 + 20Log_{10} 75$$
$$\alpha_{db} = 36.6 + 20(2.08) + 20(1.88)$$
$$\alpha_{db} = 36.6 + 41.60 + 37.60$$
$$\alpha_{db} = 115.8dB$$

In plain English, that means the amount of signal reaching the antenna of the receiver will be about 116-decibels *below* whatever was transmitted! Now we can calculate the approximate received signal strength to determine if communication is even possible.

Let's assume the aircraft transmits 4 watts of power into an antenna with 3dB gain, and that the airport receiver's antenna has 3dB gain as well.

First, let's calculate received power. We know it will be 116dB less than transmitted, so we look at path gains first, with 3dB + 3dB for each antenna gain, and then there's the 4-watts of transmitter power which is 6dB above the 0dBW reference of one-watt: (dB = 10 Log Gain or Loss = 10 Log 4/1 = 6).

So 6dBW of power plus 6dB of antenna gains equals 12dB of system gain to offset that 116dB of free-space loss. In this example, net received power (Pr) will be 116 – 12 = 104dB below 1 watt, or –104dBW.

Then:

$$dB = 10 Log (Pt \div Pr)$$
$$104 = 10 Log (1 \text{ watt} \div Pr)$$
$$104 = 10 Log (1/Pr)$$
$$104 \div 10 = Log (1/Pr)$$
$$10.4 = Log (1/Pr)$$
$$10^{10.4} = 1/Pr$$
$$2.51\times10^{10} = 1/Pr$$
$$Pr = 1 \div 2.51\times10^{10}, \text{ or}$$
$$Pr = 3.98\times10^{-11} \text{ watts,}$$
or 0.0000000000398 watts
or 39.8-picowatts

It's simple to calculate the RSL (Received Signal Level), a more meaningful figure than *received power*.

Ohms Law is our guiding light:

$$P = E^2 \div R, \text{ so:}$$

3.98×10^{-11} watts $= E^2 \div 50\Omega$ (virtually all comm systems use 50Ω antennas)

$$(50)(3.98 \times 10^{-11}) = E^2$$

$$1.99 \times 10^{-9} = E^2$$

Now take the square root of both sides, and:

$$E = \sqrt{1.99 \times 10^{-9}}$$

$E = 4.46 \times 10^{-5}$ volts $= 0.0000446$ volt, or
$44.6\mu V$ *(microvolts)*

$1\mu V$ usually permits usable communications, so we can feel pretty confident that $45\mu V$ will offer more than satisfactory results!

CAVEAT: The free-space loss formulas apply to radio waves traveling in free space only, which limits analysis to such situations as aircraft-to-aircraft, air to ground, ground to air, and space communications.

Mountain-top to mountain-top and close range communications might also qualify under the 'free space' rule.

Free space is generally that portion of the wavefront that's at least three wavelengths away from earth or any obstacle.

"Clear Line of sight" is a major property of free space, and not the only one.

PLANE-EARTH LOSS

Radio signals weaken more when passing over the surface of the earth (Plane-Earth Loss).

The model for *free-space loss* has to be modified if a radio wave passes across or appreciably near

the earth's surface, say within several wavelengths.

The reason can get fuzzy, but think of the earth as a sponge that draws power from a passing wave, or as a friction surface for a rolling ball compared to one in free flight.

Radio waves decay at a different rate from that of free space when they are in the near-field of the earth. It still amounts to a spreading loss, but different variables and rates of decay apply.

This decay model is called Plane-Earth Loss, a solution for which is as follows:

$$\alpha_{db} = 10 Log_{10} \frac{P_t}{P_r}$$

$$\alpha_{db} = 10 Log_{10} \left(3.45 \times 10^{-15} \left(\frac{R_h \times T_h}{d^2} \right)^2 \right)$$

where:

α_{db} = attenuation, decibels
P_t = power transmitted, watts
P_r = power received, watts
d = distance between antennas, miles
R_h = height of receiver antenna above ground, ft
T_h = height of transmitter antenna above ground, ft

A spreadsheet solution for Plane-Earth Loss can be constructed as follows:

Enter the height of the receiver antenna (in feet) into Cell E17.

Enter the transmitter antenna height (in feet) into cell E20.

Refer to Distance (miles) between antennas from the Great Circle calculation in Cell E47.

Then enter *this* formula into E31:

= −1*10*LOG(3.45E-15*((E17*E20)/(E47^2))^2)

The applicable Plane-Earth Loss appears, then, in Cell E31.

The Plane-Earth Loss model stands alone, as shown, only when the transmitter and receiver antennas are within optical line of sight but below the zone of the free space path.

If the two antennas are so far apart as to be below the horizon with respect to each other, or if there are appreciable mass obstacles between them, then one or both of the following models for Diffraction Loss and Shadow Loss must be calculated and the results added to the Plane-Earth Loss to determine the total path loss.

DIFFRACTION LOSS

This is a special-case *additional loss* for radio waves that pass across or near the surface of the earth where the earth's curve is a partial or complete obstacle between the Tx and Rx antennas.

This loss is additive to the Plane-Earth Loss, to derive the total path loss for the wave. Diffraction loss is best explained using a visual analogy.

Imagine a bathtub of water in the middle of which is a brick placed so that it protrudes above the surface. Now create a small ripple at one end and watch what happens as the wave approaches the brick. A portion will strike the brick head-on, while portions of the wave will go around a side.

Immediately behind the brick may be a quiet zone, but you will see where the ripples bend around and rejoin at some point close behind the brick.

Those portions of the ripples that bend lose strength more so than those which simply pass by the brick. This loss as it applies to radio waves is called diffraction loss and is a permanent loss that is additive to the plane earth loss. Diffraction loss is almost always a smaller loss than the plane earth loss, but it increases markedly with distance, and dramatically after passing the radio horizon.

Diffraction loss is almost always calculated and applied to the plane earth loss, even over short path distances where it may be less than 1dB and seemingly not significant.

After a few miles, it is always significant, even within line of sight, and must be added to the plane earth loss to gain a reasonably accurate estimate of the total path loss.

Diffraction loss is best understood as that portion of loss due exclusively to the earth's curve. These "bent" waves continue to diffract and lose strength as they travel, and at the same time they are also subject to the influences of Plane-Earth Loss.

Unfortunately, diffraction loss is variable and depends on a number of factors, including terrain characteristics, weather, and atmospheric density.

Studies have determined two cases for diffraction loss that will cover most situations. One is called the $4/3$-Earth Radius Diffraction model while the other is known as the True Earth Radius Diffraction model.

It is beyond the scope of this book to dig deeply into these variables, but the models below are reasonably conservative and will cover both good and worst cases.

$$^{4}/_{3}\alpha_{db} = 0.064950355(D^{1.438001208})$$

where:

$^{4}/_{3}\alpha_{db}$ = diffraction attenuation, decibels, based on a $^{4}/_{3}$ earth radius

D = distance between antennas, miles

0.08660047 = a "lumped" constant

1.438001208 = exponent of D, another "lumped" constant

A spreadsheet solution for Diffraction Loss can be constructed as follows: Refer Distance (miles) between antennas from the Great Circle calculation in E47, and enter this formula into E33:

=E47^(1.438001208)*0.064950355

The more conservative (worst-case) diffraction model, based on a True Earth radius, is 33% greater, or as follows:

$$^{TE}\alpha_{db} = 0.086600473(D^{1.438001208})$$

Enter this formula into **E34**:

=0.08660047*(E47^1.438001208)

SHADOW LOSS

This is another additive loss, vaguely similar to diffraction loss. Here's how it operates.

Ordinarily, one would not consider trying to communicate from Point A to Point B if a mountain were between the two sites. Surprise, but nothing *perfectly* blocks a radio signal; not even mountains.

Obstacles just attenuate signals much more so than the plane earth and diffraction influences. Obstacle or shadow attenuation can be rather severe, so much so that even modern technology can't overcome its effects, but the point is that we can quantify and evaluate that loss and know something in advance about it.

A moderate shadow loss can often be overcome with simple design techniques or informed decisions. Sometimes, a few decibels of shadow loss are not important at all; othertimes, extremely critical.

The bottom line is that the compleat scannist should know something about shadow loss, and how to estimate it. It's not a major factor, but when you're trying to squeeze every last dB from a communication channel, it's potentially important.

The formula is hairy enough that I'll not try to explain it, but can be easily applied in two steps, as follows:

(1) $\alpha_{db1} = \Phi =$

$10 \, \mathrm{Log}_{10} \, F + 20 \, \mathrm{Log}_{10} \, D - 10 \, \mathrm{Log}_{10} \, H - 55.8$

where: F = frequency, MHz

H = effective height of obstacle, ft

D = distance from obstacle to transmitter or receiver, shortest, miles

Φ = result obtained in Step (1)

e = approx 2.71828182845904 (the base of the natural logarithm)

$(0.08534)(\Phi)$ = the exponent of e in Step (2).

If α_{db} equals or exceeds 13dB, you can stop right there; the result is an accurate estimate of the shadow loss posed by that obstacle.

If less than 13dB, then proceed to Step (2):

(2) $\alpha_{db2} = 4.35459 \, e^{((0.08534)(\Phi))}$

The spreadsheet solution for Shadow Loss is constructed as follows:

Enter into **E24**, the Height of the obstacle above line of sight in feet. Enter into **E25**, the Distance in miles between the obstacle and either the transmitter or the receiver, whichever is the shortest; and enter Frequency in MHz into **E16**.

Then enter this formula into **E29**:

=IF((E24*E25*E16)>0,10*LOG(E16) +20*LOG(E24)−10*LOG(E25)−55.8,0)

Cell E29 displays an interim result and no attention to it is necessary. Finally, enter this formula into **E30**:

=IF((E24*E25*E16)=0,0,IF(E29>=13, E29,EXP(((10*LOG(E16)+20*LOG(E24) −10*LOG(E25)) − 55.8)*(0.08534))* 4.35459))

This shadow loss is added to Plane-Earth Loss and Diffraction Loss to obtain the total Path Loss.

APPLICATION

Radio waves behave according to physical laws just like gravity, mass, momentum, pneumatics, hydraulics, combustion, etc.

The performance of radio waves is predictable to a high degree of confidence with the primary uncertainties falling into categories generally beyond mankind's reach of control and full comprehension.

Weather is one such variable, which influences the diffraction loss by a factor of as much as 33%. This variance could amount to 10dB or more, which can spell the difference between good communications and none at all!

The formulas for diffraction loss that I gave you should cover most contingencies for scanner needs anyway.

In a word, most scanner communications analyses will consist of either free-space studies, or a combination of two or more of Plane-Earth, Diffraction, and Shadow Loss analyses.

If you will stick with me for a few more pages, I'll have you blueprinting your own reception radius. You can do it with little more knowledge than how to use a calculator or a spreadsheet. The hardest part will be constructing the working spreadsheet the very first time. After that, it's easy.

The fun part is entering the variables, and then munching an anchovy pizza with habañero (Scotch Bonnet – the hottest there is!!) peppers while you ponder the results. This dynamo of a spreadsheet will do all the dirty work.

Here's a brief overview of the process of analyzing VHF-UHF radio propagation between two points by adding a few more cells to the Great Circle Spreadsheet. Refer back to the spreadsheet and Technical Structure as we discuss the few action items.

If you want to be slick and professional, enter your site name, transmitter site name, your name, and the date and time in **D11** through **D14**. Enter the frequency, in MHz, into **E16**.

We need to know the distance of the path and reciprocal bearings between a transmitter and your receiver site. Enter the latitude and longitude for both sites in **C2** through **E5** on the worksheet.

The previous Great Circle spreadsheet has already been done!

Once we know distance (*calculated instantly in* **E47**), we need to know if there is any chance of "line of sight" and any possibility of free-space considerations, so let's let the worksheet calculate distances to the horizon for each site, and combine those distances to produce a maximum possible line of sight.

Requisite data for this and other calculations later include the heights of the transmitter and receiving antennas, so enter the two antenna heights into **E17** and **E20**. *These heights are not actual heights above ground as you might first think.* Rather, they're heights above *average terrain*. This could go either way.

For instance, suppose your antenna is on a 35 ft mast above ground, but your local ground is in a 20 ft deep gully.

Figure 9-4: Line of sight estimates

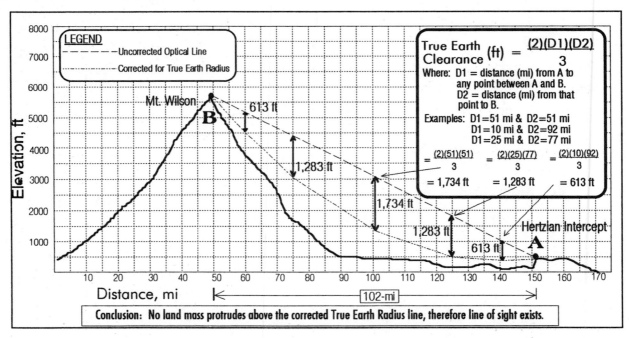

Conclusion: No land mass protrudes above the corrected True Earth Radius line, therefore line of sight exists.

The most accurate model will call for you to enter 15 ft as the height of your antenna. On the other hand, the NOAA weather station atop Mt. Wilson near Los Angeles sits at 5,710 ft AMSL (above mean sea level). My location is on a 470 ft (AMSL) mesa with no nearfield obstructions of any sort.

Therefore, I reasoned there might be a good chance of line of sight. Not sure of NOAA's antenna height above ground, I entered 5710' in **E20** and 470' + 30' mast = 500 ft for my antenna height into **E17**. The calculations for line of sight in cells **E44-E46** suggest a maximum LOS of about 138 miles in **E46**. The calculated path distance of 102 miles in **E47** seems to bear out the probability of line of sight. *Great!*

This is a good point to do a little terrain analysis. It can be as simple as stepping outside and taking a look around, or as involved as scribing the radio path over a series of pasted-up USGS topo maps and plotting a contour graph of all elevations between the two points.

There is a simple approach to evaluating this "line of sight" thing a little better. You can do it on a flat graph sheet, too! Some engineers prefer a special curved map, but anything with grid marks will do... plain old graph paper.

ENTRIES

This figure isn't real-life accurate because I didn't want to take the time to analyze a 102 mile path that is line of sight anyway.

The idea is to plot an elevation profile on a flat grid as you see in *Figure 9-4* and then correct the flatness to the earth's curve by means of the Clearance formula.

Draw a straight line between Points A and B on a topo map or other map that offers elevation data. Set a scale to your grid as I did above, and plot the elevations of A and B.

Then follow the straight line you drew on the map(s) and plot the higher elevations between A and B.

Draw a straight line on the graph between A and B. This is the flat-earth optical sight line. If any land mass protrudes into that line, you unconditionally do not have line of sight. If a landmass or object comes near the optical line, then you still may not have line of sight.

That's where the True Earth Radius Clearance correction comes into play. Any given point on the line between A and B must have the required TE Clearance beneath it, in order to have line of sight.

The examples above show that greatest clearance of 1,734 feet is required at the 51/51-mile mark and 613 feet at the 10/92 mile marks, and 1,283-feet at the 25/77 mile marks.

Drop a line straight down from the optical line scaled to the requisite clearance, and if does not hit or protrude into an obstacle or land mass, then you have line of sight and probably a free-space path. You will see with a little study that the least

required clearance is at either end of the path, and maximum is in the middle.

Enter in Cells **E18** and **E21**, the GAIN figures in dB for your antenna and for the transmitter antenna.

If you use a discone or other wideband antenna, the gain will be zero at best, and quite possibly as low as -1 to -5dB. Start with 0dB anyway. If you use a higher performance antenna, refer to its specs for the GAIN rating, in dB.

Most transmitters of a professional or business nature use antennas with anywhere from 3dB to 9dB of gain, with about 6dB typical. Start with 6dB if you're not sure.

Enter into Cells **E19** and **E22** an estimate of miscellaneous losses at each site. For your station, use the loss factor of your coax cable plus one additional dB.

The casual hobbyist will have anywhere from 3dB to 10dB of loss between the antenna and scanner.

Figure yours out, or enter 5dB as a rough estimate. Professional and commercial sites minimize their losses because of the monetary cost of waste. Allow 1-2 dB of loss at the Tx site.

It's helpful to know the transmitter's power authorization. NOAA Weather stations typically use 100 watts as do repeaters in Public Safety. Business transmitters range from 5 watts to 25 watts.

When in doubt, enter (into E23) 1 watt for handhelds, 3 watts for cellular mobiles and bases, 5 watts for other mobiles, and 25 watts for all other bases. Errors are likely to be on the conservative side, and therefore more acceptable from a results viewpoint even if they're not perfect from an engineering and technical perspective.

Now you need to analyze any obstacles that may be in the path between your receiver antenna and the remote transmitter. If there is an obstacle, enter its height in feet above the line of sight into **E24** and the shortest distance to that obstacle, whether relative to A or B, into **E25**.

Height of the obstacle is not necessarily its height above ground; rather, the height into which it penetrates above the corrected optical line shown in *Figure 9-4*. A 1,000 ft obstacle that penetrates only 100 ft into the optical zone is a 100 ft obstacle; not 1,000 ft, you see.

That's it!

About the time you enter that last number into **E25**, the entire Bearing, Distance, and Radio Propagation analysis will be waiting for you at the bottom of the page!

Now let's set up the worksheet so you can get down to brass tacks. Believe me, it will be worth your time and trouble to give this thing a shot, even if you don't have the foggiest idea of what I'm talking about so far.

This thing is awesome and will remove much of the mystery and black magic of radio for you in due time. And... without it, the Ultimate Scanner might rust, or begin leaking, or smell even worse.

FURTHER SPREADSHEET EXPLANATION

Most spreadsheets work virtually instantly.

When you enter a new value in a cell that is referred to by any of the resident formulas, a calculation takes place instantly to change all the outputs that depend on the cell that was changed. One changed entry = multiple results.

That is just right for WHAT IF situations where you need rapid feedback.

I remember my VHF-UHF days in the late 70's as a junior engineer, when I performed all these calculations by hand using a 4-function calculator and huge tables of trigonometric and logarithmic functions.

As a matter of fact, I even used a slide rule to better advantage than those old calculators. A single iteration of a radio link design was arduous enough, but then to conduct a WHAT-IF analysis sometimes took hours!

In July, 1979, Hewlett-Packard introduced their *HP-41C Programmable Calculator* – which forever changed my life.

It wasn't long before I ran these same calculations on an automated basis, reducing to minutes the time needed for WHAT-IF analysis. Now my spreadsheet will do it in seconds, even on the slowest computers.

The output/results of my Bearing-Distance & VHF-UHF Propagation Spreadsheet might well confuse many of you. Forget the confusion. Any part of it that you *do* understand will be better than nothing at all and/or the old ways.

Stick with it, and in due time you will become less confused. A little longer and you'll be explaining it to others.

Meanwhile, there is another thing you should understand: RECEIVED SIGNAL LEVEL (RSL) as expressed in microvolts (μV). $1\mu V$ is one-millionth of a volt of signal, which is pretty much the stated specification of most VHF-UHF scanners.

In practice, scanners can detect signals as weak as $0.1\mu V$, albeit with a lot of noise. Full quieting occurs in most scanners somewhere between $0.5\mu V$ and $2\mu V$.

So use my spreadsheet for all it's worth to help you understand why certain signals are hard or impossible to receive and what lengths you must go to in order to pull them in.

This spreadsheet produces interesting and useful output data starting at **E27** where the transmitter power you entered *as watts* in **E23** gets converted to *decibels relative to 1 watt* (dBW) in **E27**.

Just for play and practice, enter a variety of numbers, one at a time, into **E23** and watch the changes in **E27**. This alone can enhance your understanding of decibels (dB), logarithms, and basic ratios!

E28 is the sum of all path GAINs at both the receiver site as well as at the transmitter site. This isn't especially a very useful bit of data, but its there for a quick glance.

E29 should be completely disregarded; it has no meaning to you at all but is used as an interim step in calculating the Shadow Loss in **E30**.

If you enter a 0 in either or both of **E24-E25**, then **E30** will return zero as the shadow loss.

Plane-Earth Loss is calculated and displayed in **E31**.

E32 calculates and displays free-space loss which may or may not apply, but is useful in evaluating the best-case-possible performance from a given radio link.

E33 calculates a diffraction loss based on a 33% greater RF line of sight than optical line of sight ($^4/_3$ *Earth radius*).

Weather and terrain conditions can and do vary diffraction loss, so this "typical" case is available for view and later considerations.

E34 calculates a diffraction loss based on actual earth's curve. Any given VHF-UHF radio link can be influenced by varying levels of diffraction from one day to the next.

I'm sure you've heard the same station with strong signals at times and rather weak at other times. Variable diffraction caused by atmospheric changes is the probable cause.

So, we calculate BOTH extremes of diffraction to see the range of signals we're most likely to encounter.

Cells **E35-E37** totalize the above losses into three separate categories, with **E35** a sum of free space loss plus local system losses.

Unless you have obvious line of sight with a distant transmitter, that figure will prove to be an elusive *"best case"* with a low probability of ever coming close.

It will be valid for real free-space paths, like for ground-to-aircraft, etc. If you know a given path is line of sight, then you can rely heavily on this number.

E36 is a sum of Plane-Earth Loss, local system losses, shadow losses, if any, and the $^4/_3$ Earth radius diffraction loss.

This total system loss number in E36 is a lot more than the free space loss, but less than the loss that can occur in a worst-case scenario, so this one might be viewed as "typical" or "normal."

E37 is a total system loss based on a sum of Plane-Earth Loss, local system losses, shadow losses, if any, and the True Earth radius diffraction loss (optical line of sight). This total loss can be severe, and should be considered a worst-case scenario.

Cells **E38-E40** present anticipated received power levels in dB below 1 watt (dBW). You're not really interested in these numbers right now, but they are important to cells **E41-E43** which produce the *meat 'n taters* output for the time being, with RSL's calculated in microvolts (μV).

E41 calculates expected RSL based on a free-space path which may or may not be the actual case. The spreadsheet cannot "know" if free space conditions actually exist, so it just calculates a "best case" and lets you interpret it as you see fit.

Cell **E42** calculates an RSL based on a *"more likely"* case and **E43** calculates RSL in a *"worst case"* scenario. Among these three possible

scenarios, you will get a feel for what should be the case at your site.

E44-E46 calculate maximum possible lines of sight to help you determine the type of radio path you're evaluating. **E44** calculates the distance to the theoretical horizon for Site A.

E45 calculates the same for Site B, and **E45** sums the two, for a maximum possible line of sight distance.

To get a feel for reality, look at **E47,** the actual path distance. If E47 is less than E46, there is a possibility for line of sight and maybe a free space path. If E47 is equal to or greater than E46, there is almost no chance at all for a free-space path.

Cells E44-E46 and E47 can go a long way toward helping you determine the kind of path that exists between your site and the target signal source.

After that, call into play topo maps and your knowledge of the regional terrain to make a final assessment.

Cells **E49, E50, C52-E52, and C53-E53,** present the reciprocal directions of Sites A and B, with respect to True North. **E49-50** are in decimal degrees while **C52-E52** and **C53-E53** are in DD MM SS format.

BACK TO THE BBS

If you do not want to construct your own spreadsheets for whatever reason, these and others are available for download from my BBS, at (619) 578-9247 after 5:30pm and before 1:30pm, Pacific Time.

The file is SPRED.ZIP.

TRUE NORTH

The matter of "True North" may need some clarification, with respect to "Magnetic North." You see, the magnetic poles and the real poles of the Earth are not the same. Compasses, of course, rely on the magnetic poles for reference, but navigation and especially distances and bearings are unilaterally computed and presented with respect to the true poles, or True North.

If you have never seen or identified the Pole Star, North Star, or Polaris – whatever you want to call it – it's about time you did so. Look at *Figure 9-5.*

Polaris can be seen on a relatively clear night in a True North direction from most anywhere in the northern hemisphere. Its angle above the horizon is equal to the latitude of the observation point.

Figure 9-5: Polaris, the Pole Star

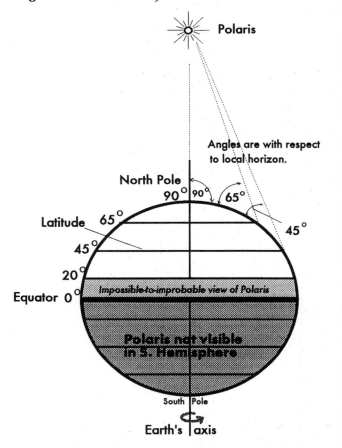

From my location, it's 34° up from the horizon. If your latitude is 45°, then Polaris will be true north

of you, exactly halfway up (45°) between your horizon and straight overhead. See *Figure 9-5*.

Polaris, the North Star (aka lots of things), has provided a True North reference since the dawn of history. You may as well use it, too.

All other stars in the sky "move" through the course of the night as our planet rotates. Not Polaris; it's immovable, day and night! Why is it "stationary?" Imagine an axle running through the earth. As it rotates about that axle, an object that lies on that axle remains stationary. It's a fine reference...

Whatever worked for the ancient Phoenicians is good enough for me.

THE END...

If you stuck with me to the end, you're hardcore!

I hope you'll agree it's been fun. It certainly has been to me. It's also incomplete. I admit it. By the time you read this there will be scanners out there that aren't covered in this book, and there are certainly mods that aren't covered.

But there's a solution. I'm like the spider at the center of the web. The information comes in and goes out at an amazing pace, and I see all of it!

Cyberspace provides my primary data input channels (BBS and the Internet). Use them, and you'll keep me up to date. The *World Scanner Report* is my primary output channel. Subscribe to that and I'll keep *you* up to date.

And meanwhile, I hope you enjoyed yourself, and that this book helps you increase the pleasure you get from our hobby.

Epilogue

Great Boogley Woogley!

I've gotta stop writing. My publisher just broke in, menacingly waving a wicked-looking pistol with a barrel so big you could stick a mop handle in it, shouting something about "I'M GONNA SHOOT THE ENGINEER!" If I don't push the *print* key and back slowly away from my keyboard, this might be my last book!

So I gotta go, but this is not the end by any stretch of the imagination. You have learned by now that *The Ultimate Scanner* isn't the "final word" in our hobby. Rather, it's the first word of a new generation, in which a scanner isn't ultimate unless a computer is part of it. So, there's more coming. Lots more. This book was like that joke about a thousand attorneys at the bottom of the Pacific. Remember? It's "just a good start." You guys 'n gals have to let my publisher know if you want more so he'll begin nagging me for it.

Meanwhile, let me leave you with a thought... and a chance.

First, the thought. Most of the scanner mod crowd is interested in the PRO-2004/5/6, 2035 and the PRO-43, and for good reason, so they get the majority of my attention. This might disappoint those looking for specific help for their SnakeBiteXR-871-YMU hardware. Well, I can do something about that if you tell me what you want, and if there's a sufficient volume of requests for that particular material. It's up to you. I apologize if you and your turnip feel slighted; *please* re-read Chapter 2.

So here's your chance: ask me to write a concise, economical Hack Report for your favorite scanner. List anything that would be useful to you and that you know isn't impossible, but don't get carried away because blood (and performance) won't come from Turnips. I will keep a database of those requests and work up documents for the more popular rigs. These will be simple, no-frills, modestly-priced reports with nothing but hard-core hacks for specific scanners.

Vote as many as you want, but do it as soon as you read this. Oh yes, I almost forgot *The Test*. This book has a certain number of deliberate errors in it, just for you perfectionists. When you find any, please let me know so we can properly grade your performance. Of course, I don't want to make it too easy for you as time goes by, so any mistake that gets found quickly will be corrected in the first revision. Let me hear from you via Internet (two ways), FidoNet, Compuserve, BBS, or *(gasp!)* U. S. Postal Service – check Chapter 1. Don't say there's no way to reach me!

Bill Cheek
San Diego, California
April, 1995

GLOSSARY

η-	Nano
μ-	Micro
ρ-	Pico
1.25-meter	Ham band from 222-225 MHz.
2-meter	Ham band from 144-148 MHz.
6-meter	Ham band from 50-54 MHz.
75-cm	Ham band from 420-450 MHz.
AC	Alternating current; flows in one direction for a period of time, and then reverses and flows in the opposite direction, usually for the same period of time. Reversal is rarely instantaneous. Time is required for a point on a wave to increase or decrease in strength or intensity. When the period of increase and decrease is repetitious, the wave is said to have a frequency equal to the reciprocal of the period of one repetition. If the period of a wave is 0.0167 sec (16.7 msec), its frequency will be 60 Hz, or 60 cycles per second.
active antenna	Combined antenna and preamplifier. If the preamplifier is good enough (GaAs FET, for instance) it may improve performance.
AM	Amplitude Modulation. Also, refers to the entertainment broadcast band from 550-1650 kHz.
amateur radio	The hobby, defined by the FCC. Don't let the name deceive: this hobby is comprised of unpaid professionals, and has amassed a pool of knowledge available nowhere else.
amplifier	Active circuit element that increases power, voltage, or both of an electrical signal.
amplitude	Voltage or power of an electrical signal. Each has it own units of measurement.
analog	Data storage and transmission techniques where *any* value whatever can be defined. Generally, this is the real world, so human perception and processing is in analog form.
angels	Military term for altitude in tens of thousands of feet, as in "Angels 40," which means 40,000'.
approach	Path of an aircraft from final navigation point to touchdown.
approach control	Traffic management facility that controls aircraft approaching an airport for landing.
ARTCC	Air Route Traffic Control Center
ASIC	Application-Specific-Integrated-Circuit, which embodies proprietary circuitry in one device. Available only to the "owner," and not usually available over the counter.
ATC	Air Traffic Control. Primary enroute air traffic management agency, with area centers linked by radio, landline, and computer.
attenuation	Reduction of strength or intensity; weaken
aviation band	118-137 MHz (military is 225-400 MHz)
bank	Array of frequencies in a scanner, usually associated with one of the number keys.
bearing	Compass direction between two points, used for angulated location-finding of radio signal emitters.
bingo	In military aviation, return to base. Alternatively, to shift to a backup frequency, as in "go to channel white, bingo red."
birdie	Signal generated within or by the tuning mechanism that deceives the radio into stopping the scan.
BNC	Common antenna connector, twist to lock.
bogie	Unidentified aircraft spotted by one of the good guys, or by ground radar. "You have a *bogie* at two o'clock, ten miles."
broadcast band	550 - 1650 kHz, amplitude modulation.
Bulletin Board System (BBS)	Computer+phone+software, permits modem-equipped callers to leave and receive messages, load and donate software, etc.
Bullington	Kenneth B., father (or at least uncle) of VHF/UHF propagation modeling
butcher brigade	A class of wannabe hackers who do more harm than good, and then send me the result with a $5 bill, to "fix"
capacitance	Storage capacity of a capacitor for an electron charge; in Farads (F) more commonly expressed as microFarads (μF) or picofarads (ρF)
capacitor	Reactive circuit component that stores energy, or passes an alternating signal while blocking a non-alternating one.

cellular	Mobile telephony, where the portable radio communicates with radios each commanding a "cell," with cells connected with the plain old telephone system "POTS."
cellular band	869-894 MHz.
center	See ARTCC
clearance	The instructions given to a pilot as to route and altitude profile from departure to destination.
coaxial cable ("coax")	Cable consisting of outer insulating sheath, flexible wire or foil layer, another insulating layer, and a central wire conductor. Used for low-loss radio frequency connections, typically with BNC connectors.
Communications Act of 1934	Legislation designed to give the FCC control over the airwaves, and to limit certain types of activity by requiring licensing and protocol compliance. Amended in 1989 to raise forfeiture limits that the FCC can impose.
compressive receiver	A sort of scanner, whereby a large segment of the spectrum is received and examined for signals.
couch potato	One who needs a little goading to launch an enterprise: Hacker-precursor.
counter	Electrical tool that can receive a signal and display its frequency.
crystal	Common frequency selection or tuning mechanism for single frequency or few-frequency radios.
CT-2	Second generation cordless phones, usually with bitstream or spread spectrum digital encoding of voice.
current	Quantity or volume of electron flow; expressed in amperes or amps (A). 1 ampere is equal to a flow of 1 coulomb of charge through 1Ω in 1 sec
CW	Continuous Wave, or Carrier Wave, without modulation.
data logger	Extended-operation tape recorder, set up to turn on when signals are detected by the scanning receiver. After recording that communication, the unit turns off and awaits the next one.
DC	Direct current; flows in one direction only. When the strength of a DC current varies with time, say from 0 volts to 5 volts and back to 0 volts, at some periodicity or interval, this is said to be an *alternating DC*, the characteristics of which are very much like those of AC, especially with respect to mathematical analysis. Therefore, an alternating waveform can still be direct current; if it flows in one direction only, it is not AC.
decibel	"dB" Unit of power ratio, expressed logarithmically. Ten times the logarithm of a ratio of two power levels = $10 \, Log_{10} \, (P_{out}/P_{in})$
delay	Scanner function, usually selectable, whereby the unit remains on frequency for perhaps two seconds following reception of a signal, thus permitting reception of the response to it.
demodulator	Receiver circuitry that extracts information from a radio signal.
departure control	Traffic management facility that controls aircraft after takeoff but still in the local control area.
diffraction	Apparent bending of electromagnetic waves in the passage across any irregularity or feature, resulting from reduction in coherence of the wave as it bends to "follow" the shape. The earth itself diffracts radio waves.
digital	Data coding, storage, and transmission technique whereby information is reduced to expressions constructed using only two symbols (for convenience, "1" and "0," though could just as easily be "on" and "off," or "green" and "Pontiac." A digital signal can only express a value in discrete increments, while an analog signal can express any value. A convenience, used in computing.
diode	Circuit element that permits electricity to flow in only one direction.
DIP	Dual In-line Package; generally describes the common IC socket, with two rows of aligned pins.
dipole	The simplest directional antenna. A TV "rabbit ears" antenna is a dipole.
direct-frequency tuning	Enables tuning a frequency by literally entering the numbers that define it rather than tuning a "dial."
directional	Antenna with greater sensitivity in some directions and less in others.
dispatch	Refers to channels and functions that control vehicle movement.
Doppler	Phenomenon whereby a frequency appears to change as the transmitter and receiver approach or separate.
Down-converter	Accessory that receives (typically) 800-900 MHz cellular and public service signals and converts them to frequencies tunable by a scanner that otherwise would not be able to operate in that band.
DPDT	Double pole, double throw; two SPDT switches in one unit
DPST	Double pole, single throw; two SPST switches in one unit

DTMF   Dual Tone Multi Frequency: the audio heard when a phone key is touched. Made up of two specific tones, with each pair corresponding to a number or function.

duplex   In two-way communications, duplex permits both sides to speak simultaneously, as over the common telephone.

DVM   Digital Volt Meter. Perhaps the most useful single tool in electronics. Typical units measure AC/DC voltage, current, resistance, and a few measure inductance and/or capacitance as well.

DX   In amateur radio, "extended distance."

dynamic range   Signal strength limits between which the unit will operate satisfactorily without malfunction, and refers to range between weakest signal detectable and strongest signal that will not produce overwhelming intermodulation and distortion.

ECPA   Electronic Communications Privacy Act of 1986, designed to prevent eavesdropping upon cellular and cordless phones, though the latter coverage was reversed by the Supreme Court.

ELF   Extremely Low Frequency band, from 0 Hz to 6 kHz, usually used by the Navy for submarine communications.

Ether "æther"   That medium through which radio signals travel.

femto-   Almost none at all. *Teeny!* Would you believe a quadrillionth?

FIDO   A network of BBSs, sharing information and processing mail for members.

flare   Raising the nose just before touchdown to cushion the landing (Navy/Marine). It's called "round out" in the USAF.

flight level   Altitude in tens of thousands of feet (civilian).

FM   Frequency Modulation. Also, a term used to refer to the high-fidelity broadcast band from 88-108 MHz.

Free Space Loss   Weakening, or decay, of radio signals due solely to distance, in compliance with the square-cube law which says that as distance doubles, perceived power is divided by four.

frequency   Specific point (periodicity of vibration, in a way) in the electromagnetic spectrum.

frequency steps   Tuning increments of a digital tuning device such as a synthesizer. Also called "resolution."

fundamental   A single-frequency signal, with neither harmonics nor subharmonics.

gain   Increase in effective radiated power (in a transmitter) or receptivity (receiver), when compared to omnidirectional antennas or passive circuitry.

GHz   Gigahertz; billion hertz; 1,000,000,000 Hz; 1,000 MHz; 1,000,000 kHz; 1 GHz

glop   A small gob, usually used in reference to silicone adhesive/seal; about 1.77cc

gloppy   Of or having to do with a glop

Great Circle   shortest arc distance between two points on the surface of the earth

ground control   Airport facility that controls and coordinates taxiing aircraft and vehicle traffic.

ground plane   Conductive or electrically reflective surface under an antenna to serve as an artificial earth ground. Also, layer within a printed circuit board that acts to reduce energy radiated from one side to the other side.

guard   A term that denotes emergency aviation frequencies, always monitored by all aircraft and by all ground control agencies. VHF – 121.5 MHz, UHF – 243.0 MHz.

guard band   "Margin" next to a selected frequency. Extra room to prevent adjacent channel interference.

Hacker   One who adapts, modifies, or alters an object of any sort to meet new needs, applications, and/or specifications not anticipated or intended by the original manufacturer. *The "war dialer" cybergang lent this term a nasty connotation. Not only that, but the legion of computer hackers desperately tries to claim the word for themselves. Computer hackers are johnny-come-lately's. Hardware hacking has been a major pursuit for a lot longer than computers and war dialers have been around.* Hacking is an honorable enterprise. *Anything* ever made by a manufacturer can be made better by a Hacker. In person, a Hacker can be identified by good looks, high IQ, and incredible agility.

Hacker's Law   *"Murphy was an optimist."*

handheld   Small, portable, battery-operated device, used to refer to radios.

harmonic   A frequency exactly twice that of a "fundamental" frequency, which appears and disappears as the fundamental is switched on and off, thereby proving a relationship.

Hertz   Unit of frequency; one cycle or repetition per second; 1 Hz

HF   High frequency band, most-used by hams.

IC	Integrated circuit; a circuit "printed" in semiconductor material on a substrate, usually of silicon. An IC can contain hundreds of thousands of transistors and other devices, connected by microscopic circuitry ("wiring")
IFR	Instrument Flight Rules, where a ground facility maintains clearance between the aircraft and ground, other aircraft, etc. Under IFR, the pilot often flies "blind."
image	When the received signal is downconverted to an intermediate frequency, an "image" is generated at twice that number.
impedance	Identical to *resistance*, except inclusive of resistive, inductive and capacitive opposition, restriction or hindrance to electron flow; expressed in Ohms (Ω). 1Ω is the impedance through which 1 amp will flow at a force of 1 volt
inductance	Storage capacity of an inductor for a magnetic field; expressed in Henries (H) commonly expressed in milliHenrys (mH) or microhenries (μH)
inductor	Reactive circuit component that passes a non-alternating signal while blocking an alternating one.
inquiry	Refers to channels used for questions.
Inter-modulation "intermod"	The new frequency products (sum and difference) when two signals are mixed. These are new frequencies, detected as radio signals, and therefore generate birdies and fool the scan mechanism into stopping.
keylock	Switch or lever that prevents inadvertent keyboard entries
kHz	Kilohertz; thousand hertz; 1000 Hz; 1 kHz
lambda (λ)	Greek symbol used to denote wavelength.
latitude	Distance from the equator or pole, expressed in degrees N or S
LF	Low Frequency band, from 30-300 kHz.
lockout	Scanner feature that skips past undesired frequencies or channels
logic	Integrated circuits that comprise the thinking mechanisms of a computer
ongitude	Position east or west, in degrees, from a great circle connecting the poles and passing through Greenwich, England
loop	Simple directional antenna
LSB	Lower Sideband. A derivative of SSB where the carrier and upper sideband are suppressed, and information is carried only on the lower sideband
Mayday!	In aviation, EMERGENCY

MF	Medium Frequency band, from 300 kHz to 3 MHz. Includes the common "AM" broadcast band.
MHz	Megahertz; million hertz; 1,000,000 Hz. 1,000 kHz = 1 MHz
micro-	Verbal prefix for "millionth
micro-processor	Also μP: the computer's brain, consisting of an array of logic.
microwave	Anything above 2 GHz in frequency.
milli-	verbal prefix for the fractional expression, "*thousandth*"; x10^{-3}
mobile	Intended for vehicle installation.
modulation	The means by which information is impressed on a fundamental radio signal
modulator	Transmitter circuitry that imposes information upon a radio signal
monitor	Scanner function that stores a frequency of interest found by searching
MTSO	Mobile Telephone Switching Office, which connects the cellular cell radios with the telephone system
Murphy's Law	"If anything can possibly break or go wrong, it will do so"
nano-	Verbal prefix for the fractional expression, "*billionth*"; x10^{-9}
NOAA	National Oceanographic and Atmospheric Administration: weather alert service.
non-volatile	Refers to memory. Non-volatile retains information even when power is removed.
NSA	National Security Agency, at Fort George G. Meade, between Baltimore and Washington DC.
octave	The range from any frequency to exactly twice that frequency, both in audio and in radio.
omni-directional	Refers to antennas with equal sensitivity to signals from every direction.
omnibus	Originally called the Omnibus Crime Control and Safe Streets Act of 1968, attempts to control eavesdropping by establishing penalties.
oscilloscope	Second most important RF test instrument (after DVM/VOM), displays waveforms in the *time domain*. That is, it shows relationships between time and amplitude (voltage) of a signal.
pan	In aviation, deferred emergency (seldom heard)
PCB	Printed circuit board
PCN	Personal Communication Network (also Personal Communication System), from 902-928MHz, also in low-microwave (1.8GHz), and at 5.4GHz.

PCS	Personal Communication Systems (see PCN)
phase noise	Specification that identifies the quality of the signal used to tune the radio/scanner, hence the selectivity.
pico-	Verbal prefix for "trillionth"
pin-line	Plugs or sockets – resembles half an IC socket, all pins in a straight line, generally one-tenth of an inch, center-to-center, top end is usually female, and bottom is usually male. The metal pins are machined in lieu of stamped and therefore, the males make a perfect fit with the females. Pin-lines can be made to serve as IC sockets, transistor sockets, quick-disconnect plugs & sockets, etc.
pirate radio	Unlicensed, unauthorized broadcasts, usually political or entertainment, often from ships at sea, or from across the border.
POTS	Plain Old Telephone Service.
power	Energy; current flow through a resistance; expressed in Watts (W). 1 watt is the energy consumed when 1 volt forces 1 amp through 1Ω
preamplifier	Also "booster," amplifies radio signals and noise, together.
priority	Scanner function. When a channel is designated "priority," every few seconds the unit returns to check for transmissions on that frequency.
propagation	Act of the transfer of electromagnetic energy through space
prototype	A functional assembly or circuit, but not in final form; subject to revision
public safety	Police, fire, ambulance, rescue, disaster relief, and other emergency services.
quartz "quartz-lock"	Refers to circuit that is tuned using a frequency synthesizer, based upon a crystal reference, rather than a reactive passive circuit.
range	That distance over which a signal can be received by a given set of factors, such as transmitter amplifier, antenna gain at each end, and receiver sensitivity.
repeater	A combined receiver and transmitter, on two frequencies, whereby a weak signal is received and re-transmitted with more power, thus increasing range.
resistance	Constriction of flow, requiring that the electrical signal give up power to pass.
resistance	Non-capacitive and non-inductive opposition, restriction or hindrance to electron flow; expressed in Ohms (Ω). 1Ω is the resistance through which 1 amp will flow at a force of 1 volt. Also see *impedance*.
resistor	In a circuit, a constriction through which electrical energy passes while giving up some of its energy.
RMS	Root-mean-square
rosin core	The *right* solder to use when working on anything electronic. "Acid core" solder is for plumbing, and should be avoided at all costs.
RTTY	Radio teletype, using the 5-bit International Telegraph Alphabet #2 (ITA2). Usually ham communication below 30 MHz, and at low data rates.
rubber duck	Rubber, flexible antenna with which most handheld scanners are equipped.
scanner	Radio capable of automatically searching for transmissions either through the spectrum, or through a pre-defined series of frequencies.
scannist	Scanner enthusiast/hobbyist. Hopefully will become widely used. Secondary definition: a "scannist" is handsome, brilliant, and knows almost everything.
scrambler	Means by which a transmission is encoded specifically to avoid eavesdropping or unauthorized reception.
search	Scanner sweeping between preset high and low frequency limits.
selectivity	Scanner specification that indicates the unit's ability to discriminate between two signals close together.
Shadow Loss	Energy loss due to partial obstacles along the line of sight
simplex	In two-way communications, simplex is a single path requiring that only one "end" speak at a time
SIP	Single In-line Package; generally describes a pin-line socket strip
skip	Radio energy propagation that "bounces" off of an ionized atmospheric layer, increasing range beyond the expected line of sight
SMA	Microwave connectors that operate over a broader frequency range than the less expensive BNC (connector)
SPDT	Single pole, double throw; a 3-pin switch, one pin common switched to either of two positions; on-on, off-off
spectrum	The delimited range of *anything,* such as color, hardness, etc. In the context of this book, refers to a range of possible periodicities, or frequencies, available to radio and other electromagnetic devices. The "spectrum" as an electromagnetic term, covers any periodicity above DC, to light and beyond.

spectrum analyzer	Instrument that depicts some segment of the spectrum and the signals detected within it. Display is in the *frequency domain*, and shows the relationship between energy and frequency.
spread spectrum	Modulation technique whereby an integrated digital code is used to distinguish the signal from other energy, allowing it to be extracted even from noise.
SPST	Single pole, single throw; a 2-pin switch, on-off
spurs	Uncommanded discrete signals generated by the tuning mechanism, sometimes heard as "birdies."
squelch	Scanner function that reduces sensitivity to all but signals of desired amplitude.
SSB	Single Sideband. A modulation strategy whereby the primary carrier is suppressed.
SSTV	Slow-scan TV, a hobbyist method of transmitting video images using relatively low data rates and narrow bandwidth.
state	In aviation, refers to fuel level, as in "What's your state?"
SWAT	Special Weapons and Tactics.
synthesizer "frequency synthesizer"	Tuning device that can generate many precision frequencies, each locked to a quartz crystal reference.
TA (tango alpha)	In aviation, a traffic advisory.
tabletop	Term ed to desc ribe a scanner (or any hobby radio) intended for base station operation.
Telephone Disclosure & Dispute Resolution Act	1992 federal legislation, originally proposed to control abuse of 900-numbers, but with addenda that cause the FCC to restrict sale/import of cellular-capable scanners.
trunking system	Public safety and industrial radio network where a bank of frequencies is available to all stations, and traffic is controlled by a computer that communicates over a management channel.
Turbo-Whopper	Extensively modified scanner, usually with leather seats and a Momo wheel

Turnip	An extensively *non*-modifiable scanner
TVRO	TeleVision Receive-Only ("satellite receiver").
USB	Upper Sideband. One derivative of SSB, where the carrier and the lower sideband are suppressed, and information is carried only on the upper sideband.
UTC	Universal Coordinated Time (World Time), once called Greenwich Mean Time. And it *is* U T C, not U C T.
VFR	Visual Flight Rules, used when weather permits. Under VFR, the pilot maintains his/her own clearance from other aircraft, terrain, etc.
VHF	Very High Frequency band, usually defined as 30-174 MHz.
Victor	Term used to identify standard numbered airways, as in "cleared to X-ray on Victor 33." Rather like an interstate highway system at 36,000'.
VLF	Very Low Frequency band, from 6 to 30 kHz.
volatile	Refers to memory. Volatile memory loses information when power is removed.
voltage	pressure or force behind electron flow; expressed in volts; 1 volt is the force required to push 1 amp through a resistance of 1Ω
VSAT	Very Small Aperture Terminal, refers to either satellite or terrestrial (point-to-point) telecommunication terminals.
wavelength	Distance between two corresponding points in a signal's repetitive waveform
whip	Simple antenna. A straight piece of wire, usually of a calculated length.
yagi	Complex directional antenna, with long, narrow, high-gain pattern. A rooftop TV antenna is somewhat like a yagi.
zulu	Refers to Greenwich Mean Time (at Greenwich, England), also "UTC."

RESOURCES

PARTS & SUPPLIES

ACTIVE
PO BOX 9100
WESTBOROUGH, MA 01581
800-343-0874
ELECTRONIC COMPONENTS SUPPLIES

ALL ELECTRONICS CORP
PO BOX 567
VAN NUYS, CA 91408
800-826-5432   213-380-8000   800-258-6666
ELECTRONIC COMPONENTS, EQUIPMENT

ALLIED ELECTRONICS
401 E. 8TH ST
FORT WORTH, TX 76102
ELEX COMPONENTS, EQUIPMENT & SUPPLIES

ALPHA WIRE CORPORATION
711 LIDGERWOOD AVENUE
ELIZABETH, NJ 07207
201-925-8000
COAX, WIRE & CABLE

AMIDON ASSOCIATES
2216 E. GLADWICK ST
DOMINQUEZ HILLS, CA 90220
213-763-5770   FAX 213-763-2250
POWDERED IRON CORES & COILS FOR RF
APPLICATIONS

AMPHENOL RF DIVISION
ONE KENNEDY AVE.
708-960-1010
DANBURY, CT 06810

PREMIUM COAX & RF CONNECTORS

ARROW ELECTRONICS
767 - 5TH AVENUE
NEW YORK CITY, NY 10153
312-397-3440
ELECTRONIC COMPONENTS, PARTS, SUPPLIES

AVERA BV
DE REIT 5, 4891 RV RIJSBERGEN
THE NETHERLANDS
+31 (0) 1606 3820, FAX 3833
EURO DSTR OF SEMICONDUCTORS

BCD ELECTRO
PO BOX 830119
RICHARDSON, TX 75083
214-690-1102
CONNECTORS, IC'S, COMPUTER ACCY'S

BELDEN WIRE & CABLE
PO BOX 1980
RICHMOND, IN 47375
800-235-3361   317-983-5200

CIRCUIT SPECIALISTS
PO BOX 3047
SCOTTSDALE, AZ 85257
800-528-1417
ELECTRONIC PROJECT KITS, PARTS

CONSOLIDATED ELECTRIC WIRE & CABLE
1104 KING ST
FRANKLIN PARK, IL 60131
312-455-8830

CUSTOM COMPONENTS CORP.
W224 S8445 INDUSTRIAL DR
BIG BEND, WI 53103
414-662-5266
ADAPTORS, CABLES, EXTENSIONS, TEST JIGS

DAVILYN CORPORATION
13406 SATICOY ST
NORTH HOLLYWOOD, CA 91605
800-235-6222
ELECTRONIC PARTS & MILITARY SURPLUS

DAYTON-GRAINGER, INC
3299 SW 9TH AVE / POB 14070
FORT LAUDERDALE, FL 33315
604-580-2443
GENERAL INDUSTRIAL SUPPLY, FANS &
BLOWERS FOR COOLING

DERF ELECTRONICS CORP.
37 PLAIN AVE
NEW ROCHELLE, NY 10801
800-431-2912 / 914-235-4600
ELECTRONIC COMPONENTS, CHIPS,
TRANSISTORS, CRYSTALS, MORE.

DIGI-KEY
HIGHWAY 32 SOUTH / PO BOX 677
THIEF RIVER FALLS, MN 56701
800-344-4539
RADIO SUPPLIES, ELECTRONIC COMPONENTS

DRAKE, R. L., COMPANY
PO BOX 3006
MIAMISBURG, OH 45343
800-568-3795   513-866-3211
DRAKE HAM RADIOS, SWL RECEIVERS, FILTERS
& OTHER RADIO PRODUCTS

EAST COAST TRANSISTOR
2 MARLBOROUGH ROAD
W. HEMPSTEAD, NY 11552
800-645-3516
SEMICONDUCTORS & ELECTRONIC PARTS

ELECTRONICS WAREHOUSE, INC.
PO BOX 624
OLD LYME, CT 06371
203-434-8308
ELECTRONICS & TECHNICAL TOOLS/SUPPLIES

GATEWAY ELECTRONICS, INC.
9222 CHESAPEAKE
SAN DIEGO, CA 92111
619-279-6802
MIL & COMMERCIAL SURPLUS EQUIP. ALSO
DENVER, ST. LOUIS, HOUSTON

HOSFELT ELECTRONICS, INC.
2700 SUNSET BLVD
STEUBENVILLE, OH 43952-1158
800-524-6464   FAX 800-524-5414
EXCELLENT SUPPLIER: NEW AND SURPLUS

JAMECO ELECTRONICS
1355 SHOREWAY ROAD
BELMONT, CA 94002
415-592-8097
SEMICONDUCTORS & ELECTRONIC PARTS, WIDE
INVENTORY, CATALOG

JONES, MARLIN P. & ASSOCIATES
PO BOX 12685
LAKE PARK, FL 33403-0685
407-848-8236   FAX 407-884-8764
COMMERCIAL SURPLUS ELECTRONICS

KEN'S ELECTRONIC PARTS
2825 LAKE ST
KALAMAZOO, MI 49001
616-345-4609
CB RADIOS, CB ACCESS, ANTENNA MOUNTS

MALLORY DISTRIBUTOR PRODUCTS COMPANY
PO BOX 1284
INDIANAPOLIS, IN 46206
317-636-5353

MCM ELECTRONICS
858 E. CONGRESS PARK DR
CENTERVILLE, OH 45459
800-543-4330   513-434-0031
ELECTRONIC PARTS & SUPPLIES

MINI-CIRCUIT LABS
PO BOX 166
BROOKLYN, NY 11235
718-934-4500
RF COMPONENTS OF ALL TYPES

MOUSER ELECTRONICS
11433 WOODSIDE AVE
SANTEE, CA 92071
619-449-2222   817-483-4422
ALSO MANSFIELD, TX 817-483-4422
COMPONENTS & SUPPLIES

MURATA-ERIE NORTH AMERICA, INC.
1420 E. EDINGER ST, SUITE 213
SANTA ANA, CA 92705
714-835-4822
CALIFORNIA SALES OFFICE

NEW-TONE ELECTRONICS
44 FARRAND ST
BLOOMFIELD, NJ 07003
201-748-5089
RESISTORS & SEMICONDUCTORS

NEWARK ELECTRONICS
5308 W. 124TH ST
ALSIP, IL 60658
312-371-9000
ELECTRONIC COMPONENTS, SUPPLIES & EQ

NTE
44 FARRAND ST
BLOOMFIELD, NJ 07003
201-748-5089
SUPPLIER OF NTE-BRAND SEMICONDUCTORS

ORA ELECTRONICS
9410 OWENSMOUTH AVE.
CHATSWORTH, CA 91311
800-423-5336   818-701-5850
JAPANESE SEMICONDUCTORS, ICS

PALADIN CORPORATION
3543 OLD CONEJO RD, #102
NEWBURY PARK, CA 91320
805-499-0318
SOLDER'G & WIRE HANDLING TOOLS, TESTERS

PARTS EXPRESS INTERNATIONAL
340 E. FIRST ST
DAYTON, OH 45402
800-338-0531   513-222-0173
ELECTRONIC PARTS & SUPPLIES

PASTERNACK ENTERPRISES
PO BOX 16759
IRVINE, CA 92713
714-261-1920
COAX CABLE PRODUCTS, CONNECTORS, MORE

QUAM-NICHOLS CO.
234 E. MARQUETTE RD
CHICAGO, IL 60637
312-488-5800
REPLACEMENT & OEM SPEAKERS

RED LION CONTROLS
20 WILLOW SPRING CIRCLE
NEW YORK, PA 17402
717-767-6511
DIGITAL COUNTERS & INDICATORS, CONTROLS

REMEE PRODUCTS CORP.
41 BRIDGE ST
FLORIDA, NY 10921
800-431-3864   914-651-4431
COAX, WIRE & CABLE

RF PARTS COMPANY
1320 GRAND AVE
SAN MARCOS, CA 92069
619-744-0700   800-854-1927
POWER DEVICES, LINEAR AMP PARTS, HAM & CB

SHOKAI FAR EAST LTD
280 N. CENTRAL AVE
HARTSDALE, NY 10530
914-681-0700
VERY LARGE IMPORTER OF ELEC EQUIPMENT &
COMPONENTS

TUCKER ELECTRONICS
1717 RESERVE ST.
GARLAND, TX 75042
800-527-4642   FAX 214-245-0357
SURPLUS ELEX TEST EQUIPMENT, COMPUTERS,
BOOKS, SUPPLIES, AND A FINE CATALOG

WORKMAN ELECTRONIC PRODUCTS, INC.
75 PACKINGHOUSE RD / PO BOX 3828
SARASOTA, FL 33578
813-371-4242
SEMICONDUCTORS & RESISTORS

SCANNERS, RADIO EQUIPMENT, ACCESSORIES

A-B-C COMMUNICATIONS
17550 15TH AVE NE
SEATTLE, WA 92065
206-364-5300
ICOM, BOOKS, ANTENNAS

ACE COMMUNICATIONS
10707 E. 106TH ST
FISHERS, IN 46038
800-445-7717
SCANNERS FROM AOL, ETC. FOR
SOPHISTICATED USERS

AMATEUR ELECTRONIC SUPPLY
5710 GOOD HOPE ROAD
MILWAUKEE, WI 53223
800-558-0411
MUCH HOBBY RADIO EQUIPMENT. ALSO IN:
    WICKLIFFE, OH 800-321-3594
    ORLANDO, FL 800-327-1917
    CLEARWATER, FL 813-461-4267
    LAS VEGAS, NV 800-634-6227
    SEATTLE, WA 206-767-8170

AMC SALES, INC
PO BOX 928
DOWNEY, CA 90241
213-869-8519
FAX 213-923-1478
LONG PLAY TAPE RECORDERS–SURVEILLANCE,
SECURITY & RADIO USE, VOX

ANTTRON ANTENNA PRODUCTS
1427 E. INDIANOLA AVE.
YOUNGSTOWN, OH 44602
216-788-9404   FAX 216-788-7709
ANTENNAS FOR SCANNERS, CB, & HAM RADIO,
GREAT SCANNER ANTENNAS!

ASSOCIATED RADIO
8012 CONSER, BOX 4327
OVERLAND PARK, KS 66204
913-381-5900   FAX 913-648-3020
NEW & RECONDITIONED RADIO EQUIP, WHSLE

ATLANTIC HAM RADIO LTD
368 WILSON AVE
DOWNSVIEW, ONT M3H 1S9 CANADA
416-636-3536
HOBBY RADIOS, ACCESSORIES AND SUPPLIES.
TRADE-INS AND REPAIRS

BARRY ELECTRONICS CORP.
25 SUTTON PLACE SOUTH
NEW YORK, NY 10012
212-925-7000
EVERYTHING, PLUS FULL-SERVICE LAB, TECHS

B.C. COMMUNICATIONS
THE 211 BLDG, DEPOT ROAD
HUNTINGTON STATION, NY 11746
516-549-8833

BURK ELECTRONICS
35 N. KENSINGTON
LAGRANGE, IL 60525
708-482-9310
MUCH HOBBY RADIO HARDWARE, PUBS,
TRADE-INS, TECH ASSISTANCE, REPAIRS

C. CRANE CO.
558 - 10TH STREET
FORTUNA, CA 95540-2350
707-725-9000   FAX 707-725-9060
SCANNERS, SHORTWAVE, RADIOS, BOOKS

COMMUNICATIONS ELECTRONICS
PO BOX 1045
ANN ARBOR, MI 48106-1045
800-872-7226
VHF-UHF SCANNER RADIOS, CB RADIOS,
MARINE RADIOS

COMMUNICATIONS SPECIALISTS
426 WEST TAFT AVENUE
ORANGE, CA 92665-4296
800-854-0547   714-998-3021
RETROFIT CTCSS TONE EQ, MODEL TS-32P.
FOR MOST RADIOS INCL SCANNERS

COPPER ELECTRONICS
3315 GILMORE INDUSTRIAL BLVD
LOUISVILLE, KY 40213
502-968-8500
HOBBY RADIO, ACCESSORIES

DANDY'S (NOW RADIO SHACK OF DERBY)
707 N. BALTIMORE
DERBY, KS 67037
HOBBY RADIO, ACCESSORIES, TRADE-INS

ELECTRONIC EQUIPMENT BANK (EEB)
516 MILL ST
VIENNA, VA 22180
800-368-3270
SWL, SCANNER RADIOS & ACCESSORIES

GALAXY ELECTRONICS
67 EBER AVE / BOX 1202
AKRON, OH 44309
216-376-2402
CB PRODUCTS/ACCY'S, SCANNER & SWL EQ

GILFER RADIO
52 PARK AVE.
PARK RIDGE, NJ 07656
201-391-7887
HOBBY RADIO, PUBLISHES ALSO

GRE AMERICA, INC.
425 HARBOR BLVD.
BELMONT, CA 94002
415-591-1400   FAX 415-591-2001
SCANNER ACCESSORIES, INCLUDING
CONVERTERS, PRE-AMPS, ANTENNAS, ETC.

GROVE ENTERPRISES, INC.
140 DOG BRANCH RD
BRASSTOWN, NC 28902
704-837-9200
SWL & SCANNER EQUIP, ANTENNAS & MONITOR
SUPPLIES, ALSO PUBLICATIONS INCLUDING
MONITORING TIMES

HAM RADIO OUTLET
EXCELLENT RESOURCE, WITH MANY HOBBY
RADIO LINES, LITERATURE, BOOKS, PARTS,
TECH HELP, AND ACCEPTS TRADE-INS. ALL
OVER:
    ANAHEIM, CA 714-533-7373
    ATLANTA, GA 404-263-0700
    DENVER, CO 303-745-7373
    OAKLAND, CA 415-534-5757
    PORTLAND, OR 503-598-0555
    PHOENIX, AZ 602-242-3515
    SALEM, NH 603-896-3750
    SAN DIEGO, CA 619-560-4900
    SUNNYVALE, CA 408-736-9496
    VAN NUYS, CA 818-988-2212
    WOODBRIDGE, VA 800-444-4799

HENRY RADIO INC.
2050 SOUTH BUNDY DRIVE
LOS ANGELES, CA 90025
800-877-7979
HOBBY RADIO, MANY LINES. TRADE-INS OK

JUN'S ELECTRONICS
5563 SEPULVEDA BLVD
CULVER CITY, CA 90230
213-390-8003
HOBBY RADIO, ACCESSORIES. DOES REPAIRS

LENTINI COMMUNICATIONS
21 GARFIELD ST
NEWINGTON, CT 06111
203-666-6227
HOBBY RADIO, ACCESS, TRADE-INS, REPAIRS

MACFARLANE ELECTRONIC, LTD
RR #2
BATTERSOA, ONT KOH 1H0   CANADA
613-353-2800
HOBBY RADIO EQ & SUPPLIES, TRADE-INS

MARYMAC INDUSTRIES, INC.
22511 KATY FREEWAY
KATY, TX 77450
800-231-3680   713-392-0747
DISCOUNT MAIL ORDER FRANCHISE DEALER
FOR RADIO SHACK PRODUCTS, SCANNERS

MFJ ENTERPRISES, INC.
POB 494
MISSISSIPI STATE, MS 39762
800-647-1800
HOBBY RADIO ACCESSORIES OF ALL SORTS

MICHIGAN RADIO
23040 SHOENHER
WARREN, MI 48089
313-771-4711
HOBBY RADIO, BROAD INVENTORY, TRADE-INS

NEVADA
189 LONDON RD, PORTSMOUTH
HAMPSHIRE, ENGLAND
0705-662145   869107 TELEX
WIDE VARIETY OF EUROPEAN SCANNERS
ACCY'S AND SHORTWAVE RADIO PRODUCTS

OPTO-ELECTRONICS
5821 NE 14TH AVE.
FT. LAUDERDALE, FL 33334
800-327-5912
FAX 305-771-2052
SSB COUNTER, HAND-HELD FREQ COUNTERS,
AUTO-TUNE RECEIVERS

PORTLAND RADIO SUPPLY
234 SE GRAND AVE
PORTLAND, OR 97214
503-233-4904

RADIO CENTER USA
630 NW ENGLEWOOD ROAD
KANSAS CITY, MO 64115
800-821-7323

RADIO CENTER USA
12 GLEN CARRAN CIRCLE
SPARKS, NV 89431
800-345-5686
HOBBY RADIO, ACCESS, ACCEPTS TRADE-INS

RADIO PLACE, THE
5675A POWER INN ROAD
SACRAMENTO, CA 95824
HOBBY RADIO, ACCESSORIES, BOOKS, REPAIRS

RADIO SHACK
1500 ONE TANDY CENTER
FT. WORTH, TX 76102
817-390-3011
OVER 7,000 STORES IN THE U.S.
COMPUTERS & SCANNERS, ANTENNAS, ACCESS

SATELLITE CITY
2663 COUNTRY ROAD 1
MINNEAPOLIS, MN 55112
800-426-2891
HOBBY RADIO EQ, REPAIRS, TRADE-INS

SCAN COMMUNICATION CO
PO BOX 911
BURLINGTON, IA 52601
319-752-3000
HOBBY RADIO, ANTENNAS, ETC.

SCANNER WORLD
10 NEW SCOTLAND AVE
ALBANY, NY 12208
518-436-9606
VHF-UHF SCANNER RADIOS, ACCESSORIES

TELE * PATH
49111 MILMONT DR
FREMONT, CA 94538
800-292-1700   415-656-5600
RADIO COMM. EQUIPT DEALER, RADIOS,
AMPLIFIERS, TEST EQUIP

TEN-TECH, INC.
1185 DOLLY PARTON PARKWAY
SEVIERVILLE, TN 37862
615-453-0364
TxRx, AMPS, ANT TUNERS, ENCLOSURES

UNIDEN CORPORATION OF AMERICA
4700 AMON CARTER BLVD.
FT WORTH, TX 76155
817-858-3300, TECH: 817-841-8615
MANY SCANNERS, ACCESSORIES

UNIVERSAL ELECTRONICS,INC.
4555 GROVES ROAD, SUITE 13
COLUMBUS, OH 43232
800-241-8171
BOOKS, SATELLITE AND SCPC RECEIVERS

UNIVERSAL RADIO
6830 AMERICANA PKWY
REYNOLDSBURG, OH 43068-4113
800-431-3939   614-866-4267
SHORTWAVE, HAM & SCANNER RADIOS, ACCESS

U. S. RADIO
377 PLAZA
GRANBURY, TX 76048
RADIO SHACK EQUIPMENT, ACCESSORIES

PERIODICALS, OTHER PUBLICATIONS

ACE BULLETIN
PO BOX 11201
SHAWNEE MISSION, KS 66207-0201
MONTHLY PUB FOR PIRATE, CLANDESTINE &
NUMBERS MONITORING SWL HOBBYISTS

AIRLINERS MAGAZINE
BOX 521-238
MIAMI, FL 33152-1238
305-477-7163   FAX 305-599-1995
MAGAZINE ON AIRLINERS, AIRLINES & AERO

AMERICAN SCANNERGRAM
50 VILLA ROAD
SPRINGFIELD, OH 45503
NEWSLETTER OF THE ALL OHIO SCANNER CLUB

ARTSCI INC
POB 1428
BURBANK, CA 91507
818-843-4080
MODIFICATIONS, LICENSE MANUALS, FREQ &
MAP BOOKS

CLANDESTINE/CONFIDENTIAL NEWSLETTER
RR#4, BOX 110
LAKE GENEVA, WI 53147
NEWSLETTER: PIRATE & CLANDESTINE RADIO

CQ COMMUNICATIONS, INC.
76 N. BROADWAY
HICKSVILLE, NY 11801
516-681-2922   FAX 516-601-2926
POPCOMM, CQ, EXCELLENT HOBBY
ELECTRONICS MAGAZINES

CRB RESEARCH BOOKS
PO BOX 56
516-543-9169   FAX 516-543-7486
COMMACK, NY 11725
HOBBY RADIO BOOKS – PERHAPS THE LARGEST
AND MOST DIVERSE CATALOG IN THE FIELD

CTM MAGAZINE
1704 SAM DRIVE
BIRMINGHAM, AL 35235
205-854-0271
COMPUTERIST & HAM RADIO, PACKET RADIO

D C ENTERPRISES
3420 TRENARY LANE
COLORADO SPRINGS, CO 80918
PUBLISHER: AIRCRAFT FREQUENCY DIRECTORY

DX LISTENING DIGEST
PO BOX 1684
ENID, OK 73702
MONTHLY PUB FOR SHORTWAVE LISTENERS

FM ATLAS PUBLISHING
BOX 336
ESKO, MN 55733-0336
PUBLISHER OF FM ATLAS AND FMEDIA
NEWSLETTER, GUIDES TO FM BROADCAST

HIGHTEXT PUBLICATIONS, INC.
7128 MIRAMAR ROAD, SUITE 15
SAN DIEGO, CA 92121
619-693-5900
HOBBY ELECTRONICS BOOKS, SHORTWAVE,
ANTENNAS, ETC.

HR BOOKSTORE
POB 209
RINDGE, NH 03461
800-457-7373
HOBBY RADIO BOOKS, SOFTWARE

INDEX PUBLISHING GROUP
3368 GOVERNOR DRIVE
SAN DIEGO, CA 92122
800-546-6707
PUBLISHER OF SCANNER BOOKS,
INCLUDING *SCANNERS & SECRET*
FREQUENCIES, EMERGENCY RADIO!
THE ULTIMATE SCANNER, TRAVELSCAN

KLINGENFUSS PUBLICATIONS
HAGENLOHER STR. 14
D-7400 TUEBINGEN, W. GERMANY
07071-62830
PUBLICATIONS ON UTILITY & RTTY SHORTWAVE

MENTOR PUBLICATIONS
135-53 NORTHERN BLVD
FLUSHING, NY 11354
BOOKS ON SECURITY, SURVEILLANCE &
RELATED ELECTRONICS

MICROWAVE SYSTEM NEWS
1170 EAST MEADOW DR
PALO ALTO, CA 94303
INDUSTRIAL, COMMUNICATIONS, ELECTRONICS,
TRADE JOURNAL

MICROWAVES & RF
PO BOX 1043
SOUTHEASTERN, PA 19398-9953
RF/ELECTRONICS TRADE JOURNAL

MOBILE RADIO TECHNOLOGY
5951 S. MIDDLEFIELD RD
LITTLETON, CO 80123
INDUSTRIAL/COMMUNICATIONS/ELECTRONICS,
TRADE JOURNAL

MODERN ELECTRONICS
76 N. BROADWAY
HICKSVILLE, NY 11801
MONTHLY MAGAZINE FOR EVERYTHING ELEX

MONITORING TIMES MAGAZINE
PO BOX 98
BRASSTOWN, NC 28902
704-837-9200
800-438-8155
MONTHLY SCANNER & SHORTWAVE MAGAZINE

NATIONAL SCANNING REPORT
PO BOX 291918
KETTERING, OH 45429
800-423-1331
MONTHLY SCANNER MAGAZINE

NUMBERS FACTSHEET, THE
PO BOX 149
BRIARCLIFF MANOR, NY 10510
"NUMBERS STATIONS"
OFFICIAL SCANNER GUIDE
PO BOX 712
LONDONDERRY, NH 03053
PUBLISHER OF FREQUENCY DIRECTORIES &
"OFFICIAL" AERO FREQUENCY DIRECTORY

POPULAR COMMUNICATIONS MAGAZINE
76 N. BROADWAY
HICKSVILLE, NY 11801
516-681-2922
RADIO COMMUNICATIONS CB, SWL & SCANNING

RADIO MONITOR NEWSLETTER
PO BOX 394
HAMPSTEAD, MD 21074-0394
NEWSLETTER FOR SCANNER & SWL
HOBBYISTS; STATE OF MARYLAND

RADIOSCAN MAGAZINE
8250 NW 27TH ST, STE 301
MIAMI, FL 33122
305-594-7734
MAGAZINE FOR RADIO HOBBYISTS &
ENTHUSIASTS, NUMBERS, CLANDESTINESE

RADIO SPORTING MAGAZINE
PO BOX 282
PINE BROOK, NJ 07058
MAGAZINE FOR HAMS & GENERAL RADIO
ENTHUSIASTS

SCANNER JOURNAL
PO BOX 542
SILVERADO, CA 92676
714-545-9551
PERIODICAL OF RADIO COMMUNICATIONS
MONITORING ASSOCIATION (RCMA)

RF DESIGN
6430 S. YOSEMITE STREET
ENGLEWOOD, CO 80111
XLNT HOW-TO RF ENGINEERING

SECRET CB
PO BOX 8189
CORPUS CHRISTI, TX 78412
512-853-2935
CB MODS, TUNEUPS

SPEC-COM JOURNAL
PO BOX 1002
DUBUQUE, IA 52004-1002
319-557-8791
FAX 319-583-6462
MAGAZINE ON SPECIALIZED COMMUNICATIONS:

STANDARD AMATEUR RADIO PRODUCTS, INC.
PO BOX 48480
NILES, IL 60648
312-763-0061
MOSTLY TRANSCEIVERS

TAB BOOKS, INC.
MONETREY LANE
BLUE RIDGE SUMMIT, PA 17214
717-794-2191
CB SERVICE DATA & RADIO/TECHNICAL BOOKS

THOMAS PUBLISHING
127 WESTWOOD
PARIS, IL 61944
217-466-4210
BOOKS ON CB RADIO MODS & TUNEUPS
TIARE PUBLICATIONS
PO BOX 493-G
LAKE GENEVA, WI 53147
PUBLICATIONS ON SW ANTENNAS, SWL, ETC.

WGE PUBLISHING, INC.
WGE CENTER
PETERBOROUGH, NH 03458
800-225-5083
PUBLISHES *73 MAGAZINE*

WINSTON ARRINGTON
7223 S. STONY ISLAND AVE
CHICAGO, IL 60649
ELECTRONIC EAVESDROPPING/SURVEILLANCE

WORLD RADIO MAGAZINE
2120 - 28TH ST / PO BOX 189490
SACRAMENTO, CA 95818
916-457-3655
AMATEUR RADIO NEWSPAPER

WORLD RADIO-TV HANDBOOK
1515 BROADWAY
NEW YORK, NY 10036
212-764-7300
212-536-5266
REFERENCE BOOK ON SHORTWAVE BROADCAST
RADIO, FREQS, MUCH MORE.

AND...

WORLD SCANNER REPORT
PO BOX 262478
SAN DIEGO, CA 92196-2478
619-578-9247   1:30PM-5:30PM, PST,
WEEKDAYS
BILL CHEEK'S SCANNER NEWSLETTER,
FOLLOWS SCANNER MODS, & MUCH
MORE. SUPPORTED BY AND
INTEGRATED WITH THE HERTZIAN
INTERCEPT BBS.

AC power supply, 9
Ace customer service, 48
AOR customer service, 48
Audio improvements, 139
Auto birdie rejection, 152
AutoLog, 152
AutoLookUp, 152
AutoProgramming, 152

Banks, memory, 91
BBS, Hertzian Intercept, The, 12
BBS, spreadsheet support of, 227
Bearcat customer service, 48
Beat frequencies, 70
Binary numbers, 96
Birdies, rejection, 152
Block identifiers, programming
    16 block, *Table 4-2*, 92
    64 block, *Table 4-3*, 98
Bullington, Kenneth, 219

Capacitor, electrolytic, markings, 162
CD-ROM, 17
CDMA (Code Division Multiple Access), 134
CE-232 computer interface, 93, 149-200
    BBS support for, 194, 227
    circuit board for, 160-161
    connectors & cables for, 169
    connections, 152
    diagnostics, 189
    documentation of, 197
    errors, common, in CE-232, 188
    functions and features, 152-153
    idiosyncrasies (no-program or no-stop), 192
    installation guide, internal, 173
    installation guide, external, 176
    keyboard matrix wiring, 184
    kits for, 198
    logic board connections, 177, 179, 183
    manual for, 155
    operation of, 194
    parts & supplies, *Table 8-1A&B*, 156-157, 198, *Table 8-9*, 199
    power source for, 181
    protection circuitry for, 180
    resource list, *Table 8-10*, 200
    resistance and continuity checks, 191
    scanner control section, 186
    schematic of, 159
    software Developer's Kit, 200
    technical support, 193
    test data matrix, 190
    troubleshooting, 185
    vendor support for, 197
    wiring plan for, *Tables 8-2 & 8-3*, 167-168
Cellular frequency allocations, 134, 136

Cellular modifications, 131-148
    legal aspects, 131
Cellular Telephone Industry Association (CTIA), 133
Cellular telephones, 133
Cellular-capable scanners, 132
Cellular-modifiable scanners, 132
Clock, system, 69
Code Division Multiple Access, 134
Compuserve, 13
Computer interface, 18, 20, 93, 149-200
    history and evolution, 149
    vendors, 150
    capturing scanner data via, 151
Continuous frequency coverage, 26
Continuous Tone Coded Squelch Systems (CTCSS), 27
CPU upgrade, 138
    chip changes, GRE, 38, 138

Data Tone Squelch (DTS), 121-130
    as opposed to SSQ, 121
    parts list for, 126
    schematic of, 127
DC power supply, 61
Decibels, 205
Decryption circuitry and software, 26
Diffraction loss, 222
Diode markings, 162
Diode matrix alteration, 39
Discriminator chips, 143
DTMF, 27

e-mail, 13
ECHO, 14
EEPROM, 86
    identifying, 106
    multiplying of, 107
Electroluminescent backlight panel, 41
Electronic Communications Privacy Act of 1986, 131

FCC frequency database, 212
Features, desirable, 24
FidoNet, 13
Finding transmitter locations, 212
Floppy disk drives, 25
Free space loss, 219
Frequency counters, 62
Frequency data on CD-ROM, 197
Frequency standards, precision, 68
Functionality issues, 24

General Research Electronics (GRE), 36
Geodetic bearings and distance, 207
    computing, 209
Global Positioning Systems (GPS), 212
Glossary, 231
GRE, *see General Research Electronics*
Great Circle, 207

Hertzian Intercept BBS, The, 12
Hookup wire, 51
Hot glue, 51
IC sockets, 54
ICOM customer service, 48
Information Superhighway, 16
Interface, computer, *see CE-232*
Internet, The, 13, 16

JFET preamplifier, 80

Kenwood customer service, 48
Keyboard design, 21

Latitude & longitude calculations, 212
LCD driver chip, 41
Legal issues, 34
Line-of-sight (LOS) estimates, 224
LINKALL Extended Memory Controller, 99
Logarithms, 204
Logic probe, 80
Logic/CPU board, 41
Losses,
    Diffraction, 222
    Free space, 219
    Plane-earth, 221
    Shadow, 222

Magnetic north, 227
Map conversions, 212
Mathematics, 204
Mechanical issues, 23
Memory banks, 91
Memory chip stacking, 104
Memory expansion, 41, 85-111, 147
Memory, programmable, 21
Memory, types of, 85
    EEPROM, 86
    SRAM, 86
    with CPU, 85
Memory, wiring and switches for, 91
Modifications, general, 47-84
Molded connectors, hi-rel, 54

Ohm's Law, 204
Oscillators, 66

Performance quantification, specs, 23
Pin-line sockets & plugs, 52
Plane-earth loss, 221
Polaris, 228
Popularity of scanners, 30
Power supplies
    AC, 9
    DC, 61
Preamp, general purpose RF (J-FET), 80
Preamp, general purpose RF (WBA-6), 73
    parts list and sources, 76
Propagation analysis spreadsheet, 218
Radio path analysis, 219
Radio Shack, 31
    sales estimates, scanners, 33
    customer service access, 48

Radio vs. Optical Line-of-Sight (LOS), 209
Regency customer service, 48
Remote control, 152
Resistor color codes, 162
Resources list, 237
Restoring mid FM-band, 139
RF detector probes, 63

S-meter, 21, 140
    from LEDs, 141
    use of to map cellular signals, 135
Satellite reception, 28
Scanner economics, 33
Schematic symbols, 203
Service manuals & technical disclosure, 30, 48
Shadow loss, 222
Shielding, 23
Signal generators, 66
Soldering techniques, 50
Specifications, 23
Spectrum analysis and analyzers, 25
Speed-ups, simple, 138, 139, 143, 145, 146
    ineligibility with CE-232, 190
Spreadsheet, 210
    terminology and symbology, *Table 9-1*, 215
    technical structure, 216
Squelch improvement, 143
SRAM, 86
    SRAM identification, *Table 4-1*, 88
SSQ, 121
Static, failures caused by, Cover-3
Status indicator, LED, 80
Subsidiary Carrier Authorization (SCA), 113-120
    SCA defined, 113
    legalities, 114
    kits for, 115

TCXO, 69
TDMA (Time Division Multiple Access), 134
Telephone Disclosure and Dispute Resolution Act of 1994
    (Public Law 102-556), 131
Television reception, 28
Test equipment, 62
Time Division Multiple Access, 134
Tools, 55, 57
Troubleshooting CE-232, 185
Troubleshooting, general, 50
True earth radius clearance, 225
True North, 227

Ultimate Scanner candidate lists, 36
Uniden
    sales estimates, scanners, 33
    customer service access, 48

VADER, 197
Voice Activated Digital Electronic Recorder (VADER), 197
Voice transmitter, converting oscillator to, 67

WWV, 70
Yaesu customer service, 48

Yes, we were late getting this book out. Our schedule and our announcements were too optimistic.
We apologize – in fact, this coupon is more than an apology: it's our payment for your inconvenience!

Use this coupon, **or the code on it,** to get an instant rebate on other scanning books. You can even save on a spare or gift copy of **Cheek**[3].

Book	Price	Rebate	Net	Copies
Scanners & Secret Frequencies (Eisenson)	$19.95	$7	$12.95	_____
Emergency Radio! (Schrein)	$14.95	$7	$7.95	_____
Scanner Modification Handbook 1 (Cheek)	$19.95	$4	$15.95	_____
Scanner Modification Handbook 2 (Cheek)	$19.95	$4	$15.95	_____
The Ultimate Scanner (Cheek)	$29.95	$5	$24.95	_____

ONE COUPON PER ADDRESS, MAXIMUM OF 3 COPIES OF ANY ONE BOOK.

Name _____ Phone _____

Address _____

City, State, ZIP _____

MC ☐
Visa ☐   Number _____
AMEX ☐
Disc ☐   Exp date _____ Signature _____

Toll-free
800-546-6707
Order Code 4255

Books _____
S/H _____
CA Tax _____
Total $ _____

$4 s/h for the first book, then $2 each. CA tax is 7.75%.

Order by e-mail (with credit card) from indexboox@aol.com, or via snail-mail with check/MO, or credit card. Send to:

Index Publishing Group, Inc.
3368 Governor Drive, Ste 273
San Diego, CA 92122

Nope. This isn't a second instant rebate. It's just an ordinary order form.
The difference is that you can use this as often as you like!

Scanners & Secret Frequencies (Eisenson)	$19.95
Emergency Radio! (Schrein)	$14.95
Scanner Modification Handbook 1 (Cheek)	$19.95
Scanner Modification Handbook 2 (Cheek)	$19.95
The Ultimate Scanner (Cheek)	$29.95
Throbbing Modems (Bagby)	$17.95
TravelScan (Eisenson)	$7.95
Cheating at Blackjack ("Marks")	$19.95
The Television Gray Market (Eisenson)	$23.75
Cellular Fraud (Thorn)	$24.95

Name _____ Phone _____

Address _____

City, State, ZIP _____

MC ☐
Visa ☐   Number _____
AMEX ☐
Disc ☐   Exp date _____ Signature _____

Toll-free
800-546-6707

Books _____
S/H _____
CA Tax _____
Total $ _____

$4 s/h for the first book, then $2 each. CA tax is 7.75%.

Order by e-mail (with credit card) from indexboox@aol.com, or via snail-mail with check/MO, or credit card. Send to:

Index Publishing Group, Inc.
3368 Governor Drive, Ste 273
San Diego, CA 92122